STATISTICS

R.C. SOLOMON

John Murray

Other titles by the author in the Advanced Level Mathematics series:

Pure Maths   ISBN 0 7195 5344 X
Mechanics   ISBN 0 7195 7082 4

First published in 1996 by
John Murray (Publishers) Ltd
50 Albemarle Street
London SW1X 4BD

Designed by Eric Drewery
Typeset in 11/12pt Times Roman by Servis Filmsetting Ltd, Manchester
Printed and bound in Great Britain by The Alden Press, Oxford

A catalogue entry for this book is available from the British Library

ISBN 0–7195–7088–3

Contents

Introduction

This book covers the statistics requirements for most A-level syllabuses. Throughout the book emphasis is put on understanding statistical operations, as well as acquiring efficiency and confidence in statistical calculations.

The use of statistics is increasing in every area of work and study. To highlight this, the examples and exercises of the book are taken from widely ranging contexts.

Structure of book

The syllabus is covered in the fifteen chapters. Each chapter contains:

- explanations of the principles involved
- worked examples
- exercises ranging from straighforward drill questions to those – marked * – which present more challenge to the student
- longer exercises to develop the theory and practice, often in unexpected ways.

There are four consolidation sections in the book. These contain:

- extra questions on the material of the chapters
- mixed exercises linking the material of the chapters
- additional longer exercises
- extra examination questions
- sets of discussion questions, in which the student is invited to consider a situation for which there may not be any exact mathematical analysis.

There are two sets of practical investigations, intended to combine the theory and practice of statistics. There are two sets of computer investigations, in which the student is encouraged to make full use of modern technology to explore statistics. At the end of the book are three mock examination papers, with the style and content of real examination questions.

Statistics involves many algebraic proofs which can be a distraction from the principles involved. These proofs have been taken from the main text and put in a Mathematical appendix.

Complete numerical solutions are provided.

Mathematical requirements

Statistics requires a great deal of pure mathematics. Below is a list of the mathematical techniques which will be needed throughout the book.

Algebra

Algebra of polynomials and rational functions. Sums of series, use of Σ notation. Powers and logarithms. Solution of linear and quadratic equations.

Calculus

Differentiation of x^n, e^x, $\ln x$, and of sums, products, quotients and compositions of functions.

Integration of basic functions. Integration by substitution and by parts.

Computers and calculators

Statistics involves a vast amount of numerical work. Nowadays most of the drudgery can be left to modern technology, ranging from scientific calculators to sophisticated statistical packages. This development is thoroughly welcome – students can now concentrate on understanding statistical principles, without being diverted and disheartened by the number-crunching connected with them. Computers can also be used to simulate statistical experiments. Investigations concerning this are given in the book.

Why study statistics?

Statistics has always developed in response to practical problems. The foundations of probability were laid in order to solve problems concerning gambling, and further contributions were made in order to understand astronomy, heredity and so on.

Nowadays the uses of statistics have spread to all subjects, including economics and sociology as well as the physical sciences. Newspapers and reports are full of statistical information and analysis, and it is necessary to be aware of statistical notions to participate fully in the modern world.

Acknowledgements

My thanks are due to the following boards for permission to include questions from their past examination papers.

The Associated Examining Board	A
University of Cambridge Local Examinations Syndicate	C
University of London Examinations and Assessment Council	L
Northern Examinations and Assessment Board	N
Northern Ireland Schools Examinations and Assessment Council	NI
University of Oxford Delegacy of Local Examinations	O
Oxford and Cambridge Schools Examination Board	O&C
The Schools Mathematics Project	SMP
Mathematics in Education and Industry project	MEI
Welsh Joint Education Committee	W

The solutions to the examination questions are the work of the author, and have neither been provided nor approved by the boards concerned.

The University of London Examinations and Assessment Council accepts no responsibility whatsoever for the accuracy or method of working in the answers given.

Analysing data

A **datum** is any fact, which may or may not be numerical. A collection of these facts consists of **data**. You may have heard of a **database**, which is a computer application enabling you to handle a great number of facts. The government of a country or state collects vast quantities of data, and seeks to analyse them. This is where the word **statistics** comes from. Originally it referred to the study of all the data collected by a state.

The facts collected are the **raw data**. It is very difficult to look at a great mass of facts and make any sense of them. It is necessary to organise the data in some way before we can draw any useful conclusions, i.e. it is necessary for the *raw* data to be *cooked*. Throughout this book you will meet many recipes.

1.1 Data

Data do not have to consist of numbers. Data which are not numerical are called **nominal data**. The list of names of all the pupils of a school consists of nominal data. The list of the ages of the pupils, however, consists of **numerical data**.

Continuous and discrete data

Throughout this book, we shall mainly be dealing with numerical data. There are two main classes of such data. Compare the following household items

- a box of matches, which contains an average of 48 matches
- a can of soup, which contains an average of 400 ml of liquid.

There could be 47 or 49 matches in the matchbox, but there could not be 48.23 matches. However many boxes we open and count the matches they contain, the results must be **whole numbers**.

In the can of soup there could be 402.45 ml, or 397.72 ml. There does not have to be a whole number of millilitres. However many cans we open and measure the contents, the results will always come from a **continuous range** of numbers.

Continuous data consist of numbers which can take any value within a given range. The volumes of the cans of soup are continuous data. Other examples of continuous data are:

- the heights of 1000 adult females
- the times taken by 100 people to run a marathon race
- the temperatures at noon at 50 seaside resorts.

Discrete data consist of values which are separated from each other. The numbers of matches inside the matchboxes are discrete data. Other examples of discrete data are:

- the marks obtained in a test taken by 40 pupils
- the numbers of copies of a newspaper sold by a newsagent on 200 days
- the number of times 100 motorists had to take their driving test before they passed.

Note

Usually discrete data consist of whole numbers. This is not essential. For example, in a test it might be possible to obtain $10\frac{1}{2}$ out of 20.

Frequency tables

One way to organise data is to arrange them in a **frequency table**. The intervals into which the data are put depend on whether the data are continuous or discrete. For continuous data, the end of one interval will be the beginning of the next. For discrete data, there will be a gap between intervals. Below are frequency tables for masses (continuous) and for exam marks (discrete).

Mass (kg)	60–70	70–80	80–90
Frequency	5	8	7

Mark	0–9	10–19	20–29	30–40
Frequency	2	8	12	7

Here the masses x kg which fall in the first interval of the first table obey $60 \leq x < 70$. The marks y which fall in the first interval of the second table obey $0 \leq y \leq 9$.

Rounding

We cannot give exact values for continuous data. The figures must be **rounded**. If a value is rounded to the nearest integer, then a value rounded to 62 could be anywhere between 61.5 and 62.5. An interval of 60–69 in a frequency table will cover values between 59.5 and 69.5. The frequency table for mass above will be written like this.

Mass (kg)	60–69	70–79	80–90
Frequency	5	8	7

Hence the masses x kg which fall in the first interval obey

$$59.5 \le x < 69.5.$$

EXERCISE 1A

1 Classify the following as discrete or continuous.

  a) the number of heads obtained when ten coins are spun

  b) the waiting time for a train

  c) the voltage of a car battery

  d) the number of customers of a shop in an hour

  e) the number of rolls of a die required to obtain a six

  f) the number of goals obtained in a hockey match

  g) the average number of children per family

  h) the time between successive customers entering a shop

  i) the number of potatoes in a bag sold in a supermarket

  j) the weight of a bag of potatoes sold in a supermarket

2 The lengths of nails are measured to the nearest cm. What range of lengths is covered in the interval 10–19?

3 The weights of ball-bearings are measured in grams correct to two decimal places. What range of weights is covered in the interval 1.10–1.19?

4 The age of a Japanese child is one year, the moment it is born. Its age increases by one year on the first of January every year. How many days could a Japanese child, aged two years, have lived?

*5 A set of bathroom scales can display weights either in kilograms or in stones and pounds. The value is given to the nearest kilogram or the nearest pound. If I find that I weigh 76 kg or 11 st 12 lb, what are the limits of my weight in kilograms? (1 kilogram is approximately 2.205 lb.)

1.2 Measures of central tendency

Having obtained our data, and perhaps sorted them into a frequency table, we may want to summarise them in some way.

The data might consist of the marks obtained in a test taken by nine students, and we might want to see how the class did as a whole. Suppose the marks are:

3 6 7 7 7 8 8 9 9

We could add all the marks and divide by 9. This would give us 7.11, the **mean** of the marks.

The middle mark is 7. This is the **median** mark.

The most common mark is 7. This is the **mode** or the **modal** mark.

The mean, median and mode are all **measures of central tendency** or **averages**. They are the three commonly used averages. The definitions are as follows.

Mean   The mean of a set of n terms is obtained by adding them and dividing by n.

Median   The median of a set of terms divides them into two equal halves, half above the median and half below. The median is obtained by arranging the terms in order and finding the term in the middle. If the number n of terms is odd, the middle one will be the $\frac{1}{2}(n + 1)$th term. If n is even, then take half-way between the $\frac{1}{2}n$th term and the $(\frac{1}{2}n + 1)$th term.

Mode   The mode of a set of terms is the most commonly occurring term.

Which to use?

Each of these three is a measure of where a data set is centred. There are advantages and disadvantages to each of them.

Mean
Advantages   It takes account of all the data. It is easy to handle mathematically.

Disadvantages   It can be distorted by a single value which is exceptionally high or low.

Median
Advantages   It is not affected by exceptional values.

Disadvantages   It does not take account of the values of all the data. It is difficult to handle mathematically.

Mode
Advantages   It is easy to find.

Disadvantages   It does not take account of all the data. If all the data are different, the mode does not exist. It may lie at one end of the data.

For most situations we use the mean. If the data are liable to be affected by extreme values then we use the median.

EXAMPLE 1.1

Find the mean, median and mode of the following set of data.

  12   17   14   18   15   15   17   16   15   19   20   23

Solution

There are 12 numbers and their sum is 201. Divide by 12, to find 16.75.

The mean is 16.75.

Arrange the numbers in order, as:

  12   14   15   15   15   16   17   17   18   19   20   23

The median value is the one in the middle. As there are 12 values, the median will be half-way between the sixth and seventh values.

Take the value half-way between 16 and 17.

The median is 16.5.

The most commonly occurring number is 15.

The mode is 15.

EXAMPLE 1.2

Two classes took the same exam. The first class, with 25 pupils, obtained a mean of 75. The second class, with 22 pupils, obtained a mean of 80. What was the mean mark for the two classes combined?

Solution

Note that we do not find the average of 75 and 80. We must take account of the fact that the numbers of pupils in the classes differ. We must find the total marks for both the classes and divide by 47, the total number of pupils.

Total for first class = $75 \times 25 = 1875$

Total for second class = $80 \times 22 = 1760$

Mean for both classes = $(1875 + 1760) \div 47 = 77.3$

The mean is 77.3.

EXERCISE 1B

1 Find the means and medians of the following data sets.

a) 26   29   18   31   28   26   32   20   30

b) 105   115   145   183   204   169   173   154

c) 0.04   0.12   0.08   0.13   0.09   0.11   0.10   0.04   0.03   0.06

d) 23   −29   10   9   −13   −18   15   17   −14   22   20

2   The weights, correct to the nearest gram, of ten cartons of orange juice were as follows. Find the mean and median weights.

   995   991   1004   1002   999   998   996   1002   1001   1002

3   The numbers of goals scored by a football team in 12 matches are shown below. Find the mean score and modal score.

   0   1   3   0   1   2   0   0   2   1   0   0

4   Ten children were asked how many brothers or sisters they had. The results are below. Find the mean and the modal number of brothers or sisters.

   0   3   2   1   1   2   1   0   1   3

5   The ages of ten people at a party were as listed below.

   9   8   9   35   10   9   8   7   8   9

Find the mean age and the median age. Which measure would you like to describe the party? Why?

6   The salaries of eight employees of a small company (in £1000s) are listed below

   13   14   11   51   16   20   21   19

Find the mean and median of these salaries. Which gives a better picture of the company?

7   In the four hours before lunch, a typist made an average of 3.5 mistakes per hour. In the three hours after lunch, she made an average of $4\frac{2}{3}$ mistakes per hour. Find the average number of mistakes per hour for the whole day.

8   The mean age of the 12 girls in a class is 12.3 years. The mean age of the 14 boys is 12.5 years. Find the mean age of the pupils as a whole.

*9   A factory tests the lifetime of its lightbulbs by switching ten of them on and seeing how long they last. Give two reasons why it is preferable to take the median time rather than the mean.

10   Another measure of central tendency is the **midrange**. For this take the mean of the greatest and least values. Find the midranges of the data in Question 1. What are the advantages and disadvantages of this measure?

Averages from frequency tables

The three averages discussed above can be obtained from data presented in a frequency table. Consider the table below, which gives the number of children in 70 families.

Number of children	0	1	2	3	4	5
Frequency	13	17	23	10	5	2

$= 70$

The total number of children is

$$0 \times 13 + 1 \times 17 + 2 \times 23 + 3 \times 10 + 4 \times 5 + 5 \times 2 = 123.$$

The mean number of children is therefore

$$123 \div 70, \text{ i.e. } 1.76.$$

If we arranged the families in order, there would be 13 families with no children, then 17 families with one child, and so on. The 35th and 36th families would both have two children, hence that is the median number.

By looking at the table, we can tell instantly that the modal number of children is 2.

Grouped data

When a frequency table contains grouped data, averages can only be found approximately.

Mean

Suppose we are given a table for the race times of a set of runners. Suppose there are 16 people in the range 15–20 minutes. The people might all have just exceeded 15 minutes, or they might all be just short of 20 minutes. In the absence of any more information, we assume that the times are evenly spread within the interval, as shown in Fig. 1.1. In finding the mean, therefore, we take the mid-interval value of $17\frac{1}{2}$ minutes. If the times are evenly spread about the middle of the interval, the 16 times will contribute $16 \times 17\frac{1}{2}$ to the total of all the times.

Fig. 1.1

Median

In the race example above, suppose that the median time lies within the interval 20–30 minutes, and that there are 20 runners in this interval, and that the median time will be between the fifth and sixth times. Again we assume that the times are evenly spread over the interval. Five runners are needed to reach the median. Estimate the median by the point $\frac{5}{20}$ of the way into the interval. This will be 22.5, as shown in Fig. 1.2.

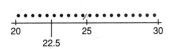

Fig. 1.2

In general, suppose there are n items in the interval, and that the median is between the rth and the $(r + 1)$th. Then the median is found by going $\dfrac{r}{n}$ of the way into the interval. This process is called **interpolation**.

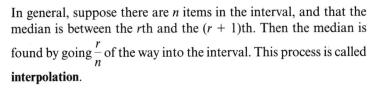

Mode

Put together the times of the runners above, as shown in Fig. 1.3. There are more runners in the interval 20–30, but there is a greater **density** of runners in the interval 15–20.

Fig. 1.3

In general, the **modal** interval is the interval which has the greatest density of data, i.e. the greatest number of data per width of interval. So for each interval, divide its frequency by the width of the interval, and pick the interval for which this result is greatest. For example, an interval of 15–20 containing 16 items of data has a greater density of data than an interval of 20–30 containing 20 items of data.

Methods of finding all three averages will be illustrated in the next example.

EXAMPLE 1.3

The table below gives the lengths of 80 fish caught by a group of fishermen. Write down the modal interval. Estimate the mean and the median.

Length (cm)	10–20	20–25	25–30	30–40
Frequency	11	19	21	29

Solution

In the third interval, there are 21 items in a width of 5 cm. In the fourth interval, there are 29 items in a width of 10 cm. The density is greatest in the third interval.

The modal interval is 25–30.

For the mean, assume that the 11 fish in the first interval have an average length of 15 cm. Make similar assumptions in the other intervals. Find the total of all the lengths and divide by 80.

$$\frac{15 \times 11 + 22.5 \times 19 + 27.5 \times 21 + 35 \times 29}{80} = 27.3$$

The mean is approximately 27.3 cm.

The median is half-way between the lengths of the 40th and the 41st fishes. There are 30 fish less than 25 cm in length, and 51 less than 30 cm. The median lies in the 25–30 interval. We need 10 fish to take the total up to 40, and there are 21 fish in the interval. So multiply 5 (the width of the interval) by $\frac{10}{21}$, and add the result on to 25. This is shown in Fig. 1.4.

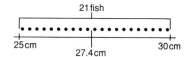

Fig. 1.4

$$25 + \frac{5 \times 10}{21} = 27.4$$

The median is approximately 27.4 cm.

EXERCISE 1C

1 The numbers of times 50 drivers had taken their driving test before passing are given in the table below. Find the mean, median and mode.

Median = 2, 25th & 26th.
between 25th & 26th

Number of tests	1	2	3	4	5
Frequency	21	13	8	5	3

= 50

2 Three coins were tossed, and the number of heads recorded. This was repeated 60 times, and the results are shown in the table below. Find the mean, median and mode.

30th and 31st
Median = 30th and 31st
= 1

Number of heads	0	1	2	3
Frequency	5	26	24	5

= 60

3 The number of people (including the driver) in a sample of 87 cars were as shown in the table. Find the mean, median and mode.

Median = 3

Number of people	1	2	3	4	5
Frequency	31	25	13	15	3

4 State the modal interval and estimate the mean and the median, for the data in each of the following tables.

a)

Range	10–20	20–30	30–40	40–50	50–60
Frequency	5	12	27	19	17

$10x$
$\dfrac{10 \times 8}{27}$
$30 +$

b)

Range	0–9	10–19	20–29	30–39	40–50
Frequency	17	27	56	62	39

$30 + (9 \times 1)$

44

c)

Range	0–0.2	0.2–0.3	0.3–0.4	0.4–0.7
Frequency	23	17	21	24

$0.3 + \left(\dfrac{0.1 \times 5}{21} \right)$ 62 =

d)

Range	100–104	105–109	110–114	115–119	120–124	125–129
Frequency	12	13	21	31	46	25

5 The journey times, correct to the nearest minute, for 100 commuters are given in the table below. Estimate the mean and median times.

Time	0–9	10–19	20–29	30–39	40–49	50+
Frequency	5	11	23	28	23	10

6 A shop records the numbers of customers who entered it per day over a period of 200 days. The results are shown in the table below. Find the mean and median of these figures.

Number	0–39	40–49	50–59	60–69	70–79	80–100
Frequency	23	18	48	53	39	19

7   The yield in pounds (lb) of an apple tree over 40 years is found. The results are shown in the table below. Find the modal interval. Find the mean and median.

Yield (lb)	60–69	70–74	75–79	80–89	90–100
Frequency	5	8	9	11	7

8   The midday temperature in a seaside resort is recorded over a period of 50 days. The results, rounded to the nearest Fahrenheit degree, are given in the table below. Find the modal interval. Find the mean and the median.

Temperature	60–69	70–79	80–84	85–89	90–100
Frequency	7	13	9	11	10

9   The lengths, in centimetres correct to one decimal place, of 60 plants are given in the table below. Find the modal interval, the mean and the median.

Length	0–9.9	10.0–14.9	15.0–19.9	20.0–30.0
Frequency	17	15	13	15

10 The pulse rates, in beats per minute, of 110 patients are given in the table below. Find the mean and median rate.

Rate	60–64	65–69	70–74	75–79	80–89	90–100
Frequency	27	21	28	16	11	7

1.3 Measures of spread

Suppose we want to compare the wealth of two nations. We might find that the people have the same average income. However, the wealths of the countries might still be very different, if in one country there is a much wider gap between rich and poor than in the other. We need a statistical measure of how widely spread the incomes are.

The measures of central tendency such as the mean, median and mode do not tell us all that we want to know about a set of data. We often want to know how widely dispersed a set of data is, as well as what its central point is.

Consider again the marks obtained in a test taken by nine students.

    3 6 7 7 7 8 8 9 9

Suppose that another class obtained the following

    1 2 4 5 6 6 8 10 10

Notice that the marks of the second class are more widely spread than those of the first. The second class has a wider spread of ability.

A number which provides information about dispersion is a **measure of spread**.

Interquartile range

The median is the point which cuts off the bottom half of the data. Similarly the **lower quartile** cuts off the bottom quarter. The **upper quartile** cuts off the top quarter of the data. If there are only a few data, we may not be able to cut off *exactly* a quarter. The convention is as follows.

Suppose there are n items of data. If $\frac{1}{4}(n + 1)$ is an integer, then take the $\frac{1}{4}(n + 1)$th term for the lower quartile. If $\frac{1}{4}(n + 1)$ is not an integer, say it lies between p and q, then take the mean of the pth and the qth terms. The upper quartile is found similarly, using $\frac{3}{4}$ instead of $\frac{1}{4}$.

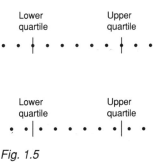

So, for example, if we have 11 items of data, the lower quartile is the third item and the upper quartile is the ninth. If we have ten items, the lower quartile is half-way between the second and the third items, and the upper quartile is half-way between the eighth and the ninth. This is shown in Fig. 1.5.

Fig. 1.5

Note
There is more than one way of defining quartiles. If n is reasonably large, there is not much difference between the definitions.

The **interquartile range** is the difference between the quartiles. It gives the width of the range which contains the middle half of the data. It is a measure of how widely spread the set of data is. The **semi-interquartile range** is half the interquartile range. So for a symmetric distribution, half the data will lie within one semi-interquartile range of the median. This is shown in Fig. 1.6.

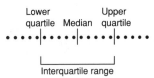

Fig. 1.6

Variance and standard deviation

Suppose we have found the mean $\bar{x}$ of a set of data. We want to find a measure of the absolute difference between each term x_i and $\bar{x}$. This can be done by squaring the difference, i.e. by finding $(x_i - \bar{x})^2$. We then find the mean of these expressions. This is the **variance** of the data.

$$S^2 = \frac{1}{n} \Sigma (x_i - \bar{x})^2$$

The **standard deviation** of the data is the square root of the variance.

$$S = \sqrt{\frac{1}{n} \Sigma (x_i - \bar{x})^2}$$

Notes

1 We took the square of the difference from the mean, $(x_i - \bar{x})^2$, in order to make it positive. Without squaring, the sum of the differences would be zero.

2 The standard deviation is measured in the same units as the original data. If the original data are in cm, then the variance is in cm^2 and the standard deviation in cm.

The form $\frac{1}{n}\Sigma\, x_i^2 - \bar{x}^2$

The variance is also written in the following form.

$$S^2 = \frac{1}{n}\Sigma\, x_i^2 - \bar{x}^2$$

The proof of this is in the Mathematical appendix on page 329. This second form is usually more convenient.

Outliers

The results we obtain from data can be distorted by exceptionally large or exceptionally small values. These can come about either through an error of measurement, or through exceptional circumstances. We often discard these exceptional values, which are called **outliers**.

By convention, we consider a value to be an outlier if it is more than 1.5 times the interquartile range distant from the nearest quartile. This is shown in Fig. 1.7.

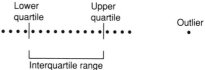

Fig. 1.7

For example, suppose we recorded the heights of 100 children. The upper quartile was 120 cm and the lower quartile 110 cm. The interquartile range is 10 cm, and hence we shall discard any value greater than $120 + 1.5 \times 10$ or less than $110 - 1.5 \times 10$. If a height of 213 cm is recorded, then it is definitely an outlier. It is quite likely that the wrong number was written down, and it should have been 113.

Which to use?

There are advantages and disadvantages for all these measures of spread.

Interquartile range

Advantages   It is not affected by extreme values, i.e. by outliers.

Disadvantages   It is difficult to handle mathematically.

Variance and standard deviation

Advantages   They are easy to handle mathematically.

Disadvantages   They can be distorted by extreme values.

For most work we use the variance or the standard deviation. In situations in which the data might be distorted by extreme values, we use the interquartile range.

Note that most scientific calculators have a facility to work out the mean and standard deviation of data. The button labelled σ_n will give the standard deviation. The button labelled σ_{n-1} will be discussed in Chapter 10.

Ordinary scientific calculators do not – and could not – have a facility to work out the median and interquartile range. This illustrates the fact that the mean and standard deviation are easier to handle mathematically than the median and interquartile range.

Often, these measures are used to compare the spread of two groups. It does not usually matter which measure is used, provided that it is the same for both groups. We could not compare the standard deviation of one group with the semi-interquartile range of the other!

EXAMPLE 1.3

Twelve people were interviewed for a job. The times of their interviews, to the nearest minute, are given below. Find the interquartile range and the standard deviation. Identify any outlier.

$$23 \quad 25 \quad 19 \quad 20 \quad 21 \quad 23 \quad 1 \quad 26 \quad 24 \quad 23 \quad 22 \quad 18$$

Solution

For the interquartile range, we need to rewrite the numbers, in order.

$$1 \quad 18 \quad 19 \quad 20 \quad 21 \quad 22 \quad 23 \quad 23 \quad 23 \quad 24 \quad 25 \quad 26$$

The value of $\frac{1}{4}(n + 1)$ is $3\frac{1}{4}$. The lower quartile is half-way between the third and fourth values, 19.5. Similarly the upper quartile is 23.5. The interquartile range is therefore 4.

The interquartile range is 4 minutes.

For the variance, we need first to find the mean.

$$\bar{x} = \tfrac{1}{12}(23 + 25 + \ldots + 18) = 20.42$$

We shall use the second version of the variance.

$$\frac{1}{n} \Sigma x_i^2 = \tfrac{1}{12}(23^2 + 25^2 + \ldots + 18^2) = 456.25$$

Hence $S^2 = 456.25 - 20.42^2 = 39.4$

Now take the square root, obtaining 6.28.

The standard deviation is 6.28 minutes.

Outliers are values more than 1.5 times the interquartile range away from the nearer quartile. These are values less than 13.5 minutes or greater than 29.5. The value of 1 minute is an outlier. Perhaps the candidate managed to annoy the interviewer the moment he entered the interview room.

The value of 1 minute is an outlier.

EXAMPLE 1.4
The IQs of ten philosophy students and twelve psychology students were measured. The results are shown in the table below. Find the mean and standard deviations for both sets of figures, and comment on the result.

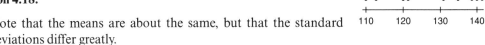

Philosophy	120	121	135	113	141	139	121	110	140	131		
Psychology	128	132	130	123	135	121	131	126	125	124	129	122

Solution
Find the means and standard deviations, using a calculator or the method above.

The IQ of philosophy students has mean 127.1 and standard deviation 10.9.

The IQ of psychology students has mean 127.2 and standard deviation 4.18.

Note that the means are about the same, but that the standard deviations differ greatly.

The group have about the same mean IQ.

The IQs of the philosophy students are more widely spread.

The difference in spread is shown in Fig. 1.8.

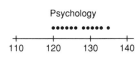

Fig. 1.8

EXAMPLE 1.5
The marks of 20 girls in an exam had mean 60 and variance 155. The marks of 25 boys had mean 58 and variance 243. Find the variance of the marks of the girls and boys combined.

Solution
Let x and y stand for the girls' and boys' marks respectively. Then the information given can be summarised as follows.

$$\tfrac{1}{20}\Sigma x = 60 \qquad \tfrac{1}{20}\Sigma x^2 - 60^2 = 155$$

$$\tfrac{1}{25}\Sigma y = 58 \qquad \tfrac{1}{25}\Sigma y^2 - 58^2 = 243$$

From these we find:

$$\Sigma x = 1200 \quad \Sigma x^2 = 75\,100 \quad \Sigma y = 1450 \quad \Sigma y^2 = 90\,175$$

From these we find that the sum of all the marks is 2650, and that the sum of the squares of all the marks is 165 275. We can now use the formula for variance again.

$$\tfrac{1}{45}(165\,275) - \left(\frac{2650}{45}\right)^2 = 204.9$$

The variance for the groups combined is 204.9.

EXERCISE 1D

1 Find the interquartile range and the variance for each of the following data sets.

a) 23   28   21   20   31   29   26   31   .33   37   38   24

b) 192   180   131   187   200   210   194   199   204   203   200

c) 1.2   1.3   1.6   1.8   1.2   1.5   1.6   2.7   1.4   1.6   1.4   1.5   1.6

2 Identify any outlier in the data sets of Question 1.

3 The temperature in a room was recorded for 12 successive days. The results are shown below. Find the interquartile range. Identify any outlier, and comment.

72   75   71   79   77   74   73   50   72   78   77   74

4 A test of manual dexterity was given to 12 applicants for a job on an assembly line. The times taken to complete the test, given correct to the nearest second, are given below. Find the mean and standard deviation. Should the data have been analysed by median and interquartile range?

45   46   34   40   58   51   98   51   55   61   48   54

5 A group of ten students took exams in Maths and French. The results are shown in the table below. Find the means and standard deviations for both exams, and comment.

Maths	66	68	51	61	73	59	61	80	72	66
French	67	34	55	91	81	62	83	29	51	81

6 I can go to work either by bus or by train. I took the bus on ten days and the train on fifteen days. The journey times, to the nearest minute, are recorded below. Find the means and standard deviations, and comment.

Bus	38	36	59	47	29	48	44	62	66	38					
Train	44	45	41	48	46	43	47	46	44	41	46	49	46	43	41

7 A food factory has two machines which make cakes. The weights, correct to the nearest gram, of samples from the machines are given in the table below. Find the means and standard deviations, and comment.

Machine A	60	62	61	59	63	60	58	62	64	63
Machine B	61	55	52	69	61	62	68	52	57	50

8   A farmer has two herds of cows. The first herd has eight animals, and their daily yield of milk, in litres, has mean 27 and variance 120. The second herd has seven animals, and their yield has mean 25 and variance 150. Find the variance of the yield of all 15 animals.

9   A doctor saw eight patients in the morning surgery, and the times spent with them had mean 14 minutes and standard deviation 9 minutes. In the evening surgery ten patients were seen, with mean time 12 minutes and standard deviation 11 minutes. Find the standard deviation for all the patients.

10   A class contains twelve girls and fifteen boys. The ages of the girls have mean 12.3 years and standard deviation 0.6 years. The ages of the boys have mean 12.4 years and standard deviation 0.8 years. Find the standard deviation of the ages of the class as a whole.

11   The sum of the first n integers is $\frac{1}{2}n(n + 1)$, and the sum of the squares of the first n integers is $\frac{1}{6}n(n + 1)(2n + 1)$. Find the mean and standard deviation of the data set 1, 2, ..., n.

12   The mean deviation of data is found by finding the mean of the absolute difference between the data and the mean, i.e.

$$\frac{\Sigma\,|\,x_i - \bar{x}\,|}{n}$$

Find the mean deviations of the data sets in Question 1.

13   The range of data is the difference between the lowest value and the highest. Find the range of the data sets in Question 1. What is the main disadvantage of this measure of spread?

LONGER EXERCISE

Other means

The mean defined in this chapter is the **arithmetic** mean. There are other sorts of mean. Here we define and investigate two others.

The **geometric** mean of n positive numbers is found by multiplying them and taking the nth root.

$$G = \sqrt[n]{x_1 x_2 ... x_n}$$

The **harmonic** mean is found by finding the arithmetic mean of the reciprocals of the data, and then dividing that into 1.

$$H = \frac{1}{\frac{1}{n}\left(\frac{1}{x_1} + \frac{1}{x_2} + ... + \frac{1}{x_n}\right)}$$

1   Find the arithmetic, geometric and harmonic means of the following data.

   25   27   30   29   19   39   18   35

2   What happens to these means if one of the data values is very small, or very large?

3 *The following illustrates the use of the geometric mean.* Suppose the retail price index at the beginning of a decade was fixed at 100, and that by the end of the decade it had risen to 350. What was the index half-way through the decade? Find both the arithmetic and geometric means.

Prices tend to rise exponentially. In this case, the index n years after the start of the decade might be given by $100 \times 3.5^{n/10}$. Which mean fits this formula better?

In what other situations would you use the geometric mean?

4 *The following illustrates the use of the harmonic mean.* A journey is divided into five stages of ten miles each. The speeds in each stage were 20 m.p.h., 65 m.p.h., 75 m.p.h., 25 m.p.h. and 10 m.p.h. Find the arithmetic and harmonic means of these speeds. Which gives the average speed for the whole journey?

In what other situations would you use the harmonic mean?

5 A computer can do all the donkey work of evaluating means. See page 156 for an investigation concerning them.

EXAMINATION QUESTIONS

1 The mean height of a sample of 15 boys is 1.38 m and the mean height of a sample of 20 girls is 1.22 m. Find the mean height of the combined sample of boys and girls.

L 1994

2 Summarised below are the values of the orders (to the nearest £) taken by a sales representative for a wholesale firm during a particular year.

a) Using interpolation, estimate the median and the semi-interquartile range for these data.

b) Explain why the median and semi-interquartile range might be more appropriate summary measures for these data than the mean and standard deviation.

L 1993

Value of order (£)	Number of orders
Less than 10	3
10–19	9
20–29	15
30–39	27
40–49	29
50–59	34
60–69	19
70–99	10
100 or more	4

3 A grouped frequency distribution of the ages of 358 employees in a factory is shown in the table.

Age last birthday	16–20	21–25	26–30	31–35	36–40	41–45	46–50	51–60	61–
Number of employees	36	56	58	52	46	38	36	36	0

Estimate, to the nearest month, the mean and the standard deviation of the ages of these employees.

Graphically, or otherwise, estimate

a) the median and the interquartile range of the ages, each to the nearest month,

b) the percentage, to one decimal place, of the employees who are over 27 years old and under 55 years old.

L 1988

4 The manager of a car showroom monitored the numbers of cars sold during two successive five-day periods. During the first five days the numbers of cars sold per day had mean 1.8 and variance 0.56. During the next five days the numbers of cars sold per day had mean 2.8 and variance 1.76. Find the mean and variance of the numbers of cars sold per day during the full ten days.

N 1991

5 In each of the twenty Olympic Games this century, there has been a Men's Discus event. The distance of the Gold medal throw has ranged from 36.04 m in 1900 to 68.82 m in 1988. The total distance of the winning throws comes to 1082.64 m. What is the mean distance?

a) The variance of the Men's Gold medal distances is 102.110 m². Calculate the total of the squares of the distances.

b) Women have had a Discus event in each of the 14 games since 1928. The mean of the Women's Gold medal throws is 56.34 m. Calculate the mean distance for Men's and Women's events combined.

c) The total of the squares of the Women's Gold medal distances is 46074.28. Use this information to calculate the variance of the distances for Men's and Women's events combined.

d) Comment briefly on the validity of combining the two collections of data.

O 1991

6 A manufacturer produces electrical cable which is sold on reels. The reels are supposed to hold 100 metres of cable. In the quality control department the length of cable on randomly chosen reels is measured. These measurements are recorded as deviations, in centimetres, from 100 metres. (So, for example, a length of 99.84 metres is recorded as -16.)

For a sample of 20 reels the recorded values, x, are summarised by:

$$\Sigma x = -86 \qquad \Sigma x^2 = 4281$$

(i) Calculate the mean and standard deviation of the values of x.

(ii) Hence find the mean and standard deviation, in metres, of the lengths of cable on the 20 reels.

(iii) Later it is noticed that one of the values of x is -47, and it is thought that so large a value is likely to be an error. Give a reason to support this view.

(iv) Find the new mean and standard deviation of the values of x when the value -47 is discarded.

MEI 1992

Summary and key points

1.1 Discrete data take fixed values. Continuous data can take any values within a range.

1.2 The mean of n numbers is found by adding them and dividing by n. The median is found by arranging them in order and taking the middle value. The mode is the most frequent value.

If data is presented in a frequency table, the modal interval is the interval with the greatest density of frequency. The mean and median can be approximated by assuming that the data is evenly spread within each interval.

When finding the mean, divide by the number of data, not by the number of intervals.

Mean, median and mode are all measures of central tendency.

1.3 The lower and upper quartiles cut off $\frac{1}{4}$ and $\frac{3}{4}$ of the frequency respectively. The difference between the quartiles is the inter-quartile range.

Suppose the mean of a set of data is $\bar{x}$. The variance of the data is found using either of the two following formulae.

$$\frac{1}{n}\Sigma(x_i - \bar{x})^2 \text{ or } \frac{1}{n}\Sigma x_i^2 - \bar{x}^2$$

The standard deviation is the square root of the variance.

Interquartile range, variance and standard deviation are all measures of spread.

Presenting data

The previous chapter demonstrated how to summarise data numerically, by averages or measures of spread. In this chapter we concentrate on presenting data pictorially, by a statistical diagram of some sort. You are probably familiar with many statistical diagrams, such as pie charts, bar charts, pictograms and so on. In this chapter we describe other sorts of diagrams.

2.1 Histograms

A **histogram** is a type of bar chart, and is used to illustrate numerical data. Frequencies are displayed by bars, and the frequency of the data falling in an interval is proportional to the *area* of the bar. The frequency is not necessarily directly proportional to the *height* of the bar.

The data in a frequency table may fall into intervals of varying widths. When planning a histogram, we need to decide upon a standard width of interval, usually the most common width. The height of a bar will then measure the frequency per standard interval. We indicate our choice by labelling the vertical axis as, for example, 'Frequency per 10 cm interval'.

Suppose we are measuring heights of children, and that the most common interval is 10 cm. Suppose part of the frequency table looks like this.

Height (cm)	60–70	70–90
Frequency	140	200

The interval 60–70 is the standard width, hence its height is 140. The interval 70–90 is twice the standard width. It can be thought of as comprising two standard intervals, of width 10 cm. If the frequency of 200 is divided equally between the standard intervals, each will receive half, 100. So we halve the frequency to obtain the height of the bar of this wide interval. This will ensure that the *area* of the bar is proportional to the total corresponding frequency. The part of the histogram is shown in Fig. 2.1.

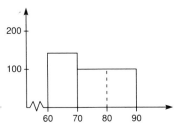

Fig. 2.1

Similarly, if an interval is a third of the standard width, then we triple the height of the corresponding bar. If an interval is half the standard width, then we double the height of its bar. Without these adjustments, the histogram would be misleading. An extra wide interval would seem to contain more data than it did. Fig. 2.2 shows the histogram without the adjustment.

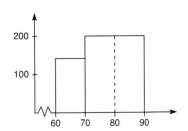

Fig. 2.2

Shape of histogram

The shape of the histogram can display facts about the distribution. This is especially useful when two distributions are being compared.

Symmetry and skewness

Some histograms are symmetrical about a central value, as in Fig. 2.3. Then that value is both the mean and median of the data.

Fig. 2.3

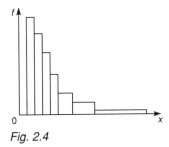

Fig. 2.4

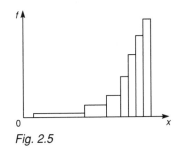

Fig. 2.5

Figures 2.4 and 2.5 show shapes which are skewed to one side. Figure 2.4 has **positive** skew, and Fig. 2.5 has **negative** skew. We can see that, in Fig. 2.4, most of the figures have low values, but there are a few high values. Two examples of data which might have positive skew are as follows.

- *Full-time salaries of employees*   Most of the employees of a firm earn roughly the same amount of money, but there are a few managers who make much more.
- *Times of a race*   Most runners finish the race in roughly the same time, but there are a few stragglers who come in much later.

These few large values will have a disproportionate effect on the mean. Hence if data has positive skew, the mean will be larger than the median. Similarly, if data has negative skew, the mean will be less than the median.

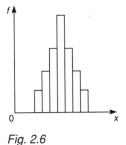

Fig. 2.6

Variance

The variance of a set of data shows how widely spread the data are. This can also be found from the shape of the histogram. In Fig. 2.6 the data is clustered closely round a central value. Hence the variance of the data will be small. In Fig. 2.7 the data is widely spread, and the variance of the data will be large.

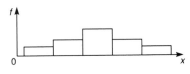

Fig. 2.7

Modal group

The modal group is the group with the highest *density* of frequency. This can be easily identified from the histogram, as the group with the tallest bar. In Fig. 2.8, which shows the distribution of marks, the modal interval is seen to be 70–75.

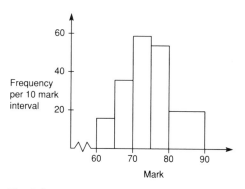

Fig. 2.8

Frequency polygon

A **frequency polygon** conveys exactly the same information as a histogram. It is constructed by drawing lines joining the midpoints of the tops of the bars. The bars themselves need not be shown. An example is shown in Fig.2.9.

Two pairs of frequency polygons are shown. The first pair, in Fig. 2.10, show data sets which have the same variance but different means. The second pair, in Fig. 2.11, show data sets with the same mean but different variances.

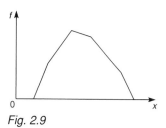

Fig. 2.9

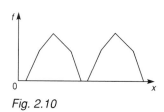

Fig. 2.10

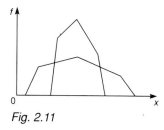

Fig. 2.11

EXAMPLE 2.1

The midday temperature in a seaside resort was measured over a period of 100 days. The results are shown in the table below. Plot a histogram to illustrate the data.

Midday temperature (°F)	60–65	65–70	70–72.5	72.5–75	75–80	80–90
Frequency	8	18	12	15	27	20

Solution

Let the standard width be 5°. There are two intervals of width 2.5°, so we double the heights of their bars. There is one interval of width 10°, so we halve the height of its bar. The histogram is shown in Fig. 2.12.

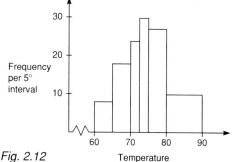

Fig. 2.12

EXAMPLE 2.2

Draw a frequency polygon to illustrate the data in Example 2.1.

Solution

No extra calculation is needed. Starting at the smallest value, at (60, 0), we draw a line to the centre of the top of the first bar, at (62.5, 8). We join this to the centre of the second bar, at (67.5, 18) and continue in this way to the largest possible value at (90, 0). The result is shown in Fig. 2.13.

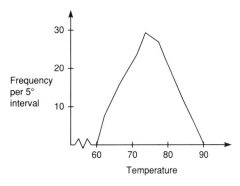

Fig. 2.13

EXERCISE 2A

1 The number of customers received per day in a shop was recorded over a period of 100 days, as shown in the table below. Construct a histogram to illustrate the data.

Number	0–19	20–29	30–39	40–49	50–80
Frequency	18	17	25	16	24

2 Certain batteries are sold as having a voltage of 6 V. A sample of 50 was tested and the results, in volts, are shown in the table below. Construct a histogram to illustrate the data.

Voltage	5.6–5.8	5.8–5.9	5.9–6.0	6.0–6.1	6.1–6.4
Frequency	9	6	13	10	12

3 The ages of a group of pensioners are given in the table below. Construct a histogram to illustrate the data. Describe the skewness of the distribution.

Age	65–69	70–74	75–79	80–89	90–
Frequency	38	25	14	16	8

4 A teacher sets an investigation, to be completed within three hours. The times, in minutes, that the students took to complete the investigation are shown in the table below. Construct a histogram to illustrate the data and describe its skewness.

Time	120–150	150–160	160–170	170–175	175–180
Frequency	12	5	11	9	14

5 The 60 employees of a firm were asked how far from work they lived. The results, in miles, are given in the table below. Construct a histogram to illustrate the data and comment on its skewness.

Distance	0–1	1–2	2–4	4–6	6–10
Frequency	13	8	15	10	14

6 A motorcycle courier firm delivers parcels throughout a city. The delivery times, in hours, of 70 parcels are given in the table below. Construct a histogram to illustrate the data and comment on its skewness.

Time	0–0.5	0.5–1	1–1.5	1.5–2	2–3	3–5
Frequency	12	21	13	9	11	4

7, 8 and 9   Construct frequency polygons to illustrate the data of Questions 1, 2 and 3.

10 The numbers, in thousands, of patients per year contracting a particular disease over a period of 60 years are given in the table below. Construct a histogram to illustrate the data. Explain the shape of the distribution.

Number	0–10	10–30	30–50	50–70	70–100
Frequency	17	13	5	10	15

2.2 Stem and leaf diagrams

If data are organised into frequency tables, information may be lost. In Example 2.1 above, we know that the midday temperature was between 60° and 65° on eight days. We don't know whether the data are closer to 60 or to 65.

A **stem and leaf diagram** is a type of bar chart in which information is not lost. They have become fashionable over the past few years. (There are fashions in Statistics as well as in clothing.) In a stem and leaf diagram, the numbers themselves form the bars.

Suppose the data are organised into groups of ten: 10 to 19, 20 to 29, 30 to 39 and 40 to 49. The stems will consists of the first digits, 1, 2, 3 or 4. The leaves consist of the second digit, laid along the appropriate stem. The final diagram might look like this.

```
1 | 0  2  3  5  8  8  8  9
2 | 0  0  1  1  3  4  6  7  8  8  8  9  9  9
3 | 0  1  2  3  3  4  8  9
4 | 0  2  2  4
```

It is important to explain the entries. In this diagram, for example,

    2 | 1 means 21.

If the data contain the values 2.1, 2.3, 3.2 and so on, the explanation would be:

    2 | 1 means 2.1.

Stem and leaf diagrams are useful when we have two groups of data. The diagrams are placed 'back to back', so that comparisons can be made. Sometimes the stems may be written as 10, 20 etc instead of 1, 2 etc.

EXAMPLE 2.2

A teacher sets the same end-of-year test to classes in two successive years. The results are given below. Construct a stem and leaf diagram to illustrate the data, and comment.

1995 results					**1996 results**				
23	34	38	39	19	35	39	31	29	35
17	21	44	31	23	31	29	19	20	34
43	12	39	37	24	32	37	27	36	34
15	41	38	31	27	32	35	30	24	30
10	27	20	27	39	30	31	32	37	33

Solution

Take stems of 1, 2, 3 and 4. The data can be arranged 'back to back', so that the two years can be compared. The result is shown below.

```
                   1995   1996
          9 7 5 2 0 |1| 9                                          | 2| 4 means 24
      7 7 7 4 3 3 1 0 |2| 0  4  7  9  9
  9 9 9 8 8 7 4 1 1 |3| 0  0  0  1  1  1  2  2  2  3  4  4  5  5  5  6  7  7  9
              1 3 4 |4|
```

Note that the 1996 figures are more concentrated.

The 1996 class has a narrower range of ability.

If we want to show more detail, we might choose to have two lines per stem instead of one. Each line then represents a spread of five instead of ten.

EXAMPLE 2.3

The IQs of 30 students are listed below. Construct a stem and leaf diagram, using two lines per stem and stems of 11, 12 and 13. From the diagram find the median.

110	122	119	114	135	134	130	138	124	127	123	120	114	128	125
113	131	117	128	116	123	117	114	132	128	121	132	137	117	126

Solution

The first line has a stem of 11 and will include 110 up to 114, and the second stem will include 115 up to 119. The completed diagram is as follows.

```
11 | 0  3  4  4  4
11 | 6  7  7  7  9
12 | 0  1  2  3  3  4        12| 3 means 123
12 | 5  6  7  8  8  8
13 | 0  1  2  2  4
13 | 5  7  8
```

The median is half-way between the 15th and 16th terms. This can be found from the diagram, as 123.5.

The median is 123.5.

EXERCISE 2B

1 A group of 30 people were asked to guess how many apples there were in a bag. The results are listed below. Construct a stem and leaf diagram, using stems of 2, 3 and 4.

```
28   35   31   47   21   44   30   37   28   30   46   43   27   36   40
31   26   29   33   42   37   32   35   31   26   33   41   42   46   40
```

2 The scores obtained by a basketball team are listed below. Contruct a stem and leaf diagram, using stems of 0, 1, 2, 3, 4 and 5.

```
38   48   51   29   9   35   41   28   30   38   35   27   19   15   28   39
```

3 The ages of a group of voters were as listed below. Construct a stem and leaf diagram, using stems of 1, 2, 3, 4 and 5.

```
43   18   20   39   58   34   54   29   19   19   40   39   20   40   44

55   51   36   37   39   53   57   19   18   29   40   38   32   31   42
```

4 A group of people were asked how many credit cards they possessed. The results are shown below. Construct a stem and leaf diagram, with stems 0 and 1, and two lines per stem.

```
0   2   1   3   1   6   1   11   0   2   1   5   12   4   2   0   1
```

5 Construct a stem and leaf diagram for the data in Question 1, using stems of 2, 3, 4 and 5, and two lines per stem.

6 Construct a stem and leaf diagram for the data in Question 3, using stems of 1, 2, 3, 4 and 5, and two lines per stem.

7 The driving test was taken by 40 people, of whom 20 passed and 20 failed. Their ages are listed below. Construct a back to back stem and leaf diagram, and comment.

Passing	**Failing**
17 28 23 17 18 19 22 31 33 21	18 19 17 17 26 39 31 22 17 19
18 17 19 27 29 31 17 30 20 27	17 17 29 20 18 17 30 41 20 17

8 The points scored by two rugby teams over 20 games are as listed below. Construct a back to back stem and leaf diagram, and comment.

Team A	**Team B**
12 3 21 5 10 14 7 35 9 16	20 31 19 6 19 31 39 9 18 25
8 6 0 11 10 0 21 13 16 3	25 43 17 29 3 12 0 42 21 19

9 Two journalists were compared for egotism. Ten articles by each journalist were investigated and the number of occurrences of 'I', 'me' etc were recorded, as shown below. Construct a back to back stem and leaf diagram, and comment.

Journalist A   **Journalist B**

10 12 9 8 10 17 18 7 14 16   5 8 3 11 6 9 1 13 10 6

10 Use the stem and leaf diagram for Question 3 to find the median age of the voters.

11 Use the stem and leaf diagram for Question 7 to find the medians and interquartile ranges for the two groups. Comment on the differences.

12 Use the stem and leaf diagram for Question 8 to find the medians and interquartile ranges for the two teams. Comment on the differences.

2.3 Cumulative frequency

Suppose an exam is set, for which the bottom 30% of the candidates will fail, the next 60% will pass and the top 10% will get a distinction. To find the pass mark, the examiners will need to find the mark which cuts off the bottom 30%. At the pass mark, the **cumulative frequency** will be 30% of the total frequency.

Suppose the frequency table showing the marks of 1000 candidates is as follows.

Number	0–19	20–39	40–59	60–79	80–100
Frequency	98	287	406	147	62

We then see that 385 scored under 40, 791 under 60 and so on. These frequencies, found by totalling all the preceding frequencies are the cumulative frequencies. If we plot the cumulative frequencies against the corresponding marks, we obtain the graph of Fig. 2.14.

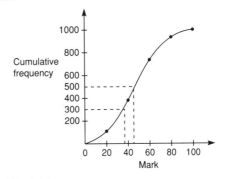

If 30% fail then 300 candidates will fail. From the graph we can see that about 300 candidates scored less than 38. Hence the passmark is about 38.

In general, cumulative frequencies are found by adding (i.e. accumulating) all the frequencies up to certain values. A graph of the cumulative frequencies is a **cumulative frequency graph**, or **ogive**. The points are plotted at the left ends of the intervals, not in the middles. In the graph above, illustrating the marks obtained in an exam, the point (40,385) on the graph indicates that 385 candidates got less than 40 marks.

Fig. 2.14

Median and quartiles

The median is the value which separates the top half of the data from the bottom. Hence at the median the cumulative frequency is half the total frequency. The **lower quartile** and **upper quartile** are the values at which the cumulative frequencies are a quarter and three-quarters of the total, respectively. The median and the quartiles can be found from the cumulative frequency graph. The median mark for the exam above corresponds to the 500th mark, which is shown to be about 46.

Percentiles

Using the cumulative frequency graph, we can find the value which cuts off any given proportion of the frequency. These proportions can be given as percentages, and the cut-off points are **percentiles**. The tenth percentile, for example, will cut off the bottom 10 per cent of the total frequency.

EXAMPLE 2.5

A piece of music was played to a group of 80 people and afterwards they were asked to estimate how long it had lasted. The estimates, in minutes, are given in the table below. Find the cumulative frequencies and plot a cumulative frequency curve.

Find the median and the interquartile range. If in fact the music lasted 17.5 minutes find how many people overestimated the time.

Time	10–14	15–19	20–24	25–29	30–34
Frequency	4	19	27	25	5

Solution

We find the cumulative frequencies by making a running total of the frequencies.

Cumulative Frequency	4	23	50	75	80

From this, we see there were four people whose estimate was less than 15. Plot a point at (15, 4). Similarly, plot points at (20, 23), (25, 50), (30, 75) and (35, 80). Join the points by a **smooth** curve. The result is shown in Fig. 2.15.

There are 80 people altogether, and hence 40 people will estimate less than the median time. Find 40 on the cumulative frequency axis, go across to the curve, then down to the time axis. This gives 23 minutes approximately.

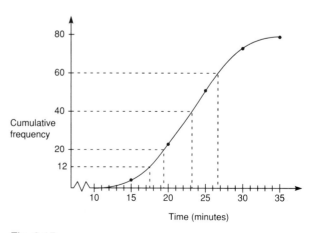

Fig. 2.15

The median is 23 minutes.

The quartiles correspond to cumulative frequencies of 20 and 60. The lower and upper quartiles are therefore approximately 19 and 27. The interquartile range is 8.

The interquartile range is 8 minutes.

From the graph, the cumulative frequency corresponding to a time of 17.5 minutes is 12. Hence 68 people estimated a time greater than 17.5 minutes.

The time was overestimated by 68 people.

EXERCISE 2C

1   The IQs of 120 students are listed in the table below. Draw a cumulative frequency curve, and from that estimate the median and the interquartile range.

IQ	100–104	105–109	110–114	115–119	120–124	125–130
Frequency	9	18	38	31	17	7

2   The 80 employees of a firm were asked how long they had taken getting to work. The results, in minutes, are listed in the table below. Draw a cumulative frequency curve, and from that estimate the median and the interquartile range.

Time	0–10	10–20	20–30	30–40	40–50
Frequency	11	17	21	17	14

3   An exam is taken by 800 students. The results are listed in the table below. Draw a cumulative frequency curve. If about two-thirds of the students are to pass, what is the pass mark? If the top eighth of the students will get a distinction, what mark will they achieve?

Mark (%)	30–39	40–49	50–59	60–69	70–79	80–100
Frequency	63	142	219	162	141	73

4   The salaries, in £1000s, of the 200 employees of a company are given in the table below. Draw a cumulative frequency curve. From your curve, estimate the median salary. Estimate the mean salary.

Salary	10–15	15–20	20–25	25–30	30–40	40–60
Frequency	32	87	45	24	8	4

5   The times, in minutes, that 100 patients spent waiting to be seen by a doctor are given in the table below. Draw a cumulative frequency curve, and from that estimate the median. Estimate the mean time.

Time	0–5	5–10	10–20	20–30	30–40	40–60
Frequency	23	31	19	11	9	7

6 In a nation, the annual inflation rate has been measured over 40 years. The results are listed in the table below. Draw a cumulative frequency curve, and from that estimate the median and the quartiles.

Rate (%)	0–5	5–10	10–15	15–20	20–25
Frequency	11	17	5	4	3

7 The scores obtained by a cricketer in 50 innings are given in the table below. Construct a cumulative frequency curve, and estimate the median. Estimate the tenth percentile.

Score	0–9	10–19	20–39	40–79	80–110
Frequency	11	8	12	12	7

8 The weights of 100 apples are given in the table below. Construct a cumulative frequency graph from the data. The apples are to be classified as small, medium and large in approximately equal numbers. Estimate the weights between which the medium apples lie.

Weight (grams)	80–90	90–100	100–110	110–120	120–130
Frequency	9	25	37	17	12

9 A new insecticide spray is tested in a room containing 100 mosquitoes. The numbers of insects still alive after given periods of time are given in the table below. Draw a curve to illustrate the data. After what time will half the insects be dead?

Time (minutes)	5	10	15	20	25	30
Number alive	92	67	41	17	8	0

*10 What region on a cumulative frequency graph will correspond to the modal interval?

2.4 Box and whisker plots

Another way of displaying data is a **box and whisker plot**, also called a **box plot**. An example of this type of diagram is shown in Fig. 2.16.

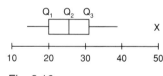

Fig. 2.16

The central half of the data, the values between the quartiles, are shown in a box. From the box stretch lines, the 'whiskers', to the rest of the data. The lower quartile, the median and the upper quartile are often denoted by Q_1, Q_2 and Q_3 respectively. In Fig. 2.16, $Q_1 = 20$ and $Q_3 = 31$.

Outliers

As we saw in Chapter 1, unusually large or small values are called **outliers**. Often they are not included in the whiskers, but instead are shown by crosses. The convention is that a value is an outlier if its distance from the nearer quartile is greater than 1.5 times the interquartile range.

The interquartile range in Fig. 2.16 is 11. Multiply this by 1.5, obtaining 16.5. The value of 50 is more than 16.5 distant from the upper quartile, 31. Hence it is shown by a cross.

Median

The median can be marked on the box. If the data has a symmetrical distribution, then the median will lie in the middle of the box. If the data has positive skew, then the median will be closer to the lower quartile than to the upper, and vice versa, as shown in Fig. 2.17.

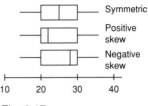

Fig. 2.17

Comparison

Two groups can be compared by showing their box and whisker plots next to each other. Figure 2.18 shows the marks achieved by two classes. We can see that Class A achieved higher marks overall, and that Class B has a narrower spread of ability.

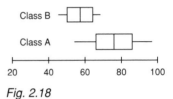

Fig. 2.18

EXAMPLE 2.4

A motorist keeps a record of his journey time to work. The results, to the nearest minute, for 20 working days are given below. Construct a box plot for the data and comment on the skewness of the data.

45 52 43 48 46 49 44 58 62 68

78 48 46 51 54 59 56 46 47 50

Solution

Arrange the data in increasing order.

43 44 45 46 46 46 47 48 48 49 50 51 52 54 56 58 59 62 68 78

The median is 49.5. The lower and upper quartiles are 46 and 57. The interquartile range is 11, and hence any value more than 1.5 $\times$11 from the nearest quartile will be an outlier. The only outlier is 78. Excluding this outlier, the whiskers stretch to 43 on the left and 68 on the right. The completed diagram is shown in Fig. 2.19.

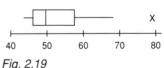

Fig. 2.19

Note that the right-hand whisker is longer than the left. The data is more concentrated in the lower half. Notice also that the median is closer to the lower quartile than to the upper.

The data has positive skew.

EXERCISE 2D

1 The manageress of a shop keeps records of the times, in minutes, between successive purchases. The results are listed below. Construct a box and whisker plot to illustrate the data, indicating any outliers. Describe the skewness of the distribution.

    2   3   8   1   2   12   5   6   2   3   1   1   2   3   4   2   5   6   16   3   2

2 Over a period of 20 working days, the number of typing errors made by a typist in a given hour are as listed below. Construct a box and whisker plot to illustrate the data, indicating any outliers. Describe the skewness of the distribution.

    7   3   2   4   3   6   10   6   7   8   23   7   8   5   3   6   8   9   11   8

3 Over a period of 18 days, the numbers of people who saw a particular film in a cinema are as listed below. Construct a box and whisker plot to illustrate the data, indicating any outliers. Describe the skewness of the distribution.

    57   68   17   62   69   55   42   38   63   51   37   38   37   49   51   61   58   66

4 The numbers of hours spent sleeping, by a group of 20 teenagers, are listed below. Construct a box and whisker plot, identify any outliers, and comment on the skewness.

    8   6   7   9   12   7   9   10   8   9   8   9   10   7   8   8   7   9   10   8

5 Delivery times, in days, of items sent by two mail order companies are listed below. Construct box and whisker plots next to each other, and comment on the differences.

Company A								Company B							
10	15	6	23	12	9	3	3	11	12	13	10	9	12	15	12
19	20	5	4	32	18	12	17	15	12	13	15	16	13	10	9

6 The lengths of words in crosswords from the *Daily Sneer* and the *Shout* were examined. The results are listed below. Construct box and whisker plots next to each other, and comment on the differences.

Daily Sneer										Shout									
4	14	12	7	8	5	6	6	9	10	5	6	7	4	5	3	6	7	8	9
13	3	7	5	6	8	8	4	3	9	4	5	3	6	7	8	4	6	5	4

7 The ages at marriage for 20 couples are as listed below. Construct box and whisker plots next to each other, and comment on the differences.

Men										Women									
23	19	38	21	18	25	38	41	29	25	18	16	18	20	25	22	21	19	20	21
19	16	35	30	23	24	38	23	19	26	23	26	27	21	23	20	17	19	21	20

8 Two machines both make bolts which should have a length of 31 mm. Samples of ten bolts are taken from each machine. The results, in mm, are given below. Construct box and whisker plots next to each other, and comment on the differences.

Machine A					Machine B				
31.1	31.2	31.0	30.8	30.9	30.5	31.7	31.2	31.0	31.9
30.8	31.2	31.0	29.8	31.3	30.7	31.2	32.1	31.5	31.8

9 In two countries, the workers have approximately the same median income, but the spread of income is much wider in one country than in the other. Sketch box and whisker plots to illustrate these facts.

10 Batsman A is usually out for less than 20 runs, but occasionally he makes a large score. Batsman B usually scores between 40 and 60, and never makes a large score. Construct box and whisker plots to illustrate these facts.

11 Sketch box and whisker plots to illustrate the weights of

    a) 100 randomly selected cats,   **b)** 100 randomly selected dogs.

LONGER EXERCISE

Population pyramids

Figure 2.20 is an example of a population pyramid. It shows the structure of a population, classified by age and sex. Each bar gives, as a percentage of the total population, the proportion of men or women in each age range.

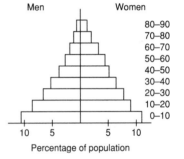

Fig. 2.20

1 State some facts about the population illustrated in Fig. 2.20.

2 Sketch population pyramids for:

    a) a country with high infant mortality

    b) a country with a rapidly growing population

    c) a country with a declining population

    d) a country which fought a very bloody war, 20 years ago.

3 A country with a stable age structure will have enough people of working age to support both the elderly and the young. Sketch a population pyramid for such a country.

4 How would a population pyramid for Britain today differ from one in 1200, or in 1800, or in 1918?

EXAMINATION QUESTIONS

1 The following table shows the time, to the nearest minute, spent reading during a particular day by a group of school children.

Time	10–19	20–24	25–29	30–39	40–49	50–64	65–89
Number of children	8	15	25	18	12	7	5

    a) Represent these data by a histogram.

    b) Comment on the shape of the distribution.

L 1993

2 A random sample of 51 people were asked to record the number of miles they travelled by car in a given week. The distances, to the nearest mile, are shown below.

```
67  76  85  42  93  48  93  46
52  72  77  53  41  48  86  78
56  80  70  70  66  62  54  85
60  58  43  58  74  44  52  74
52  82  78  47  66  50  67  87
78  86  94  63  72  63  44  47
57  68  81
```

a) Construct a stem and leaf diagram to represent these data.

b) Find the median and quartiles of this distribution.

c) Draw a box plot to represent these data.

d) Give one advantage of using:

   (i) a stem and leaf diagram,   (ii) a box plot,

   to illustrate data such as that given above.

L 1992

3 The haemoglobin levels in a sample of 100 people were measured correct to one decimal place. The results are summarised in the table on the right.

Haemoglobin level	Number of people
9.0–9.9	1
10.0–10.9	10
11.0–11.9	14
12.0–12.9	15
13.0–13.9	23
14.0–14.9	21
15.0–15.9	13
16.0–16.9	3

(i) Draw a cumulative frequency graph for this data and hence estimate the median, and the 15th and 85th percentiles.

(ii) Calculate estimates for the mean and standard deviation of the haemoglobin levels. Your working must be clearly shown.

C AS 1992

4 As part of a GCSE Mathematics coursework assignment the following grouped frequency distribution of the heights of the 32 pupils in a class was compiled.

Height (cm)	130–145	145–155	155–160	160–165	165–180
Number of pupils	3	10	8	7	4

(i) Draw, on graph paper, the histogram for this distribution. Indicate clearly the scales to which it is drawn.

(ii) Estimate the probability that a pupil chosen at random from the class was less than 150 cm tall.

(iii) Find the largest possible value for the mean height of the 32 pupils consistent with this distribution.

SMP 1993

Summary and key points

2.1 A histogram displays the density of frequency of data. The modal group is the group with the greatest density, i.e. the tallest bar.

If the intervals containing the data are not equal, then adjust the heights of their bars. If an interval is twice the standard width, for example, then halve the height of its bar.

If the histogram is not symmetrical, then it is skew. The skewness is positive or negative depending on whether the peak appears to the left or the right of the mean.

2.2 A stem and leaf diagram contains all the original data. For two-digit data, the stems consist of the first digits, and the leaves of the second digits.

2.3 The cumulative frequency at a value is the running total of the frequencies up to that value. Cumulative frequencies can be illustrated on a cumulative frequency graph.

Be sure to put the points of the graph at the left ends of intervals, not in the middles.

The median and quartiles can be found as the values which cut off 50%, 25% and 75% of the frequency.

2.4 A box and whisker plot shows the region between the quartiles as a box, and the rest of the data as whiskers. Any point more than 1.5 times the interquartile range away from the nearer quartile is an outlier, and is shown by a cross rather than as part of a whisker.

CHAPTER **3**

Probability

Chapter outline

3.1 Combinations of probabilities
3.2 Tree diagrams
3.3 Permutations and combinations
3.4 Conditional probability

The probability of an event measures our belief that it is true. If an event is impossible, we give it a probability of 0. If it is certain, we give it a probability of 1. If an event is just as likely to happen as not to happen, we give it a probability of $\frac{1}{2}$.

The ideas of probability are used throughout statistics. In particular, statistics are often concerned with picking items at random from a population. In an opinion poll, 1000 or so people may be picked from the electorate. When a factory tests the quality of its output, it may pick a sample of the day's production. We often have to work out the probability that a certain collection of items is picked – that an opinion poll contains a certain proportion of Labour voters, or that a quality control sample contains a particular proportion of defective items.

3.1 Combinations of probabilities

The meanings of words used in probability are not always exactly the same as their everyday usage. We speak of **experiments, outcomes** and **events**.

Experiments

An **experiment** or **trial** is some activity with a variable result. The experiment might be to roll a die, or to pick a person at random from the population.

Outcomes and sample space

The possible results of an experiment are the **outcomes**. Possible outcomes of the experiments above are that the die gives a 5, or that *you* are the person selected. The set of all possible outcomes is the **sample space**. The basic rule used to find probability is:

If an experiment has n equally likely outcomes, then each outcome has probability $\frac{1}{n}$.

So if the die is fair, the probability of each number is $\frac{1}{6}$. If the population is 60 000 000, the probability that you are picked is 1/60 000 000.

A sample space cannot always be broken down into a finite number of equally likely events. The sample space might, for example, be infinite.

Events

An **event** is a result concerning an experiment. In the case of the die, the event might be that the number thrown is even. In the population example, the event might be that the person chosen is female.

Theoretical and experimental probability

Consider the following two experiments and connected events.

a) A can of beans is thrown on the floor, and it lands on a flat face.
b) A die is rolled and a 5 is obtained.

In **a)**, we cannot calculate the probability of the event. We have to find it by experiment. Perhaps we throw the can 50 times, and find that it lands on a flat face 17 times. We then have an **experimental probability** of $\frac{17}{50}$.

In **b)**, if the die is fair and the rolling is random, then the probability of the event is $\frac{1}{6}$. This is a **theoretical probability**. We have deduced, from probability theory, that if there are six equally likely outcomes the probability of each is $\frac{1}{6}$.

In practice, it is impossible for a die to be absolutely fair, or to throw it in an absolutely random fashion. The theoretical probability of $\frac{1}{6}$ is obtained from a **model** of reality. If the die is well manufactured and it is allowed to turn many times before settling, then the results predicted by the model will be close to those found in practice.

EXERCISE 3A

1 For the following, decide whether the probability of the event mentioned is theoretical or experimental. Find the theoretical probabilities. Describe how you would find the experimental probabilities.

a) A member of your family is picked at random. The person is female.

b) A stray dog is captured. The dog weighs more than 20 kg.

c) A coin is spun. It comes up heads.

d) A card is drawn from a well-shuffled pack. It is an ace.

e) A drawing pin is thrown on the floor. It lands point upwards.

2 Show how each of the following experiments can be broken up into equally likely outcomes. Hence find the probability of the event given.

a) Two dice are rolled. The total is 8.   **b)** Four coins are spun. There are two heads and two tails.

c) Three people A, B and C play a game which is determined purely by chance. They finish in the order ABC.

d) Two marbles are drawn from a box containing four marbles, coloured red, blue, green and yellow. The two marbles drawn are red and blue.

3 A spinner has three sides, labelled 1, 2 and 3, which are equally likely to come up. In three spins, what is the probability that the same number comes up each time?

4 A tetrahedral (four-sided) die is thrown twice. What is the probability that on both occasions it lands on the side labelled 2?

5 In a pack of four oranges two are mouldy. If I select two at random what is the probability that both are mouldy?

6 Three envelopes are addressed for three letters. However, the letters are put into the envelopes at random. What is the probability that each letter is in the correct envelope?

*7 The manufacturer of a cereal puts one card showing a film-star in each package. There are three different film-stars, and the cards are made in equal numbers. If I buy three packets, what is the probability I shall have the three different cards?

Venn diagrams

Probabilities can be illustrated on a **Venn diagram**. The rectangle represents the entire sample space, and the circle represents the event A, as shown in Fig. 3.1.

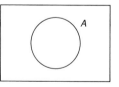

Fig. 3.1

When dealing with events, the words *and* and *or* are sometimes replaced by the symbols $\cap$ and $\cup$ respectively. The event of A not happening is sometimes written as A'. Combinations of probabilities can be shown on a Venn diagram, as follows.

A and B, i.e. $A \cap B$ This is the overlap of the regions corresponding to A and B as shown in Fig. 3.2. It is common to write 'A and B' as 'A & B'.

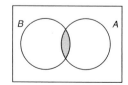

Fig. 3.2

A or *B*, i.e. *A* ∪ *B*   This is the region of points in either the *A* region or the *B* region (or both). Note that the word *or* is inclusive. '*A* or *B*' means '*A* or *B* or both', as shown in Fig. 3.3.

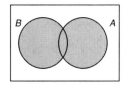

Not *A*, i.e. *A'*. This is the region outside the *A* region, as shown in Fig. 3.4.

Fig. 3.3

P(*A* or *B*) = P(*A*) + P(*B*) − P(*A* & *B*)

Suppose that 54 per cent of the electorate are women, and that 15 per cent of the electorate are over 65. Suppose also that 9 per cent of the electorate are women over 65. The Venn diagram of Fig. 3.5 shows the situation. What proportion of the electorate are either female or over 65?

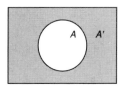

Fig. 3.4

If we add 54 per cent and 15 per cent, the women over 65 will have been counted twice. Hence to find the proportion, we must discount 9 per cent.

> Proportion which are female or over 65
> = 54% + 15% − 9% = 60%

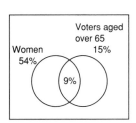

In general, consider the region *A* ∪ *B*. If we combine the regions of *A* and *B*, then the region *A* ∩ *B* will have been counted twice. Hence we have the following rule.

> Region of (*A* ∪ *B*)
> = region of *A* + region of *B* − region of (*A* ∩ *B*)
>
> P(*A* or *B*) = P(*A*) + P(*B*) − P(*A* & *B*)

Fig. 3.5

Exclusive events

Consider a population which is broken up into three groups: those under 18, those between 18 and 65, and those over 65. Suppose a person is picked at random. Let us label events as follows.

A   The person is under 18.   *B*   The person is between 18 and 65.

C   The person is over 65.   *D*   The person is female.

A person cannot both be under 18 and between 18 and 65. The events *A* and *B* are **exclusive**. The probability of either of them happening is the sum of the individual probabilities.

> P(*A* or *B*) = P(*A*) + P(*B*)

Notes
1 This follows from the rule above. Events *A* and *B* cannot happen together, hence P(*A* & *B*) = 0.

2 Note that *A* and *D* could happen together. These events are *not* exclusive.

> P(*A* or *D*) = P(*A*) + P(*D*) − P(*A* & *D*) < P(*A*) + P(*D*)

3 The events A and A' are exclusive. Note also that, if $P(A) = x$, then $P(A') = 1 - x$.

EXAMPLE 3.1

Two fair dice are rolled, and the total score is found. Events are as follows.

A The first die shows 3. B The total is 8. C The total is 7.

Which pair of events is exclusive?

Solution

Event A could happen with either B or C. Events B and C cannot happen simultaneously.

Events B and C are exclusive.

EXAMPLE 3.2

For events A and B, $P(A) = 0.4$ and $P(B) = 0.3$. Find $P(A$ or $B)$ in these cases.

a) Events A and B are exclusive.   **b)** $P(A \& B) = 0.1$

Solution

a) As A and B are exclusive, we can add their probabilities.

$$P(A \text{ or } B) = P(A) + P(B) = 0.4 + 0.3$$

P(A or B) = 0.7

b) Use the formula for $P(A$ or $B)$.

$$P(A \text{ or } B) = P(A) + P(B) - P(A \& B)$$

$$= 0.4 + 0.3 - 0.1 = 0.6$$

P(A or B) = 0.6

EXERCISE 3B

1 A fair die is rolled. Which pairs of the following are exclusive?

   A The result is even. B The result is odd. C The result is a prime.

2 A card is drawn from the standard pack. Which pairs of the following events are exclusive?

   A The card is red. B The card is a spade. C The card is an ace.

3 For events A and B, $P(A) = \frac{1}{4}$, and $P(B) = \frac{2}{3}$. Find $P(A$ or $B)$ in these cases.

   a) Events A and B are exclusive.   **b)** $P(A \& B) = \frac{1}{8}$

   What is the least possible value of $P(A$ or $B)$?

4 For events A and B, P(A or B) = 0.8, P(A & B) = 0.3 and P(A) = 0.5. Find P(B).

5 Events A and B have probabilities 0.5 and 0.3 respectively. The probability that both occur is 0.2. Find the probability that neither A nor B occurs.

6 Events A and B have probabilities 0.4 and 0.3 respectively. The probability that either occurs is 0.6. Find the probability that they don't both occur.

7 Of the married couples in a certain country, 60 per cent of the husbands and 30 per cent of the wives have full-time jobs. For 10 per cent of the couples, both have full-time jobs. Find the proportion of couples in which at least one member has a full-time job. Find the proportion of couples in which neither has a full-time job.

8 The probability that a day will be too cold for playing tennis is $\frac{1}{4}$. The probability that it will be too wet to play is $\frac{1}{3}$. The probability that the day is both too cold and too wet is $\frac{1}{10}$. What is the probability that a day will be suitable for tennis?

9 In a certain town, 70 per cent of households own at least one car, and 80 per cent own a video recorder.

a) What is the greatest possible proportion with neither a car nor a video recorder?

b) If 15 per cent of households own neither a car nor a video recorder, what proportion own both?

*10 Find a rule to expand P($A \cup B \cup C$).

Independent events

Consider again the population broken up into people under 18, between 18 and 65, and over 65. Suppose that, in this population, the proportion of females under 18 is the same as the proportion of females overall. In this case, knowing that A is true (that the person picked is under 18) does not make D (that the person is female) any more or less likely. These events are **independent**. In this case, to find the probability that both A and D are true, we multiply their individual probabilities.

P(A & D) = P(A) $\times$ P(D)

Now consider events C (that the person is over 65) and D. There are more women over 65 than men, hence C and D are *not* independent. If we know that a person is over 65, it makes it more likely that the person is female.

Note

If events are not independent, that does not necessarily mean that one event *causes* the other. Being over 65 does not *cause* one to be female, or vice versa. Independence is a matter of knowledge, not of cause and effect.

EXAMPLE 3.3

Let two fair dice be rolled, as in Example 3.1. The events A, B, and C are

A The first die scores 3. B The total is 8. C The total is 7.

a) Find P(A), P(B) and P(C).
b) Find P(A & B), P(A & C).
c) Which pairs of events are independent?

Solution

The probability of A is $\frac{1}{6}$. There are 36 possible outcomes for the rolling, of which five give a total of 8, and six give a total of 7.

a) The probabilities of A, B and C are $\frac{1}{6}$, $\frac{5}{36}$ and $\frac{1}{6}$ respectively.

If A and B occur, then the first die shows 3 and the second shows 5. This has probability $\frac{1}{36}$. Similarly, the probability for A and C occurring is also $\frac{1}{36}$.

b) The probabilities of A & B and A & C are both $\frac{1}{36}$.

Note that P(A & B) $\neq$ P(A) $\times$ P(B), but that P(A & C) = P(A) $\times$ P(C).

c) Events A and C are independent.

EXERCISE 3C

1   A random digit is picked from 0, 1, 2, 3, 4, 5, 6, 7, 8, 9. Find the probabilities of the events below. Which pairs of events are independent?

   A The digit is odd. B The digit is prime. C The digit is over 3.

2   A card is drawn from the standard pack. Events A, B and C are listed below. Which pairs of events are independent?

   A The card is red. B The card is a spade. C The card is an ace.

3   For events A and B, P(A) = 0.6 and P(B) = 0.4. If A and B are independent find P(A & B) and P(A or B).

4   For events A and B, P(A) = 0.3 and P(B) = 0.2. If P(A or B) = 0.42 show that A and B are not independent.

5   The probability that a day will be cold is $\frac{1}{3}$, and the probability that it will be rainy is $\frac{1}{4}$. If these events are independent of each other find the probability that the day will be either cold or rainy (or both).

6   Of the 25 pupils in a form, 12 play cricket, eight play soccer and four play both. A pupil is picked at random: show that the events that the pupil plays soccer and that the pupil plays cricket are neither exclusive nor independent.

7 A college has 500 students, of whom 270 are female, and 100 study maths. There are 60 female maths students. If a student is picked at random, show that the events of picking a female student and picking a maths student are neither exclusive nor independent.

8 A college has 2000 students, of whom 800 are female, and 200 study French. If choice of subject is independent of sex, find the number of female students who study French.

9 For two events A and B, $P(A) = 0.3$, $P(B) = 0.4$, and $P(A \text{ or } B) = 0.6$. Find $P(A \& B)$. Show that A and B are neither exclusive nor independent.

10 For two events A and B, $P(A) = 0.4$, and $P(B) = 0.5$. Find $P(A \& B)$ in the following cases.

a) Events A and B are exclusive.   **b)** Events A and B are independent.

11 For two events A and B, $P(A) = 0.3$ and $P(A \& B) = 0.1$. Given that A and B are independent, find $P(B)$ and $P(A \text{ or } B)$.

12 A car is advertised in two local newspapers, the *Trumpet* and the *Clarion*. The probabilities of at least one response from these papers are 0.6 and 0.5 respectively. Find the probability of at least one response from either newspaper, making clear any assumption that you make.

13 Events A and B are independent with probabilities p and q respectively. Find the following probabilities in terms of p and q.

a) $P(A \& B)$ **b)** $P(A \text{ or } B)$ **c)** $P(A')$ **d)** $P(A \& B')$

3.2 Tree diagrams

A useful way to illustrate the outcomes of several experiments is with a **tree diagram**. Suppose that the adult population is evenly divided between men and women, and that the proportion of support for a political party is 30 per cent for men and 35 per cent for women. What is the probability that a voter picked at random supports the party?

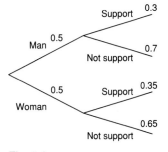

Fig. 3.6

Figure 3.6 shows a tree diagram for the situation. The first pair of lines corresponds to whether a man or a woman has been picked. The second pairs correspond to whether the person supports the party. The probabilities are written on each line.

The top branch corresponds to a male supporter. It has probability 0.5×0.3. The third branch corresponds to a female supporter, with probability 0.5×0.35. The probability that the voter supports the party is therefore:

$$0.5 \times 0.3 + 0.5 \times 0.35 = 0.325$$

In general, the outcomes of the first experiment are shown by lines leading from a fixed point. From the ends of these lines lead lines corresponding to the outcomes of the second experiment, as in Fig. 3.7. The probability of each outcome is written above its line. The probability of the event at the end of each branch is found by multiplying the probabilities along the branch.

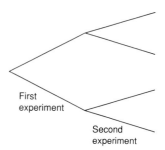

First
experiment

Second
experiment

Fig. 3.7

Sampling with and without replacement

Suppose we are drawing two items from a group. We select the first. If we return it before making the second selection, then we are sampling **with replacement**. If the first item is not returned, then we are sampling **without replacement**.

Suppose the group consists of ten red and eleven black balls. The probability that the first is red is $\frac{10}{21}$. If the sampling is with replacement, then the probability that the second is red is still $\frac{10}{21}$. If the sampling is without replacement, then after drawing a red for the first ball, the probability that the second is also red is now $\frac{9}{20}$.

Let A and B be the events of a red ball on the first and second drawings.

- If the sampling is *with replacement*, then the occurrence of A will not alter the probability of B. Hence A and B are independent.
- If the sampling is *without replacement*, then the occurrence of A makes B less likely. Hence A and B are not independent.

Note
If the sampling is taken from a very large population, then there is little difference between 'with replacement and without replacement'. Opinion polling consists of sampling without replacement. However, there are many million supporters of the major parties, and if the first person in an opinion poll is a Conservative supporter, that makes little difference to the probability that the second person will also be a Conservative supporter. Opinion polling can be considered as sampling with replacement.

EXAMPLE 3.4
A box contains five red and six blue marbles. Two are drawn out. Find the probabilities that they are both red if the drawing is done:

a) with replacement,   **b)** without replacement.

Solution
There are two successive drawings. They are illustrated on the tree diagram shown in Fig. 3.8.

a) In this case, there are five red marbles out of eleven for both drawings. Hence the probability of a red marble is $\frac{5}{11}$ for both drawings. Square $\frac{5}{11}$ to obtain the probability of two reds.

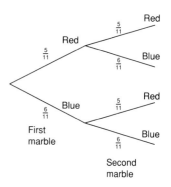

Red

$\frac{5}{11}$

Red

$\frac{5}{11}$

$\frac{6}{11}$

Blue

$\frac{6}{11}$

Blue

$\frac{5}{11}$

Red

First
marble

$\frac{6}{11}$

Blue

Second
marble

Fig. 3.8

$$\left(\frac{5}{11}\right)^2 = \frac{5 \times 5}{11 \times 11} = \frac{25}{121}$$

The probability of drawing two red marbles is $\frac{25}{121}$.

b) In this case, if a red marble is drawn first, there are four red marbles left out of ten. Hence the probability that the second is red is $\frac{4}{10}$, as shown in the tree diagram, Fig. 3.9. To find the probability that both are red, multiply $\frac{5}{11}$ and $\frac{4}{10}$.

$$\frac{5}{11} \times \frac{4}{10} = \frac{2}{11}$$

The probability of drawing two red marbles is $\frac{2}{11}$.

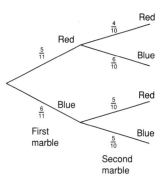

Fig. 3.9

EXERCISE 3D

1 In a multiple choice test, there are five possible answers for each question. If a candidate answers two questions at random, find the probabilities that:

a) both are right,   **b)** both are wrong,   **c)** only one is right.

2 The probability of a rainy day is $\frac{1}{3}$. Assuming independence, find the probability that of Monday and Tuesday only one day will be rainy.

3 If a day is rainy, the probability that the next day will also be rainy is $\frac{1}{2}$. If a day is sunny, the probability that the next day will be rainy is $\frac{1}{4}$. If the probability that Monday is rainy is $\frac{1}{3}$, find the probability that of Monday and Tuesday only one day is rainy.

4 Assuming that boys and girls are born in the ratio 51:49, find the probability that of two babies only one is a girl.

5 Two shots are fired at a target. The probability that the first shot hits the target is $\frac{1}{4}$. Find the probability that exactly one shot hits the target in the following cases.

a) The second shot is independent of the first, and has probability $\frac{1}{4}$ of being a hit.

b) If the first shot is a hit, the probability that the second is a hit is $\frac{3}{8}$. If the first shot misses, the probability that the second misses is $\frac{1}{8}$.

6 The probability of a windy day is 0.3. When a golfer makes a given shot, the probability that it will land on the green is $\frac{1}{4}$ if it is a still day, and $\frac{1}{8}$ if it is a windy day. Find the probability that a shot will land on the green.

7 The proportion of the adult population of a town in employment is 80 per cent. 70 per cent of the employed adults and 40 per cent of the unemployed adults own a car. What is the probability that an adult picked at random owns a car?

8 A small club has 60 members, of whom 40 voted Labour and 20 voted Conservative. What is the probability that two people picked at random both voted Labour?

9 In a general election, 35 per cent of the electorate voted Labour. If two voters are picked at random, find the probability that both voted Labour.

10 A pub holds a raffle, in which the tickets are either red or blue. Twenty red tickets and ten blue tickets are sold. Find the probability that the first two tickets drawn are red.

11 A national charity holds a raffle, in which a quarter of the tickets sold are blue. Find the probability that the first two tickets drawn are blue.

12 It is thought that 92 per cent of households have a television, and that of these 84 per cent have a television licence. If a household is picked at random, find the probability that it will not have a television licence.

13 A sales representative finds that 10 per cent of his calls result in a sale. Assuming independence, find the probability that of three calls exactly one results in a sale.

14 The probability that a day will be wet is $\frac{1}{3}$. A football team's chances of winning, drawing and losing on a wet day are $0.4, 0.4$ and 0.2 respectively. The probabilities on a dry day are $0.3, 0.3$, and 0.4 respectively. If a match is picked at random, what is the probability that the team will lose it?

15 In Shakespeare's *The Merchant of Venice*, the suitors of Portia are shown three caskets: one made of gold, one of silver and one of lead. The first suitor to pick the casket containing a picture of Portia will gain her hand in marriage. Bassanio is the third suitor. Assuming that the selections are made at random, find the probability that he will gain her hand in the following cases.

a) Each suitor is unaware of the results of the previous attempts.

b) Each suitor is aware of the results of the previous attempts.

16 In the game of Russian Roulette, a bullet is put into one of the six chambers of a revolver. The chambers are spun round, the first player points the revolver at his head and pulls the trigger. If the gun fires the game ends. Otherwise the gun is passed to the next player, who has a go. Find the probability that the second shot will be fatal in the following cases.

a) The chambers are not spun after each shot.   **b)** The chambers are spun after each shot.

The gun is passed between two players until a shot is fatal. Find the probability that the first player will be killed in the following cases.

c) The chambers are not spun after each shot.   ***d)** The chambers are spun after each shot.

3.3 Permutations and combinations

If we make more than two selections from a group, then a tree diagram becomes complicated. Another method of calculating the probability of a given selection involves counting the number of ways it can be made. For example, suppose that there are four entrants, A, B, C and D, for a race. The ways in which they could finish are listed below.

ABCD ABDC ACBD ACDB ADBC ADCB

BACD BADC BCAD BCDA BDAC BDCA

CABD CADB CBAD CBDA CDAB CDBA

DABC DACB DBAC DBCA DCAB DCBA

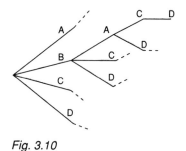

There are 24 alternatives here. If all the ways are equally likely, then the probability that the runners will end in the order ABCD is $\frac{1}{24}$.

The probability *could* be found using a tree diagram. Part of it is shown in Fig. 3.10. The complete diagram would have 24 branches!

Fig. 3.10

n factorial

It is laborious to write out all the arrangements, and we are liable to make errors. In this section we shall find ways to calculate the number of arrangements.

Above we had four letters to be arranged in an order. The first one can be picked in four ways. There are now three letters left, and so the second can be picked in three ways. The third letter can be picked in two ways, and there is only one choice for the fourth letter. Hence the number of ways is:

$$4 \times 3 \times 2 \times 1 = 24.$$

This is written as 4!, and said as 'four factorial', or 'four shriek'. In general, the number of ways *n* objects can be arranged in an order is *n*!, which we say as '*n* factorial'. It is given by the formula:

$$n! = n(n - 1)(n - 2) \ldots 3 \times 2 \times 1$$

Justification
The first object can be picked in *n* ways. There are now $(n - 1)$ objects left, so the second object can be picked in $(n - 1)$ ways. Continue this process, down to 3, 2 and 1. Part of the selection process is shown in Fig. 3.11.

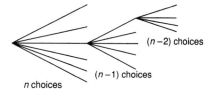

n choices

$(n-1)$ choices

$(n-2)$ choices

Fig. 3.11

Permutations and combinations

Sometimes we want to make a selection from a set. The number of ways will depend on whether or not the *order* of selection is important.

Consider a class of 25 pupils who are to receive three gifts, which are to be awarded at random. If the gifts are different, of values £30, £20 and £10, then the order of selection of recipients is important. The first recipient can be selected in 25 ways, the second in 24 ways, and the third in 23 ways. The number of ways the three gifts can be awarded is $25 \times 24 \times 23$, i.e. 13 800.

If the three gifts are equal, all of value £20, then the order in which the recipients are chosen is unimportant. There are 13 800 ways of awarding three different gifts. As the gifts are equal, the three recipients can be rearranged, in any of 3! ways. The number of ways of selecting the recipients is 13 800 ÷ 3!, i.e. 2300.

In general, suppose we have n objects, and we select r of them in a particular order. These are **permutations** of r objects out of n. The number of ways this can be done is written ^nP_r.

$$^nP_r = n(n-1)(n-2) \ldots (n-r+1) = \frac{n!}{(n-r)!}$$

Justification
The first object can be picked in n ways. There are now $(n-1)$ objects, giving the number of choices for the second object. This is continued up until the rth object, which can be picked in $(n-(r-1))$ ways, i.e. $(n-r+1)$ ways.

Suppose we have n objects, and we select r of them without regard to order. These are **combinations** of r objects out of n. The number of ways this can be done is written ^nC_r or $\binom{n}{r}$.

$$^nC_r = \frac{^nP_r}{r!} = \frac{n!}{r!(n-r)!}$$

Justification
The number of ways the objects can be selected with regard to order is ^nP_r. If we aren't bothered by the order, the r selected objects can be rearranged in $r!$ ways without altering the selection. Hence the number of combinations is found by dividing the number of permutations by $r!$.

Notes
1 When we picked three children to receive the first, second and third gifts, the number of ways was $^{25}P_3 = 13\ 800$. When we picked three children to receive equal gifts, the number of ways was $^{25}C_3 = 2300$.
2 A scientific calculator will have a button to evaluate $n!$, and may have buttons for ^nC_r and ^nP_r.

EXAMPLE 3.6
In a magazine competition, ten desirable qualities of a washing machine are listed. The entrant has to pick the most important three, in order. How many possible entries are there?

Solution
The entrant must pick three items out of ten, in order. The number of ways of doing this is $^{10}P_3$, i.e. $10 \times 9 \times 8$.

There are 720 possible entries.

EXAMPLE 3.7

A class contains ten boys and twelve girls. Six pupils are selected at random as class representatives. Find the probability that there will be equal numbers of boys and girls selected.

Solution

The number of ways of selecting three boys out of 10 is $^{10}C_3$. For each of these selections, there are $^{12}C_3$ ways of selecting three girls.

Hence the number of ways of selecting three boys and three girls $=$ $^{10}C_3 \times ^{12}C_3$

The total number of selections without regard to sex is $^{22}C_6$. Divide this into the expression above.

$$\frac{^{10}C_3 \times ^{12}C_3}{^{22}C_6} = 0.354$$

The probability is 0.354.

EXERCISE 3E

1 Evaluate the following.

   a) $5!$ **b)** $6!$ **c)** $^5P_2$ **d)** $^{10}P_3$ **e)** $^{12}C_3$ **f)** $^{13}C_{10}$

2 Simplify the following.

   a) $(n + 1)n!$ **b)** $n! \div n$ **c)** $^nP_1$ **d)** $^{10}C_{10}$ **e)** $^nC_r \times r!$ **f)** $^nC_r \times (n - r)!$

3 Show that $^nC_r + {}^nC_{r-1} = {}^{n+1}C_r$.

4 In a competition the contestants have to rank ten properties of a car in order of importance. Find the total number of possible orders. If a contestant puts down the order at random, find the probability that it will match the winning order.

5 There are twelve entrants in a horse race. Find the number of ways in which the first three places could be filled.

6 In the football pools, an entry consists of a selection of eight matches. How many selections of eight matches can be made from twelve matches?

7 In Bridge, a hand of 13 cards is dealt from a pack of 52. Find the number of possible Bridge hands.

8 A committee of five is picked at random from a list of eight men and seven women. What is the probability that three men and two women will be chosen?

9 A selection of six chocolates is made from a box containing nine with hard centres and 13 with soft centres. If the selection is at random find the probability that the selection contains equal numbers of each type.

10 A parliamentary committee is made up from a pool of 20 Conservative MPs and 15 Labour MPs. Find the number of ways of selecting the committee if there are to be four Conservative and three Labour members on it.

11 A football club contains 20 forwards, twelve defenders and six goalkeepers. No member is more than one of these. How many ways can a football team of four forwards, six defenders and one goalkeeper be selected?

12 An exam contains Sections A and B with five questions in each. Candidates should answer seven questions. In how many ways can the selection be made:

a) if there are no restrictions,

b) if the candidate must answer four from one section and three from the other.

13 Find the probability that a Bridge hand contains all four aces.

14 A student is studying maths and physics. In the library there are available seven suitable books on maths and five on physics. In how many ways can the student select five books, three on maths and two on physics?

15 There are twelve points on a piece of paper, no three in a straight line.

a) How many straight lines can be drawn joining pairs of points?

b) How many triangles can be drawn with the points as vertices?

16 Components are produced in batches of 100. A sample of ten is taken from the batch, and the batch is rejected if the sample contains a faulty item. If a particular batch contains 15 faulty items, find the probability that it will be rejected.

17 A woman has four grandchildren. She has bought six identical boxes of chocolates. In how many ways can she give them to the children, ensuring that each child gets at least one box?

18 There are six entrants in the final of a greyhound race. The entrants are the two fastest dogs from each of three heats, which also have six entrants. What is the number of possible sets of entrants for the final?

19 A cereal company promotes its products by putting a plastic model of a famous politician in each packet. There are eight different politicians to be collected, and they are manufactured in equal numbers. If I buy eight packets, what is the probability that I have a complete set?

20 What is the probability that, in a class of 25 children, at least two will have the same birthday? (Ignore leap years and assume that each day is equally likely.)

21 A box contains disks labelled 1 up to n, where n is unknown. To guess n, ten disks are drawn out, and n is taken to be the largest number showing on one of these disks. If in fact n is 100, find the probability that the guess is correct.

22 Four fair dice are rolled. What is the probability that they show different numbers?

23 A launderette contains ten machines, of which three are faulty. A customer picks two machines at random. What is the probability that both machines chosen are faulty?

3.4 Conditional probability

Suppose you have placed a bet on a horse to win a race. You hear that it rained heavily during the night before the race. Have your chances of winning increased or decreased? If the horse goes well on sticky ground, your chances have improved. If it prefers a dry surface, then they have deteriorated. In either case, the information about rain has altered the probability that the horse will win.

In general, suppose we have two events A and B which are not independent. If we know that B is true, then the probability of A changes. The new probability of A is the **conditional probability** of A, given that B is true.

The conditional probability of A given that B is true is written $P(A|B)$. It is found from the following formula.

$$P(A|B) = \frac{P(A \ \& \ B)}{P(B)}$$

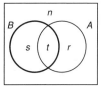

Fig. 3.12

Justification
Suppose that the sample space contains n equally likely outcomes. Suppose r, s and t outcomes are in A, B and ($A \ \& \ B$) respectively, as shown in Fig. 3.12.

If we know that B is true, then the sample space is reduced to B. The probability of A is now the number of outcomes in ($A \ \& \ B$), divided by the number of outcomes in B.

$$P(A|B) = \frac{t}{s} = \frac{P(A \ \& \ B)}{P(B)}$$

Note
If A and B are independent, the top line of the fraction above becomes $P(A) \times P(B)$.

$$P(A|B) = \frac{P(A \ \& \ B)}{P(B)} = \frac{P(A) \times P(B)}{P(B)} = P(A)$$

This is to be expected, as knowledge of B's occurrence does not affect the probability of A.

EXAMPLE 3.8
In a certain crime-ridden area, the probability that a house will be

burgled on a particular night is 0.04. A burglar alarm is installed in a house in the area. If the house is burgled, the probability that the alarm will go off is 0.95. If the house isn't burgled, the probability that it will go off by accident is 0.1. Find the probability that the house *has* been burgled, if the alarm has gone off.

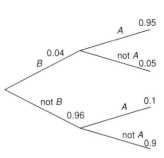

Solution

Let *B* be the event that the house has been burgled, and *A* the event that the alarm goes off. We want to find $P(B|A)$.

The tree diagram of Fig. 3.13 shows the probabilities. From the diagram:

Fig. 3.13

$$P(B \text{ \& } A) = 0.04 \times 0.95.$$

$P(A)$ is given by:

$$P(A) = 0.04 \times 0.95 + 0.96 \times 0.1$$

Now use the formula.

$$P(A|B) = \frac{P(B \text{ \& } A)}{P(A)} = \frac{0.04 \times 0.95}{0.04 \times 0.95 + 0.96 \times 0.1} = 0.284$$

The probability is 0.284.

EXERCISE 3F

1   For events *A* and *B*, $P(A) = 0.3$, $P(B) = 0.4$, and $P(A \text{ \& } B) = 0.2$. Find $P(A|B)$ and $P(B|A)$.

2   With *A* and *B* as defined in Question 1, find $P(A|B')$ and $P(A'|B)$.

3   For events *A* and *B*, $P(A) = \frac{1}{4}$, $P(B) = \frac{1}{3}$ and $P(A|B) = \frac{1}{8}$. Find $P(A \text{ \& } B)$ and $P(A \text{ or } B)$.

4   It is known that the proportion of the population with a certain disease is 5 per cent. There is a test for the disease, which gives a positive result for 90 per cent of those with the disease and for 2 per cent of those without. A person is tested.

   a) If the result is positive, what is the probability that the person has the disease?

   b) If the result is negative, what is the probability that the person doesn't have the disease?

5   If a person with Brod's syndrome is given treatment, the probability of recovery is 0.7. The recovery rate for those not given treatment is 0.4. If a quarter of the sufferers from the syndrome are given the treatment, find the probability that someone who recovers has received the treatment.

6   In a certain tropical country, the proportion of people who regularly eat *Gueule de Feu* chilli peppers is 30 per cent. The tongue cancer rates among people who eat these peppers and those who don't are 10 per cent and 5 per cent respectively. What is the probability that someone with tongue cancer has regularly been eating these peppers?

7 A manufacturer is supplied with components from factories A and B in the ratio 3:2. The proportions of defective items from these factories are 2 per cent and 5 per cent respectively. What is the probability that a defective item has come from factory A?

8 There are two workers assembling products on a line. The first worker works twice as fast as the other, but makes a mistake in the assembly three times as frequently. What is the probability that an incorrectly assembled product comes from the first worker?

9 A canteen serves three-course meals. Everyone has the main course, but only 10 per cent have all three courses. The proportions having the first and third courses are 40 per cent and 30 per cent respectively. What is the probability that a customer having the third course also had the first?

10 In a constituency, 45 per cent of the male voters and 43 per cent of the female voters support the Purple Party. Assuming equal numbers of male and female voters, what is the probability that a Purple Party supporter is male?

11 The proportion of people who take the newspaper the *Daily Sneer* is 1 per cent. The proportion taking the weekly magazine *New Moaner* is 0.5 per cent. If the probability that a *Sneer* reader takes the *New Moaner* is 0.4, find the probability that a *New Moaner* reader takes the *Sneer*.

12 A student is taking A-levels in Alchemy and Astrology. The probabilities that she will pass these subjects are 0.8 and 0.7 respectively, while the probability that she will pass both is 0.6.

a) If she passes Alchemy, what is the probability she will also pass Astrology?

b) If she passes only one of these subjects, what is the probability it was Alchemy?

13 An insurance company has clients in three areas, A, B and C, in the ratio 3:2:4. The probabilities that a client from one of these areas will send in a claim in a given year are 0.01, 0.02 and 0.05 respectively. If a claim is received by the company, find the probability it came from a client in area C.

14 Of two coins, one is fair and the probability of the other coming up heads is $\frac{1}{3}$. A coin is picked at random and spun, and it comes up heads. Find the probability that it was the fair coin.

15 A coffee company claims that its instant coffee cannot be distinguished from real coffee. This claim is to be tested by offering people a cup of either instant or real coffee, with equal probability, and asking them which it is.

Suppose that real coffee is correctly identified in 70 per cent of the cases, and instant coffee is correctly identified in 60 per cent of the cases. If someone says that a cup contains real coffee what is the probability that this is true?

LONGER EXERCISE

The problem of the points

The theory of probability largely came about through correspondence between two French mathematicians, Blaise Pascal and Pierre Fermat, in the seventeenth century. They wrote many letters to each other about the following problem.

Suppose there are two gamblers of equal skill, who are playing a game of successive points. When one player has won six, he will then gain all the prize money. They are interrupted when one player has won five points and the other three. How should the prize money be divided?

Generalise the problem, setting different numbers of points to win, and with the players having gained different numbers of points.

To make it even more general, consider cases when the players have different levels of skill.

EXAMINATION QUESTIONS

1 One plastic toy aeroplane is given away free in each packet of cornflakes. Equal numbers of red, yellow, green and blue aeroplanes are put into the packets.

Faye, a customer, has collected 3 colours of aeroplane but still wants a yellow one. Find the probability that:

(i)   she gets a yellow aeroplane by opening just 1 packet,

(ii)   she fails to get a yellow aeroplane in opening 4 packets,

(iii)   she needs to open **exactly** 5 packets to get the yellow aeroplane she wants.

Henry, a quality controller employed by the cornflakes manufacturer, opens a number of packets chosen at random to check on the distribution of colours. Find the probability that:

(iv)   the first 2 packets he opens both have red aeroplanes in,

(v)   the first 2 packets he opens have aeroplanes of different colours in,

(vi)   he gets all 4 different colours by opening just 4 packets.

MEI 1994

2 Two porcelain factories A and B produce cheap china cups in equal numbers. If closely examined, a cup from A will be found flawless with probability $\frac{3}{4}$; but the probability of one from B being flawless is only $\frac{1}{2}$. Jim picks two cups from a batch at a shop. The shopkeeper says that all the cups in the batch come from the same factory, but the batch is equally likely to come from factory A or from factory B.

(i)   Copy this tree diagram, and mark the appropriate probabilities on each branch.

(ii)   What is the probability that the first cup Jim examines is flawless?

(iii)   Given that the first cup is flawless, what is the conditional probability that the batch came from factory A?

(iv)   Draw a new version of the tree diagram, using your answer to (iii) to show the probabilities *after* the first cup has been found to be flawless.

(v)   Unfortunately, Jim drops the second cup before he can examine it. Given that the first cup was flawless, find the conditional probability that the second cup was also flawless before the accident.

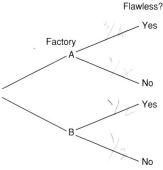

Fig. 3.14

SMP 1989

3 The contingency table compares a group of London surgeons by category and base.

		Base	
		Office (O)	*Hospital (H)*
Category	*General (G)*	15	15
	Specialist (S)	25	45

(i) For a randomly selected surgeon in the group, find P(*S*) and find P(*H*).

(ii) Show that, with the figures given, *H* is not independent of *S*.

(iii) Construct a new contingency table, for a group of 100 surgeons, based on the hypothesis that *S* and *H* are independent. You should retain the values of P(*S*) and P(*H*) calculated in (i) above.

SMP 1993

4 The events *A* and *B*, are such that

$$P(A') = \tfrac{3}{4}, \qquad P(A|B) = \tfrac{1}{3}, \qquad P(A \cup B) = \tfrac{2}{3},$$ where *A'* denotes the event '*A* does not occur'. Find

(i) P(*A*),   (ii) P(*A* ∩ *B*),   (iii) P(*B*)   (iv) P(*A*|*B'*),

where *B'* denotes the event '*B* does not occur'. Determine whether *A* and *B* are independent.

(Answers may be given as fractions in their lowest terms.)   *O&C 1991*

5 A factory has three machines A, B, and C producing a particular type of item. In a day's output 50% of the items are produced on A, 30% on B, and 20% on C. A randomly chosen item from those produced on A has probability 0.01 of being defective, the corresponding probabilities for items produced on B and C being 0.02 and 0.03, respectively.

(i) If an item is chosen at random from a day's output calculate the probability that it will be defective.

(ii) Given that two items chosen at random from a day's output were produced on the same machine and were both defective, calculate the conditional probability that both items were produced on A.   *W 1992*

6 Three events, *A*, *B* and *C*, are such that

$$P(A) = 0.5, P(B) = 0.4, P(C) = 0.3, P(A \cup B) = 0.62.$$

The events *B* and *C* are independent. The events *A* and *C* are mutually exclusive.

(i) Find P(*B* ∩ *C*).   (ii) Find P(*A* ∩ *B*).   (iii) Find P(*A*|*B*).

(iv) Show that *B* cannot occur without *A* or *C* also occurring.

N 1992

7 (In this question, give your answers in decimal form, correct to three significant figures.)

A choir has 7 sopranos, 6 altos, 3 tenors and 4 basses. The sopranos and altos are women and the tenors and basses are men. At a particular rehearsal, three members of the choir are chosen at random to make the tea.

(i)   Find the probability that all three tenors are chosen.

(ii) Find the probability that exactly one bass is chosen.

(iii) Find the conditional probability that two women are chosen, given that exactly one bass is chosen.

(iv) Find the probability that the chosen group contains exactly one tenor or exactly one bass (or both).

C 1991

Summary and key points

3.1 If an experiment has n equally likely outcomes, the probability of each is $\frac{1}{n}$.

Two events A and B are exclusive if they cannot happen together. In this case :

$$P(A \& B) = 0 \text{ and } P(A \text{ or } B) = P(A) + P(B).$$

Two events A and B are independent if knowledge of one of them does not affect the probability of the other. In this case

$$P(A \& B) = P(A) \times P(B).$$

3.2 Tree diagrams are often useful in finding probabilities concerning two events.

3.3 The number of ways n objects can be arranged is $n!$

The number of ways r objects can be selected from n objects in order is:

$$^{n}P_{r} = \frac{n!}{(n - r)!}$$

The number of ways r objects can be selected from n objects without regard to order is:

$$^{n}C_{r} = \frac{n!}{r!(n - r)!}$$

3.4 The probability of A once we know that B is true is the conditional probability of A given B. It is found from the formula:

$$P(A|B) = \frac{P(A \& B)}{P(B)}$$

Do not write the top line of this fraction as $P(A) \times P(B)$, unless you know that A and B are independent.

CHAPTER 4

Sampling

Chapter outline

4.1 Populations and samples   **4.2** Random samples

4.3 Other methods of sampling

In a general election the whole adult population of the country is able to vote for members of Parliament. In between elections the mood of the country is found by regular opinion polls. These can influence the political parties in their strategies for winning the next general election.

The electorate of the United Kingdom is about 40 000 000. In an opinion poll, however, only about 1000 people are questioned. The results of the opinion poll could therefore give a false impression of the voting intentions of the whole electorate. There are two ways in which this could occur.

Statistical error   Just by chance, it might happen that the sample of 1000 people questioned contained an abnormally high number of supporters of one particular party. This sort of error is unavoidable.

Bias   In the selection of the 1000 people, one group of the population might be over-represented. This sort of error can be avoided, or at least minimised. The main topic of this chapter is the selection of samples which are not biased.

4.1 Populations and samples

The techniques of statistics are used to obtain information. The set that we want to investigate is called the **population**. For example, if we want to find out about the voting intentions of people in the United Kingdom, then the population is its electorate. The population does not have to be finite, nor to consist of actual objects. If we are investigating whether a die is biased, then the population is the set of all possible rolls of the die.

If the population is large or even infinite, it may not be possible to investigate every single item. In this case only a part of the population is investigated. This part is called a **sample**. In the example about voting above, the sample consists of the 1000 people who are chosen for the opinion poll. In the case of the suspect die, we could not investigate all possible rolls. There are infinitely many! Instead we take a sample of these rolls, perhaps by rolling the die 100 times.

In a manufacturing process, the testing procedure may involve the destruction of the item. If a food manufacturer tested all its cakes by eating them there would be nothing left to sell! Only a sample of the cakes can be tested. Some other examples of populations and samples are as follows.

Factory production

The production manager of a factory would want to ensure that the goods produced are satisfactory. It may not be possible to test every item. Instead, every day, just a few items are tested. The day's production is the population. The items tested form the sample.

Roulette wheel

The authorities in charge of gaming might test a roulette wheel to check that it was not biased. The population consists of every possible spin of the wheel. The sample consists of the test spins.

Market for a teenage magazine

A publisher is considering bringing out a new magazine aimed at 13–18 year olds. They might ask 100 people in that age range what they would like the magazine to contain. Here the population consists of all the 13–18 year olds in the country. The sample consists of the 100 people questioned.

EXERCISE 4A

1 Explain why it is not possible for a fireworks factory to test all the day's production of fireworks.

2 A manufacturer of climbing ropes wishes to ensure that the breaking strength is sufficient. This is done by hanging more and more weight on the rope until it breaks. Explain why only a sample of the day's production is tested.

3 The Government wishes to find out how many people in the UK are over 65. Explain how this could be done by

   a) a census,   b) a sample survey.

   What are the advantages and disadvantages of each method?

4 A new medicine for arthritis is developed. Show how it could be tested before being put on sale, describing clearly the population and the sample.

5 An educationalist wishes to reform the way children are taught to read. The new methods are tested on a particular primary school. Describe the population and the sample for this situation.

6 A transport users' group wants to report on the proportion of intercity coaches which arrive late. Explain how this could be done, stating clearly what the population and the sample are.

7 A road safety organisation wishes to find out the proportion of cars with defective brakes. Explain how this could be done, stating clearly what the population and the sample are.

8 The presence of certain viruses in a patient's body is found by testing the patient's blood. Explain why it is necessary to use sampling. Describe the population and the sample.

4.2 Random samples

The results obtained from a sample should be as reliable as possible. There is no point in taking an opinion poll, unless its results give a reliable impression of the voting intentions of the electorate. The views of one section of the population should not be represented more than any other.

A **random** sample is one in which each member of the population has an equal chance of being picked for the sample. Hence the sample is not biased towards any particular section of the population. In order to obtain a random sample we need a representation of the whole population, such as a list of its members. This representation is the **sampling frame**.

Suppose that there are 1000 pupils in a school, and that we want to select a random sample of size 20. On the school list a different number can be assigned to each pupil. This is the sampling frame. If we pick 20 numbers at random from 1 to 1000, then the pupils corresponding to these numbers will be our random sample. There are several ways of selecting numbers at random.

- *From a computer* Computers have the facility to generate random numbers.
- *From a calculator* On a scientific calculator there is often a button which returns a three-digit random number.
- *From a table of random numbers* Books of statistical tables often contain tables of random numbers. An extract from the table might be as below.

42599	30209	35314	29446	96279	75433	18820
32548	96246	11220	84947	89875	70394	20482
21662	72958	96054	86153	32807	59475	63107

Note
The numbers found by these methods are not strictly random. They are generated by a formula, but one so complicated that its results cannot be predicted. The numbers are said to be **pseudo random**. The *Pure Mathematics* book in this series contains a computer investigation involving functions which generate pseudo random numbers.

There are many other ways of obtaining random numbers, for example with cards, a spinner and so on.

EXAMPLE 4.1

There are 700 voters in the electorate of a local authority ward. A sample of size 10 is to be taken. Show how a random sample can be obtained, using the following digits which were obtained from a computer.

0 1 5 4 2 2 2 6 5 2 3 9 0

0 0 2 9 4 7 4 8 3 2 2 6 5

7 4 4 2 7 0 5 2 2 4 6 0 0

6 8 3

Solution

The voters' names are listed in the electoral register. Suppose that they are numbered from 1 to 700. The numbered list is the sampling frame.

Rewrite the random numbers and arrange them in groups of three, as shown below.

015 422 265 239 000 294 748 322 657 442 705 224

600 683

Of these 748 and 705 are greater than 700, so we discard them. The group 000 appears, which can also be discarded. The results are

015 422 265 239 294 322 657 442 224 600 683

This is a random sample from 1 up to 700. The people corresponding to the first ten of these numbers form a random sample.

Notes

1 There are many ways of going from the random digits to the selection. In this example the group 000 occurred, which we had to discard. To avoid this, we could have added 1 to all the three-digit numbers. Alternately, we could have numbered the voters from 0 to 699 instead of from 1 to 700. The next example will use this sort of numbering.

2 The method of picking the random numbers must be decided before the calculations are done. It would be very suspicious if the investigator looked at the random digits and then decided what method to use.

EXAMPLE 4.2

A class contains 23 pupils. Three are to be selected at random to be class representatives. Use the following random digits to select the pupils.

4 5 9 7 2 8 9 1 6 1 9 4 7 4

Solution

Number the pupils from 0 to 22. As above, regroup the digits in pairs.

45   97   28   91   61   94   74

It would be wasteful to discard all the pairs greater than 22. We use more of the pairs if we allow more than one pair per pupil. We can split the pairs into four groups of 23 numbers.

00 to 22   23 to 45   46 to 68   69 to 91

Now we only need to discard the numbers greater than 91. We allot 00, 23, 46 and 69 to the pupil numbered 0. We allot 01, 24, 47 and 70 to the pupil numbered 1, and so on. In general, find the remainder when the pair is divided by 23. If this remainder is n, then pick the nth pupil. The results are below.

$45 = 23 + 22$	Pick the pupil numbered 22.
97 is greater than 91.	Discard.
$28 = 23 + 5$	Pick the pupil numbered 5.
$91 = 3 \times 23 + 22$	The pupil numbered 22 has been picked already.
$61 = 2 \times 23 + 15$	Pick the pupil numbered 15.

The pupils numbered 5, 15 and 22 are selected.

EXERCISE 4B

1   A school has 856 pupils. Six are to be selected at random to appear in a television documentary. Make the selection using the random numbers below.

2   6   3   7   0   6   4   8   4   7   1   5   4   0   9   9   5   3   7   2   3

2   A primary school has 73 pupils. Four will be selected at random to go on a trip. Use the following random numbers to make the selection.

3   6   1   7   8   0   5   7   3   2   4   1   3   6   7   4   5   4

3   In the National Lottery six balls are selected by machine from balls numbered 1 to 49.

One week the machine breaks down, and it is resolved to select the balls from a table of random numbers. Use the following random digits to obtain the numbers.

6   3   4   6   9   4   7   8   8   5   0   9   5   2

4   A government decided to make three days in the year bank holidays. The days were to be selected at random from the 365 days in the year (ignoring leap years). The following random digits were obtained.

3   2   8   4   2   6   8   9   8   1   6   1   4   5   0   9   7   2   9   7   6   0   4   7

Make the selection:

a) by grouping the digits in threes, and discarding 000 and any number greater than 365,

b) by grouping the digits in threes, and alloting 000 and 365 to 1 January, 001 and 366 to 2 January and so on.

5   A prize draw with three top prizes has attracted 62 034 entries. Use the following random numbers to select the winning entries.

　　0 5 7 6 8 9 4 0 3 3 5 0 4 7 4 5 1 6 2 0 2

6   A cabinet comprises 19 ministers. Two are to be selected at random to take the blame for a disastrous government policy. Make the selection using the following random numbers.

　　6 1 1 4 4 8 6 6 2 0

7   A computer program is written to simulate a dice game. Obtain ten rolls of the die from the following random numbers.

　　7 4 2 0 6 6 2 3 6 0 2 9 9 5 3

8   A computer program is written to simulate the spinning of a roulette wheel in which there are numbers 1 to 36. Use the following random digits to simulate six spins.

　　1 2 6 2 7 6 6 0 4 7 4 7 9 5 1 9 0 0 3 0 7

9   A Poker hand consists of five cards dealt from a pack of 52. Use the following random numbers to pick a random hand. Describe carefully your sampling frame and your selection method.

　　8 6 9 1 3 8 4 6 6 2 0 0 0 8 1 1 6 6 7 5 8 7 9 8 3 6 9

10   You can try to pick random numbers in your head. Quickly write down 40 teenage ages, i.e. 40 numbers from 13 up to 19. Arrange them in a frequency table. How random are they? Is your own age over-represented, or under-represented?

(In Chapter 13 we shall discuss techniques for finding out how truly random your sample is.)

4.3 Other methods of sampling

A random sample is not always the most appropriate. There are many different ways to select the sample, which are outlined below.

Systematic sampling

This method relies on some systematic way of picking the sample from the population. We might, for example, pick every tenth item on the sampling frame.

This sort of sampling is used in factories. If every tenth item produced by a machine is tested, then that will provide a check that the machine is operating properly. It is preferable to random sampling, as the testing procedure is carried out at a constant rate throughout the day.

Systematic sampling is inappropriate if it leads to one group of the population being over-represented in the sample. For example, suppose the use of a railway station is to be investigated. If we picked every seventh day to do the testing, then the same day of the week would be tested on each occasion. If that day happened to be Sunday, that would result in a very inaccurate picture of the use of the station.

Stratified sampling

Suppose a population is divided into different groups. If a purely random sample is used, then just by chance one group may be over-represented. It is more reliable to ensure that the sample contains representatives from each group in proportion to their numbers in the population.

Consider the railway station example above. A stratified sample might select 70 days on which to investigate, and pick at random ten Sundays, ten Mondays and so on.

Quota sampling

This method is similar to stratified sampling. It is often used in market research. The population is broken up into different groups, and the investigator is given fixed numbers (the **quotas**) for each group. The sample must contain the appropriate number from each group. The selection may be made in any way, as the investigator decides. Hence the selection within each group may not be random. For example, suppose the popularity of a new magazine is to be investigated. The market researcher might be told to question 20 women under 30, 25 women over 30, 15 men under 30 and 20 men over 30. These are the quotas. The researcher can find the people by stopping them in the street (and guessing their age) or from the electoral register or the phone book.

Cluster sampling

Market research and opinion polling are often very expensive to carry out. A random sample might result in a sample spread all over the country, and it would be expensive to send the researcher to question all of them. A **cluster sample** consists of a sample drawn from one small area.

A random sample selects from the whole population. A cluster sample is confined to one or more areas, chosen as representative of the whole population. All the items within those areas are investigated. For example, there might be some geographical areas of a nation which have roughly the same age range, class range, ethnic mix and so on as the nation as a whole. If the sample is restricted to one of these areas, then its results will give a reasonably reliable picture of the nation as a whole. It will have been cheaper to confine the investigation to one small area.

EXERCISE 4C

1 The word *decimate* is often wrongly used to mean reduce to a tenth. In fact it mean reduce *by* a tenth. A Roman legion that had disgraced itself was sometimes punished by making the soldiers line up and then executing every tenth man. How could you classify this method of obtaining a sample of the legion?

2 A recipe includes certain naturally occurring ingredients such as mushrooms, hazelnuts and so on. The cook sends a child out to the woods to gather the correct amounts of each ingredient. How could you classify this collection of ingredients?

3 The United States used to select conscripts by picking a few days from the year and calling up all the men within a certain age range who had been born on those days. What sort of sampling is this?

4 A firm bottles mineral water from a spring. Every 100th bottle is tested for purity. What sort of sampling is this?

5 A local education authority wishes to canvass the opinions of its secondary school pupils on the education they are receiving. The following methods of obtaining a sample are suggested.

a) Combine all the school lists, and make a random selection from the combined list.

b) Select one school and question every pupil in that school.

c) Select ten pupils at random from each school.

Classify the sampling method for each suggestion. Will they all lead to an unbiased impression of the opinion of school pupils?

6 An adult education college offers 50 examinable courses (called schedule 2) and 70 non-examinable course (non-schedule 2). The college is to be inspected. The inspectors have time to visit 24 classes. How could the classes be selected

a) by a random sample,   b) by a stratified sample?

7 Professional soccer in England is divided into four leagues. A sociologist wants to investigate the extent of crowd violence at matches. Describe how a selection of matches to be visited could be made by:

a) a random sample,   b) a stratified sample,   c) a cluster sample.

What are the advantages and disadvantages of each method?

8   A market gardener owns an orchard of 100 apple trees. He wants to find the proportion of apples which contain maggots. How might this be done by:

a) a random sample,   **b)** a stratified sample,   **c)** a cluster sample?

What are the advantages and disadvantages of each method?

9   A large block of flats contains 200 flats, with groups of five dwellings sharing a common entrance door to the street. A sample of 20 flat-dwellers are to be questioned. Explain why a systematic sample of taking every tenth flat might not result in a fair sample.

10   A fruit farmer has a field of 150 apple trees, arranged in a 15 by 10 rectangle. He wants to find out whether the fruit is contaminated by pollution from a nearby road. Explain why a systematic sample of every tenth tree might not result in a fair sample.

11   The tickets for a raffle come in five colours: red, green, blue, yellow and white. Explain how the prizes could be selected by:

a) a random sample,   **b)** a stratified sample.

Comment on the advantages and disadvantages of each method.

12   A transport users' group wants to report on the proportion of intercity trains to London which arrive late. Explain how the trains could be selected by:

a) a random sample,   **b)** a cluster sample,   **c)** a stratified sample.

What are the advantages and disadvantages of each method?

Bias

If the results of a statistical investigation are likely to give an inaccurate picture of the population, then the investigation is **biased**. This can often arise because the sample is not representative of the population. Two famous examples of this are discussed below.

The Roosevelt-Landau election
Before the 1936 US presidential election, a poll was taken by ringing up voters and asking them for whom they would vote. There were more than twice as many supporters of Landau than of Roosevelt, and so it was predicted that Landau would win the election. At that time, though, only richer people had telephones, and hence this sample was biased towards them. In fact, Roosevelt won the election handsomely.

The Kinsey Report
In the 1940s Kinsey and Martin conducted a survey into the sexual behaviour of Americans. They concluded that about 10 per cent of adult American males were homosexual. However, their information was obtained from volunteers, and it is unlikely that people

prepared to volunteer information about their sex lives form an unbiased sample from the whole population. Recent surveys, which have taken great pains to use unbiased samples, have revealed a much lower percentage.

EXERCISE 4D

In each of Questions 1 to 5 state, with reasons, whether or not the sample data described is likely to be biased.

1 To investigate the extent of steroid-taking among athletes, 100 randomly chosen athletes are asked whether or not they have ever taken steroids.

2 A university wishes to find out how well their graduates are doing financially. It sends out a letter to all its graduates of ten years ago, asking them to state their income. The data is obtained from the responses to the letter.

3 Blood given by volunteers at a blood donor clinic is tested for blood group and for the HIV virus. The data is used to estimate:

a) the proportion of the population with blood group A,

b) the proportion of the population infected with the HIV virus.

4 The researcher for an opinion poll stands on a street corner and asks passers-by which political party they support. This is done:

a) at a shopping centre on Wednesday at 11 a.m.

b) outside a station on Wednesday at 6 p.m.

c) at a shopping centre on Saturday at 11 a.m.

5 After a radio programme on cannabis, the listeners are invited to write in saying whether they think it should be legalised. The data is obtained from the letters received.

6 A school wants to survey the opinion of a sample of the parents of its pupils. The school list is available. Why might this not be a suitable sample frame?

What could the sample frame be? How could a random sample of 30 be obtained?

7 A survey is taken to find the average adult income in a town. A random sample of 50 dwellings is selected, and an interviewer is sent to each dwelling to ask the head of the household their income. Will the data obtained by this method be unbiased? How could the method be improved?

8 A computer programmer is trying to simulate a dice game. The program picks random digits, divides them by 6, takes the remainder and adds 1.

Explain why this is not a random sample from 1, 2, 3, 4, 5, 6. How could a random sample be obtained?

*9 A sampling frame contains a list of people numbered from 0 up to n, where n is less than ten. A sample of people is selected in the following way. Take random digits, and find the remainder after division by n. Select the people whose numbers occur as a remainder.

For what values of n will this result in a random sample?

LONGER EXERCISE

Embarrassing questions

However careful we are in picking a sample of people to answer a questionnaire, there is always the possibility that their answers may not be truthful. This is likely to be the case if they are asked whether they have indulged in activities which are embarrassing or even criminal. A way round the difficulty is as follows.

Hand each person a die, and ask them to roll it without showing you the result. They are to answer 'A' if either of the following holds.

- The die gives 1 or 2 and the answer to the embarrassing question is *yes*.
- The die gives 3, 4, 5 or 6 and the answer to the embarrassing question is *no*.

They are to answer 'B' if either of the following holds.

- The die gives 1 or 2 and the answer to the embarrassing question is *no*.
- The die gives 3, 4, 5 or 6 and the answer to the embarrassing question is *yes*.

If the true proportion of people who should answer *yes* is p, find the proportion of people who answer 'A'.

What would you expect the proportion of people answering 'A' to be if p is 0? What if it is 1?

This method was used to find the proportion of taxpayers who had submitted a false income-tax form. The proportion of people answering 'A' was 45 per cent. What can be concluded?

Think up an embarrassing question of your own, and conduct a survey using this method.

EXAMINATION QUESTIONS

1 A random sample of 100 people listed in a residential telephone directory is not likely to be representative of the adult population of the area covered by the directory. Name two groups of people which are likely to be under-represented.

N 1991

2 A market research company is to conduct a party political opinion poll in a by-election. In this context, explain briefly what is mean by:

a) systematic sampling,   **b)** stratified sampling.

In practice, quota sampling is often used.

c) Explain briefly why this is done and how it is carried out.

A AS 1992

3 A manufacturer of a new type of chocolate dessert wishes to predict the likely volume of sales in a city. Three schemes, as outlined below, are proposed for selecting people for a questionnaire. Discuss, briefly, the advantages or disadvantages of each scheme.

(i)   Select every 30th name on the electoral register of the city;

(ii) Pick, at random, one name from each page of the telephone directory and telephone them;

(iii) Select customers entering a supermarket, ensuring that the numbers in each sex, age and social class category are proportional to the number in the population.

Choose one of the schemes, explaining why you think it is best.

NI 1991

4 A college of 3000 students has students registered in four departments, Arts, Science, Education and Crafts. The Principal wishes to take a sample from the student population to gain information about likely student response to a rearrangement of the college timetable so as to hold lectures on Wednesday, previously reserved for sports.

What sampling method would you advise the Principal to use? Give reasons to justify your choice.

L 1994

5 a) Explain briefly:

(i)   why it is often desirable to take samples,

(ii) what you understand by a sampling frame.

b) State two circumstances when you would consider using,

(i)   clustering   (ii) stratification

when sampling from a population.

c) Give two advantages and two disadvantages associated with quota sampling.

L 1992

Summary and key points

4.1 A population is the complete set that we want to investigate. A sample consists of a selection from the population.

4.2 A random sample is one in which every member of the population has an equal chance of being selected. Random samples can be made by the use of random numbers, which are available in tables or from a computer or calculator.

4.3 There are other methods of sampling, for example stratified, systematic, quota and cluster sampling.

It is important to ensure that selection of the sample does not lead to a bias in favour of one group over another.

Consolidation section A

Chapter 1

1 Find the mean, median and mode of the following sets of data.

   a) 56   51   56   61   49   52   56   68   67   63   59

   b) 10.6   10.2   9.8   10.4   10.0   10.3   10.1   9.9   10.7   10.5

2 The electrical current along a wire is measured 100 times. The results, in amperes, are given in the table below. Find the modal interval, and estimate the mean and the median.

Current	10–20	20–25	25–30	30–40
Frequency	17	21	29	33

3 Calculate the variance and interquartile range for the data in Question 1.

4 Estimate the standard deviation and interquartile range of the current in Question 2.

5 Two people measure the diameters of components produced by a machine. The diameters of the 20 components checked by the first person had mean 1.25 cm and variance 0.0002 cm^2, the diameters of the 25 components checked by the second person had mean 1.26 cm and variance 0.0003 cm^2. Find the mean and variance of the measurements as a whole.

6 At a village fête the vicar invites people to guess his weight. The results, in stones and pounds, are shown in the table below. Would the mean or the median be a better average to use? Give reasons.

   12 st 6 lb   11 st 13 lb   12 st 4 lb   13 st 5 lb

   12 st 4 lb   13 st 10 lb   12 st 1 lb   11 st 8 lb

   11 st 9 lb   11 st 8 lb   13 st 0 lb   30 st 6 lb

   13 st 9 lb   11 st 10 lb   13 st 9 lb   13 st 1 lb

Chapter 2

7 In order to compare prices in 100 different shops, the total cost of the same selection of items was found in each. The results are shown in the table below. Construct a histogram to illustrate the data.

Cost (£)	25–29.99	30–31.99	32–33.99	34–34.99	35–40
Frequency	5	23	41	17	14

8 The ages of the 30 members of a tennis club are listed below. Construct a stem and leaf diagram to illustrate the data, taking as your stems 1, 2, 3 and so on.

19 27 34 21 32 68 41 35 25 26 19 20 26 30 40

26 32 39 47 44 19 34 30 29 47 21 22 25 46 20

9 The weights, in kilograms, of two teams of footballers are given below. Construct a back to back stem and leaf diagram, and comment.

Team A	**Team B**
71 79 78 77 83 81 79 74 72 80 73	77 86 80 72 70 81 92 88 68 79 73

10 Construct a cumulative frequency diagram to illustrate the data of Question 7. From it, estimate the median and the quartiles.

11 The weekly take-home pay, in £, of 20 female and 20 male employees of a factory is given below. Construct a box and whisker plot for each group, and comment.

Male					**Female**				
250	362	302	281	404	194	241	274	305	216
482	491	294	375	482	228	251	220	178	262
168	529	391	234	401	240	328	360	243	231
492	258	361	320	284	261	302	321	283	234

Chapter 3

12 For two events A and B, $P(A) = 0.6$, $P(B) = 0.2$, $P(A \text{ or } B) = 0.7$. Find $P(A \& B)$. Show that A and B are neither exclusive nor independent.

13 If two cards are drawn without replacement from the standard pack, find the probability that neither is a heart.

14 The probability that a snooker player will win the first frame of a match is 0.4. If he wins, the probability he will win the second is 0.6, while if he loses the probability he will win the second is 0.3. Find the probability he wins exactly one of the first two frames.

15 In how many ways can you predict the order of the first four teams in a league of 22 teams?

16 Three of the 50 teachers at a school are to sit on the board of governors. How many possible selections of representatives are there?

17 Four people are picked at random from a group containing 12 men and 13 women. What is the probability that two men and two women will be picked?

18 With events A and B as defined in Question 13, find $P(A|B)$ and $P(A|(A \text{ or } B))$.

19 A student is taking Maths and Physics at A-level. Her probabilities of passing these subjects are 0.6 and 0.8 respectively, and her probability of passing both is 0.5. If she passes exactly one subject, find the probability that it was Maths.

Chapter 4

20 Five workers are to be picked at random from a workforce of 83. Describe how this can be done using the following random digits.

6 3 0 3 8 9 9 2 3 8 1 0 0 0 4 5 6 7

21 Twenty workers are to be selected from a factory. The sample should reflect the sex, age and ethnic make-up of the factory. Explain how this could be done by:

a) stratified sampling, **b)** quota sampling.

22 Certain GCSE projects are marked by the teachers themselves. To ensure standardisation, the examining board then asks to see projects from across the ability range. Explain how this could be done by

a) stratified sampling, **b)** cluster sampling.

MIXED QUESTIONS

1 If a distribution has positive skew, then it is usual that mode $<$ median $<$ mean.

Find data for which:

a) median $<$ mode $<$ mean, **b)** median $<$ mean $<$ mode.

2 A box contains counters numbered 1, 2, ..., n, where n is unknown. A sample of size r is taken out, and n is estimated as the largest number from the sample. What is the probability that n is estimated correctly? If $n = 100$, how large must r be for the probability of estimating n correctly to be at least $\frac{1}{2}$?

3 A tenth of the people with a certain psychiatric disorder receive psychoanalysis, which will bring a cure in 25 per cent of the cases. Only a quarter of those not receiving treatment will recover. Find the probability that someone who recovers had received psychoanalysis.

4 You meet a girl who says she comes from a family with three children. What is the probability that she has an elder brother?

5 A woman has four grandchildren. She buys five different presents. In how many ways can she give them out, if each child receives at least one present?

6 When is it true that $P(A|B) = P(B|A)$?

7 If A and B are independent, show that A' and B' are independent.

8 If two events A and B are independent, then $P(A \& B) = P(A) \times P(B)$. A set of events is *pairwise* independent if any pair of events is independent.

Find a set of three events, A, B and C, which are pairwise independent but for which $P(A \& B \& C)$ = 0. (Consider the spinning of two coins. A, B and C each have probability $\frac{1}{2}$.)

DISCUSSION QUESTIONS

1 To compare prosperity today with that of just after World War 2, it was said that in the 1940s the average man owned only one pair of trousers. Discuss this claim, with particular reference to the 'less than average' man.

2 A common exercise in probability is to show that when three coins are spun, the probability that they all show the same is $\frac{1}{4}$. What is wrong with the following argument?

At least two of the coin must show the same. Say they show heads. The probability that the third coin shows the same as the other two is $\frac{1}{2}$.

3 Most scientific calculators have the facility to work out the mean and variance of data entered into them. How does it do it? Which formula for the variance does it use? Why can't it work out the median of the data?

4 What would be the best way to measure the relative safety of different modes of transport, in terms of numbers of journeys, number of vehicles and so on?

LONGER EXERCISES

56 virtues

In about AD 960, Bishop Wibold of Cambrai in France enumerated 56 virtues, and associated them with the arrangements in which three identical dice can land. Show how to list these arrangements.

Public lending right

Public lending right is a scheme for paying authors for the loans of their books from public libraries. There is a ceiling of £6000 for any single author. The table below, for a recent year, gives the numbers of authors receiving amounts within given ranges.

Amount earned (£)	0	1–99	100–499	500–999	1000–2499	2500–4999	5000–5999	6000
Number of authors	3505	11 204	3061	572	406	148	25	55

Analyse these data. Are they discrete or continuous? You might find it interesting to prepare diagrams showing:

a) the proportions of authors in the different ranges,

b) the proportions of money going to authors in the different ranges.

Quartiles

The definition of quartile given in Chapter 1 is not the only one. Two other rules for finding the lower quartile are given below. In both cases there are n data.

a) If $\frac{1}{4}n$ is an integer, say $\frac{1}{4}n = i$, then take the average of the ith term and the $(i+1)$th term. If $\frac{1}{4}n$ lies between i and $i+1$, take the $(i+1)$th term.

b) First find the median m. The lower quartile is the median of those terms less than m. (This value is also called a **hinge**.)

Use these definitions on some of the data sets in Chapter 1. Do they give different results for the lower quartile? For what values of n will they give the same values? For what data would the different definitions give very different values?

A statistical program on a computer gave 2.75 for the lower quartile of the following data.

$\quad$ 1$\quad$ 2$\quad$ 3$\quad$ 4$\quad$ 5$\quad$ 6$\quad$ 7$\quad$ 8$\quad$ 9$\quad$ 10

What rule was the program following? What would it give for the upper quartile?

EXAMINATION QUESTIONS

1$\quad$ In an investigation of delays at a roadworks, the times spent, by a sample of commuters, waiting to pass through the roadworks were recorded to the nearest minute. Shown below is part of a cumulative frequency table resulting from the investigation.

Upper class boundary	2.5	4.5	7.5	8.5	9.5	10.5	12.5	15.5	20.5
Cumulative number of commuters	0	6	21	48	97	149	178	191	200

$\quad$ **a)** For how many of the commuters was the time recorded as 11 minutes or 12 minutes?

$\quad$ **b)** Estimate (i) the lower quartile, (ii) the 81st percentile, of these waiting times.

$\hfill$ *L 1994*

2$\quad$ Give two reasons for considering the use of:

$\quad$ **a)** cluster sampling,$\qquad\qquad$ **b)** quota sampling.

$\quad$ **c)** Give two advantages and two disadvantages associated with stratified sampling.

$\quad$ A class contains 35 children and the teacher wishes to take a simple random sample of 10 children from the class.

$\quad$ **d)** Write down the procedure the teacher might use if the sample is to be taken using random numbers.

$\hfill$ *L 1995*

3$\quad$ A marketing company always buys new cars on 1st August. Before making any purchases on 1st August 1992, they reviewed their fleet of cars. The following table shows the age, x, in years, of the cars in the fleet.

Age (x)	1	2	3	4	5	6	7	8	9	10	11
Number of cars (f)	14	20	16	14	12	8	6	4	3	2	1

Find:

a) the mode   b) the median and quartiles   c) the mean

of this distribution.

Draw a boxplot to represent these data.

The distribution is positively skewed. Use your calculations to justify this statement.

L 1993

4 a) Mr and Mrs Patel are members of a committee of 17 people from which a delegation of 6 people will be chosen to represent the committee at a civic function. The delegation will consist of 3 men chosen at random from the 12 men on the committee, and 3 women chosen from the 5 women on the committee. Calculate the probability that:

(i) Mr and Mrs Patel will both be chosen,

(ii) at least one of Mr and Mrs Patel will be chosen,

(iii) exactly one of Mr and Mrs Patel will be chosen.

b) An athlete attempts a gymnastic exercise three times. The probability of success at the first attempt is 0.45. For each of the second and third attempts the probability of success is 0.6 if the athlete has been successful at the preceding attempt, and 0.45 if the athlete has not been successful at the preceding attempt. Find the probability that the athlete succeeds on exactly two out of the three attempts.

C AS 1992

5 Two events A and B are such that:

$$P(A) = \tfrac{8}{15}, \qquad P(B) = \tfrac{1}{3}, \qquad P(A|B) = \tfrac{1}{5}.$$

Calculate the probabilities that:

(i) both events occur

(ii) only one of the two events occurs,

(iii) neither event occurs.

N 1990

6 A box contains 10 videos of which 6 are films and 4 are educational. If 4 of these videos are chosen at random calculate the probabilities that

(i) all four will be films

(ii) two will be films and the other two educational.

W 1992

7 On September 1st the frequency distribution of the ages (in completed years) of the pupils in Forms 1–5 in a certain school is given in the following table:

Age (in completed years)	11	12	13	14	15
Frequency	111	119	150	159	161

(i) Draw the cumulative frequency polygon and estimate the median age of these pupils.

(ii) Calculate estimates for the mean and the standard deviation of the ages of these pupils.

If, in addition, it is known that the mean and the standard deviation of the ages of the 100 pupils in Form 6 are 16.9 and 0.8 years respectively, find estimates for:

(iii) the mean and the standard deviation of the ages of all the pupils in the school.

(iv) the median age of all the pupils in the school.

W AS 1991

8 A frequency diagram for a set of data is shown in Fig. A1.

(i) Find the median and the mode of the data.

(ii) Given that the mean is 5.95 and the standard deviation is 2.58, explain why the value 15 may be regarded as an outlier.

(iii) Explain how you would treat the outlier if the diagram represents

(A) the ages (in completed years) of children at a party,

(B) the sums of the scores obtained when throwing a pair of dice.

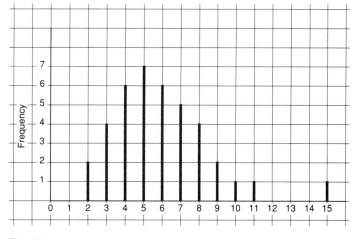

Fig. A1

(iv) Find the median and the mode of the data after the outlier is removed.

(v) **Without doing any calculations** state what effect, if any, removing the outlier would have on the mean and on the standard deviation.

(vi) Does the diagram exhibit positive skewness, negative skewness or no skewness? How is the skewness affected by removing the outlier?

MEI 1993

9 To withdraw money from a cash machine with my plastic card, I need to type in my Personal Identification Number (PIN). The PIN is 4 digits long, and can take any value from 0000 to 9999 inclusive.

(i) How many different PINS are there?

Unfortunately, the only thing I can remember about my PIN is that all 4 digits are different.

(ii) How many possibilities are there for my PIN?

On further thought, I can recall that the digits in my PIN are 1, 4, 5, 9, but I cannot remember the order.

(iii) How many possibilities are there now for my PIN?

The cash machine allows me up to 3 attempts to get my PIN right, but if all 3 attempts are incorrect then the card is confiscated. I choose randomly from the possible PINs (as in part (iii) above), but I take care not to try a wrong PIN twice. Find the probability of each of the following events.

(iv) I get the PIN right at the first attempt.

(v) I get the PIN right at the second attempt.

(vi) The card is confiscated.

MEI 1993

Discrete random variables

In earlier work, and in the previous chapters of this book, you have dealt with data. These have come from surveys, questionnaires or experiments. They have been organised into frequency tables, illustrated by pie charts or histograms, analysed by their measures of central tendency or their measures of spread.

The distributions of the data were **practical** or **experimental** distributions. They were found from real, practical figures. Much of statistics, however, is concerned with **theoretical** distributions, for which the data do not come from real life, but are obtained from some mathematical formula. The distinction between experimental and theoretical distributions is very similar to that between experimental and theoretical probability.

Statistical models

Throughout this book we shall refer to **models**. A statistical model consists of mathematical equations, formulae and so on, which we try to use to predict behaviour in the real world. There are often simplifications and assumptions involved in a model.

A theoretical distribution can be used as a statistical model of an experimental distribution. Data, obtained from the theoretical distribution, may be compared with real life data. If the match is close, then the model is successful and we can continue using it. If there is a wide difference between the theoretical and the practical values then the model is not successful. Either we shall abandon it or we shall modify it until its results are close to the real ones.

For example, it might be found that the number of attempts people take to pass the driving test may be found to have a distribution as shown in the bar chart of Fig. 5.1. We might find a mathematical formula which fits these values very closely. The authority in charge of testing could then use this formula to plan its provision of tests.

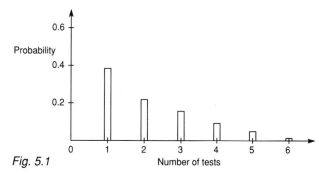

Fig. 5.1

The formula may not be a perfect fit of the bar chart. For example, no one has taken 1000 driving tests, so the experimental probability of this is zero, although the formula might give a small but non-zero probability of this happening. That does not necessarily matter. The formula provides a mathematical model for the distribution of the number of tests and, provided that it is accurate for the large majority of people, then it is a successful model.

5.1 Discrete distributions

A **random variable** is a quantity X which takes different values with various probabilities. The **probability distribution** of X tells us these values and the corresponding probabilities.

There are two main classes of random variable, which correspond to the two main classes of data defined in Chapter 1.

A **continuous** random variable takes real-numbered values within a fixed range. A continuous random variable could be used to model:

a) the time taken to run a race
b) the weight of a randomly selected pea
c) the length of a randomly selected snake.

The probability that a continuous variable takes any given value is zero. For example, the probability that someone will run a race in *exactly* 12 seconds is zero. By contrast, a **discrete** random variable takes any of its possible values with non-zero probability. A discrete random variable could be used to model:

d) the score obtained when a die is rolled
e) the number of bulls-eyes obtained when 20 darts are thrown at a board
f) the number of rolls of a die needed to obtain a 6.

Usually, but not always, the values taken by a discrete random variable are whole numbers. The values taken in examples **d)**, **e)** and **f)** are all whole numbers. We could, however, make a peculiar die which displayed fractional values on its faces. Example **f)** shows that a discrete random variable can take infinitely many possible values. In theory, there is no limit to the number of times you will have to roll a die before obtaining the first 6.

In this chapter we shall consider probability distributions of discrete random variables.

Notation
We shall use capital letters such as X, Y and Z for the random variables and lower case letters such as x, y and z for the values that

they take. We shall write the possible values of X as x_1, x_2 and so on. So we shall write, for example:

$$P(X = x_2)$$

to mean the probability that X takes the value x_2.

Definition
X is a discrete random variable if it takes values x_1, x_2, ... , x_i, ... with probabilities $p_1, p_2, ... , p_i, ...$ respectively, such that:

$$p_i \geq 0 \quad \text{for all } i$$

$$\Sigma \, p_i = 1$$

We give the probability distribution of X by stating the values x_i and the corresponding probabilities p_i. This can be done by listing, by a table or by formula.

EXAMPLE 5.1
Let X be the number obtained when a fair die is rolled. Construct a table giving the probability distribution of X.

Solution
The variable X can take any of the values 1, 2, 3, 4, 5 or 6. The die is fair, so each of these values has probability $\frac{1}{6}$. Draw up a table giving these values of X and the corresponding probabilities.

i	1	2	3	4	5	6
$P(X = i)$	$\frac{1}{6}$	$\frac{1}{6}$	$\frac{1}{6}$	$\frac{1}{6}$	$\frac{1}{6}$	$\frac{1}{6}$

Note
The example of a fair die is one that we have used many times already. Note that the distribution above is a theoretical distribution. We have constructed it on the assumption that the die is absolutely fair and that the roll did not favour any face above another.

EXAMPLE 5.2
The random variable X takes values 1, 2, 3 or 4, with probabilities given by the formula:

$$P(X = i) = ki,$$

where k is constant. Find k.

Solution
The sum of all the probabilities must be 1. Hence:

$$k1 + k2 + k3 + k4 = 1$$
$$k(1 + 2 + 3 + 4) = 1$$

Hence $k = \frac{1}{10}$

The value of k is $\frac{1}{10}$.

EXERCISE 5A

1 Two fair coins are spun. Let X be the number of heads obtained. Construct a table showing the probability distribution of X.

2 The proportion of a population with blood group O is 40 per cent. Two people are picked at random, and X is the number of those people with blood group O. Construct a table showing the probability distribution of X.

3 A box contains ten counters. Five of the counters have the number 1 written on them, three have 2, two have 3. A counter is drawn out, and X is the number on it. Construct a table showing the probability distribution of X.

4 The dwellings in a housing estate have two, three or four bedrooms in the ratio 2:5:3. A dwelling is picked at random. Write down the probability distribution of the number, X, of bedrooms it contains.

5 Two fair dice are rolled. Let X be the number of 6s obtained. Construct a table showing the probability distribution of X.

6 A motorist encounters two sets of traffic lights in succession. At each set the probability that he will be stopped is $\frac{2}{3}$, and each set is independent of the others. Construct a table showing the probability distribution of the number, X, of sets at which he stops.

7 A fair die is rolled, and X is the *square* of the number showing. Construct a table for the probability distribution of X.

8 Assuming that a baby is equally likely to be a boy or a girl, construct a table showing the probability distribution of the number of boys in a family with two children.

9 In a game a fair die is rolled and then a fair coin is spun. If the coin gives a head, then X is the score on the die. If the coin gives a tail, then X is twice the score on the die. Construct a table showing the probability distribution of X.

10 The random variable X takes values 0, 1, 2, 3 with probabilities given by:

$$P(X = i) = k(i + 1)^2$$

where k is constant. Find k.

11 The random variable X has a probability distribution given by:

$$P(X = i) = ki^2 \qquad \text{for } i = 1, 2 \text{ or } 3$$
$$= k(7 - i)^2 \text{ for } i = 4, 5 \text{ or } 6$$

Find k, given that it is constant.

12 Suppose that X has a probability distribution given by:

$$P(X = i) = \frac{k}{i^2}, \quad \text{for } i = 1, 2, 3, 4, \ldots$$

Use the result that $\sum_{i=1}^{\infty} \frac{1}{i^2} = \frac{\pi^2}{6}$ to find k, given that it is constant.

*13 A fair die is rolled until a six is obtained. Let X be the number of rolls required. Show that the probability distribution of X is given by:

$$P(X = i) = \frac{1}{6}(\frac{5}{6})^{i-1}, \quad \text{for } i = 1, 2, 3, 4, \ldots$$

Use the formula for the sum of a geometric series to show that the sum of these probabilities is 1.

5.2 Expectation and variance of discrete random variables

In Chapter 3 we defined the mean and variance for experimental distributions. We can also define them for theoretical distributions.

Consider Example 5.1, which involved the score obtained when a fair die was rolled. Suppose you are playing a gambling game in which the die is rolled and you receive the score in £. How much money do you expect to gain if you play the game a large number of times?

You receive £1 on $\frac{1}{6}$ of the games.

You receive £2 on $\frac{1}{6}$ of the games.

...

You receive £6 on $\frac{1}{6}$ of the games.

Hence your expected gain, per game, will be:

$$£1 \times \tfrac{1}{6} + £2 \times \tfrac{1}{6} + \ldots + £6 \times \tfrac{1}{6} = £3.50$$

A **fair game** is one in which the expected gain is zero. This particular game will be fair if you pay £3.50 for playing it.

We see that the expected gain (in £) is obtained by multiplying each possible gain by its probability and then adding. This will apply to all discrete distributions. If X is a discrete random variable, then its expected value is obtained by multiplying each possible value by its probability and then adding the products. The general definition is below.

Expected value
Suppose X is a discrete random variable which takes values x_1, x_2, ... , x_i, ... with probabilities p_1, p_2, ... , p_i, ... respectively. Then the expected value of X, written $E(X)$, is:

$$E(X) = x_1 p_1 + x_2 p_2 + \ldots + x_i p_i + \ldots = \Sigma\, x_i p_i$$

Variance

Suppose we have found the expected value of X to be $E(X)$. We define the variance of X in accordance with the definition of variance for experimental data in Chapter 1.

$$\text{Var}(X) = E((X - E(X))^2)$$

That is, we take each value of $(X - E(X))^2$, multiply by its appropriate probability, then add the products.

$$\text{Var}(X) = \Sigma\, (x_i - E(X))^2 p_i$$

It is often more convenient to write the variance in the equivalent form:

$$\text{Var}(X) = E(X^2) - (E(X))^2 = \Sigma\, x_i^2 p_i - (E(X))^2$$

The proof of the equivalence is in the Mathematical appendix on page 329.

Expectation of a function of X

The expectation of any function of X is defined similarly.

$$E(f(X)) = \Sigma\, f(x_i)p_i$$

For example, the expectation of $5X + 2$ is:

$$E(5X + 2) = \Sigma(5x + 2)p_i$$

EXAMPLE 5.3
Find the expected value and variance of the random variable of Example 5.1.

Solution
Here X takes the values 1, 2, 3, 4, 5 and 6, each with probability $\frac{1}{6}$. Hence:

$$E(X) = 1 \times \tfrac{1}{6} + 2 \times \tfrac{1}{6} + \ldots + 6 \times \tfrac{1}{6} = 3\tfrac{1}{2}$$
$$E(X^2) = 1^2 \times \tfrac{1}{6} + 2^2 \times \tfrac{1}{6} + \ldots + 6^2 \times \tfrac{1}{6} = 15\tfrac{1}{6}$$
$$\text{Var}(X) = 15\tfrac{1}{6} - (3\tfrac{1}{2})^2 = 2\tfrac{11}{12}$$

X **has expected value** $3\tfrac{1}{2}$ **and variance** $2\tfrac{11}{12}$**.**

EXAMPLE 5.4
The table below gives the probability distribution of a discrete random variable with expected value 4.15. Find x and y.

i	1	2	3	4	5	6
$P(X = i)$	0.1	0.2	0.1	x	y	0.4

Solution
We have two unknowns. We can find two equations: one from the

fact that the sum of all the probabilities is 1, and the other from the fact that the expected value is 4.15.

$$x + y + 0.8 = 1$$

Hence $x + y = 0.2$ (1)

$$0.1 + 0.4 + 0.3 + 4x + 5y + 2.4 = 4.15$$

Hence $4x + 5y = 0.95$ (2)

Solve equations (1) and (2) to obtain $x = 0.05$ and $y = 0.15$.

$x = $ **0.05** and $y = $ **0.15.**

EXAMPLE 5.5
With X as defined in Example 5.4, find the expected value of $3X - 7$.

Solution
When X takes the values 1, 2, 3, 4, 5, 6, $(3X - 7)$ takes the values $-4, -1, 2, 5, 8, 11$. Multiply each of these values by the appropriate probability and add the products.

$$E(3X - 7) = \Sigma(3x_i - 7)p_i$$

$$= -4 \times 0.1 + -1 \times 0.2 + 2 \times 0.1 + 5 \times 0.05$$
$$+ 8 \times 0.15 + 11 \times 0.4$$
$$= 5.45$$

The expected value is **5.45.**

EXERCISE 5B

1 Each of the tables below gives the probability distribution of a discrete random variable. In each case find the expected value and variance.

a)

i	0	1	2	3	4
$P(X = i)$	0.2	0.4	0.2	0.1	0.1

b)

i	1	2	3	4
$P(X = i)$	0.2	0.3	0.2	0.3

c)

i	0.5	1	1.5	2	2.5	3
$P(X = i)$	0.1	0.2	0.3	0.3	0.05	0.05

2 The probability distribution of X is given by $P(X = i) = ki$, for $i = 1, 2, 3, 4$ and 5. Find k, and find the expected value and variance of X.

3 The probability distribution of X is given by $P(X = i) = k(4 - i)$, for $i = 0, 1, 2$ and 3. Find k, and find the expected value and variance of X.

4 The number of cracked eggs in a carton sold in a supermarket will be 0, 1, 2 with probabilities $\frac{1}{2}, \frac{1}{3}, \frac{1}{6}$. Find the expected value and variance of the number of cracked eggs in a carton.

5 A simplified fruit machine has two reels, each of which has ten lemons and five strawberries. If one reel shows a strawberry you win £1, and if two strawberries show you win £3. Letting X be your gain on one play, construct a table showing the distribution of X. Find the mean and variance of X.

6 A certain species of bird always lays three eggs. The number, X, of eggs which hatch successfully has probability distribution as given below. Find the expected value and variance of X.

i	0	1	2	3
$P(X = i)$	0.1	0.2	0.3	0.4

7 In the game of *Crown and Anchor* three dice are rolled. You bet on one of the numbers. If your number comes up once you receive twice your original stake, if it comes up twice you receive thrice your original stake, and if it comes up on all three dice you receive four times your original stake.

Find the mean and variance of your gain, if you bet £1.

8 A die has six faces, with the numbers 1, 1, 1, 2, 2 and 3 on them. It is rolled, and you receive the score on the die, in £. What should you pay to play the game if it is to be fair?

9 A fair die is rolled twice. You receive £10 if a double 6 is obtained, and £1 if one six is obtained. Otherwise you receive nothing. If the game is to be fair, how much should you pay to play it?

10 In a game two cards are dealt, without replacement, from a standard pack. You receive £1 if one card is a heart, and £5 if both are hearts. If the game is to be fair, how much should you pay to play it?

11 In a game a fair die is rolled three times. If a 6 first appears on the first, second or third roll you receive £5, £2 or £1 respectively. If no 6 appears you receive nothing. If the game is fair, how much should you pay to play it?

12 X is a random variable with probability distribution as given in the table below. The expected value of X is 4.4. Find x.

i	2	3	5	x	10
$P(X = i)$	0.2	0.4	0.2	0.1	0.1

13 X is a random variable with probability distribution as given in the table below. The variance of X is 8. Show that $x^2 - 2x - 35 = 0$. Find x, given that it is positive.

i	1	x
$P(X = i)$	$\frac{1}{3}$	$\frac{2}{3}$

14 X is a random variable with probability distribution as given in the table below. The expected value of X is 3.25. Find x and y.

i	1	2	3	4	5
$P(X = i)$	0.15	0.2	x	y	0.15

15 X is a random variable with probability distribution as given in the table below. The expected value of X is 10.3 and its variance is 9.01. Find x and y, given that they are integers.

i	5	8	x	y
$P(X = i)$	0.1	0.3	0.4	0.2

16 The random variable X takes the values 1, 2, 3, 4, 5, 6 and 7. The probabilities that X is 1, 2, 3 or 4 are all equal to x, and the probabilities that X is equal to 5, 6 or 7 are all equal to y. The expected value of X is 3.5. Find x and y.

17 The number, X, of times per term a certain book is taken out of the library is modelled by the formula below.

$$P(X = i) = k(5 - i), \quad \text{for } i = 0, 1, 2, 3.$$

Find k, given that it is constant. Find the expected value and variance of X.

18 The number X of taxis outside a station has a probability distribution modelled by:

$$P(X = i) = k(7 - i)(i + 1), \quad \text{for } i = 0, 1, 2, 3, 4, 5, 6$$

Find k, given that it is constant. Find the expected value and variance of X.

19 The number, X, of kittens born in a litter has a probability distribution modelled by the formula below.

$$P(X = i) = ki^2(7 - i), \quad \text{for } i = 1, 2, 3, 4, 5, 6$$

Find k, given that it is constant. Find the expected value and variance of X.

20 With X as defined in Question 1a), find:

a) $E(2X + 1)$ **b)** $E(X^3)$ **c)** $E(X(X - 1))$.

21 With X as defined in Question 2, find:

a) $E(4X - 1)$ **b)** $E(7 - 3X)$ **c)** $E(X^2 + 1)$.

5.3 Uniform distribution

There are several special discrete distributions which arise in natural contexts. Here we give examples of one of these special distributions, the **uniform** distribution.

Uniform

The number given by a fair die is a discrete variable which takes values 1 to 6 with equal probabilities. It is an example of a uniform distribution.

In general, suppose X takes n values with equal probabilities $\dfrac{1}{n}$. Then X has a uniform distribution.

If X takes the values 1, 2, 3, ..., n, the expected value and variance of X are given by

$$E(X) = \tfrac{1}{2}(n + 1) \qquad \mathrm{Var}(X) = \tfrac{1}{12}(n^2 - 1)$$

The proofs of these appear in the Mathematical appendix, on page 329.

EXAMPLE 5.6
A roulette wheel has holes numbered 1 to 36. If the ball is equally likely to land in any of these holes, find the mean and variance of the number of the hole it lands in.

Solution
The number of the hole has a uniform distribution, taking the values 1, 2, up to 36. Apply the formulae, with $n = 36$.

$$\begin{aligned}
E(X) &= \tfrac{1}{2}(36 + 1) \\
&= 18\tfrac{1}{2} \\
\mathrm{Var}(X) &= \tfrac{1}{12}(36^2 - 1) \\
&= 107\tfrac{11}{12}
\end{aligned}$$

The mean is $18\tfrac{1}{2}$ and the variance is $107\tfrac{11}{12}$.

Triangular

When two identical independent uniform variables are added, the distribution of the sum has a **triangular** distribution. The most familiar example of this is the total score obtained when two dice are rolled.

EXAMPLE 5.7
Two fair dice are rolled and their total T is found. Find the distribution of T and illustrate it by a bar chart showing the probabilities. Find the mean and variance of T.

Solution
The table in Fig. 5.2 shows the possible outcomes of the dice. Each of the 36 squares is equally likely. Note that 2 occurs in one of the squares, hence its probability is $\frac{1}{36}$. Find the other probabilities in a similar way. Fill in a distribution table.

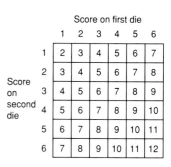

Score on first die

		1	2	3	4	5	6
	1	2	3	4	5	6	7
Score	2	3	4	5	6	7	8
on	3	4	5	6	7	8	9
second	4	5	6	7	8	9	10
die	5	6	7	8	9	10	11
	6	7	8	9	10	11	12

Fig. 5.2

i	2	3	4	5	6	7	8	9	10	11	12
$P(T=i)$	$\frac{1}{36}$	$\frac{1}{18}$	$\frac{1}{12}$	$\frac{1}{9}$	$\frac{5}{36}$	$\frac{1}{6}$	$\frac{5}{36}$	$\frac{1}{9}$	$\frac{1}{12}$	$\frac{1}{18}$	$\frac{1}{36}$

A bar chart of the probabilities is shown in Fig. 5.3. Notice the triangular shape of the diagram.

Find $E(T)$ and $Var(T)$ using the methods described in Section 5.2.

$E(T) = 7$ and $Var(T) = 5\frac{5}{6}$.

Note

The mean and variance of T are twice the mean and variance of the score on a single die.

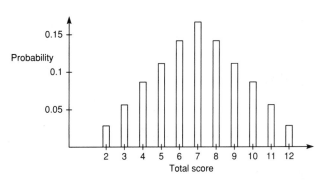

Fig. 5.3

EXERCISE 5C

1 Verify that the expected value and variance of the score on a fair die, as found in Example 5.3, agree with those given by the formulae.

2 A calculator is used to pick a random number from 1 to 9 inclusive. Find the expected value and variance of the number obtained.

3 A roulette wheel has holes numbered 0 to 36. Find the mean and variance of the number in which the ball lands.

4 A janitor has seven similar keys, only one of which will open a door. He tries them in turn, until he finds the one that fits. Find the expected value and variance of the number of keys he tries.

5 A fair tetrahedral (four-sided) die is rolled. Find the mean and variance of the number obtained.

6 A time of day is chosen at random. Find the expected value and variance of the number of minutes, rounded up to the nearest whole number, that would have elapsed since the hour was struck.

7 A spinner has the numbers 1 to n on its sides, and each number is equally likely. Find n in the following cases

   a) The expected value of the number is 4.5.   b) The variance of the number is 4.

8 Two fair tetrahedral dice are rolled. Construct a table showing the probability distribution of the total score. Find the expected value and variance of the total score.

9 A fair die is rolled twice, and the scores on the first and second roll are X and Y respectively. Let $Z = X - Y$. Construct a table showing the probability distribution of Z. Plot a bar chart for Z. Find the expected value and variance of Z. How are these connected with the expected value and variance of X?

10   Two fair dice are rolled, and the positive difference Z of the scores (i.e. $|X - Y|$, where X and Y are the scores on the dice) is found. Construct a table showing the probability distribution of Z. Plot a bar chart for Z. Find the expected value and variance of Z.

11   Two fair dice are rolled. Let X be the greater of the scores obtained. (If the dice show the same number, then X is that number.) Find the probability distribution of X. Draw a bar chart showing the distribution. Find $E(X)$ and $\text{Var}(X)$.

5.4 Practice in discrete distributions

We shall now look at some examples and problems involving discrete distributions. We shall need to find probabilities and permutations and combinations.

EXAMPLE 5.8
An archer shoots arrows at a target. The score, X, obtained by each arrow has the following distribution.

i	1	2	3	4
$P(X = i)$	0.4	0.3	0.2	0.1

Assuming that the scores for the arrows are independent of each other, find the distribution of the number of arrows shot before the total score is 3.

Solution
Let Y be the number of shots. Then Y could be 1, 2 or 3, in the following ways.

$Y = 1$. Score 3 or 4 with the first arrow.

$$P(Y = 1) = 0.2 + 0.1 = 0.3$$

$Y = 2$. Score 2 with the first arrow, then any score with the second. Score 1 with the first arrow, then 2, 3 or 4 with the second.

$$P(Y = 2) = 0.3 + 0.4 \times (0.3 + 0.2 + 0.1) = 0.54$$

$Y = 3$. Score 1 with the first and second arrows, then any score with the third.

$$P(Y = 3) = 0.4 \times 0.4 = 0.16$$

Hence the distribution is given by:

i	1	2	3
$P(X = i)$	0.3	0.54	0.16

EXAMPLE 5.9
Three children are chosen at random from a class containing ten

boys and twelve girls. Find the distribution of the number of girls selected.

Solution

Let X be the number of girls, so X could be 0, 1, 2 or 3. The number of ways of selecting three out of 22, regardless of sex, is $^{22}C_3$. The number of ways of selecting three boys from ten is $^{10}C_3$. The ratio of these will give us the probability that the three selected were all boys, i.e. that $X = 0$.

$$P(X = 0) = \frac{^{10}C_3}{^{22}C_3} = \frac{120}{1540} = \frac{6}{77}$$

Find the other probabilities similarly.

$$P(X = 1) = \frac{^{10}C_2 \times \, ^{12}C_1}{^{22}C_3} = \frac{540}{1540} = \frac{22}{77}$$

$$P(X = 2) = \frac{^{10}C_1 \times \, ^{12}C_2}{^{22}C_3} = \frac{660}{1540} = \frac{3}{7}$$

$$P(X = 3) = \frac{^{12}C_3}{^{22}C_3} = \frac{220}{1540} = \frac{1}{7}$$

The distribution of X is given by:

i	0	1	2	3
$P(X = i)$	$\frac{6}{77}$	$\frac{27}{77}$	$\frac{3}{7}$	$\frac{1}{7}$

Note

In both these examples, we can check the calculation by adding the probabilities to confirm that their sum is 1.

EXERCISE 5D

1 A fair die is rolled until the total of the scores is 3 or greater. Find the probability distribution of the number X of rolls required. Find the expected value of X.

2 Six cards each have one of the numbers 1, 2, 3, 4, 5 and 6 on them. They are shuffled, and two are dealt out. Find the probability distribution of the total X of the numbers on the cards drawn. Find the mean and variance of X.

How do your results compare with those obtained from the triangular distribution of Example 5.7?

3 Two cards are drawn, without replacement, from a standard pack of cards. Let X be the number of hearts obtained. Construct a table showing the probability distribution of X.

4 Assuming that a baby is equally likely to be a girl or a boy, construct a table showing the probability distribution of the number X of girls in a family of three children.

5   An urn contains eight black balls and seven white balls. Two are drawn out. Find the probability distribution of the number, X, of black balls obtained if the balls are drawn

a) with replacement,   b) without replacement.

6   When a letter is sent from A to B or from B to A, the number, X, of days it takes has the following probability distribution.

i	1	2	3	4	5
$P(X = i)$	0.3	0.4	0.1	0.15	0.05

A letter is sent from A to B, and a reply is sent back immediately. Assuming that the travel times are independent, find the expected value of the total time taken.

7   Five cards each have one of the numbers 1, 2, 3, 4 and 5 written on them. Two cards are dealt at random. Find the probability distribution of the maximum of the two numbers found. Find the expected value of this maximum.

8   A marksman fires at a target, and the score, X, he obtains has the following probability distribution.

i	1	2	3	4
$P(X = i)$	0.5	0.3	0.1	0.1

He fires twice. Assuming that the shots are independent, find the distribution of the total score.

9   The independent variables X and Y have the following probability distributions.

i	1	2	3
$P(X = i)$	0.2	0.4	0.4

i	0	1
$P(Y = i)$	0.7	0.3

Let $Z = XY$. Find the probability distribution of Z. Find $E(X)$, $E(Y)$ and $E(Z)$.

10   Two fair coins, one gold and one silver, each have 1 on one side and 2 on the other. They are both spun, and the numbers showing are taken as X and Y on the gold and silver coins respectively. Letting $Z = X \div Y$, find the probability distribution of Z. Find $E(X)$, $E(Y)$ and $E(Z)$.

11   A box contains three black socks and two white socks. I draw socks out at random, without replacement. Find the probability distribution of the number of drawings required to obtain:

a) a pair of the same colour,   b) a black pair.

In each case find the expected value of the number of drawings.

12   Three socks are picked at random from a box containing seven black and three white socks. Find the probability distribution of the number of white socks obtained.

*13 A box contains seven marbles coloured red, orange, yellow, green, blue, indigo and violet. Two are picked out, and I guess which colours have been chosen (in either order). Find the probability distribution of the number, X, of correct guesses. Find $E(X)$ and $Var(X)$.

*14 A secretary writes three letters and addresses three envelopes. Being in a hurry, she puts the letters into the envelopes at random. Find the probability distribution of the number of letters in the correct envelopes.

LONGER EXERCISE

The National Lottery

In the National Lottery, six numbers, from 1 to 49, are chosen at random. An entrant guesses six numbers. What is the probability that an entrant will win the jackpot by guessing all the numbers correctly?

Let X be the number of correct guesses. Construct a table showing the distribution of X.

At present, each entry costs £1. Half the money goes on administration and to charities, the other half is distributed as prizes. Three correct guesses wins a prize of £10. The remaining prize money is divided among those who got four right, five right and six right in the ratio 11:13:26. What do you expect would be the prizes for these results?

EXAMINATION QUESTIONS

1 A curiously shaped six-sided die produces a score, X, for which the probability distribution is given in the following table.

r	1	2	3	4	5	6
$P(X = r)$	k	$\frac{1}{2}k$	$\frac{1}{3}k$	$\frac{1}{4}k$	$\frac{1}{5}k$	$\frac{1}{6}k$

Show that the constant k is $\frac{20}{49}$. Find the mean and variance of X.

The die is thrown twice. Show that the probability of obtaining equal scores is approximately $\frac{1}{4}$.

MEI 1991

2 The discrete random variable X has the probability distribution shown in the following table.

r	-1	0	1
$P(X = r)$	$\frac{1}{4}$	$\frac{1}{2}$	$\frac{1}{4}$

(i) Write down the expectation of X, and find the variance of X.

A second random variable Y has the same distribution as X, and the two random variables are independent.

(ii) List all possible values of $X + Y$. Show that $P(X + Y = -2) = \frac{1}{16}$ and find $P(X + Y = 0)$.

(iii) Show in a table the complete probability distribution for $X + Y$.

(iv) Verify that, for these random variables, Var($X + Y$) = Var(X) + Var(Y).

MEI 1993

3 a) When a particular type of coin is tossed the probability of obtaining a head is a constant p. Find, in terms of p, the probability distribution of X, the number of heads obtained when such a coin is tossed twice.

b) Determine whether or not **each** of the following represents a probability distribution of the type described in (a). When the answer is in the negative give a reason, and when the answer is in the affirmative find the value of p and describe the nature of the coin.

(i) $P(X = 0) = \frac{1}{4}$, $P(X = 1) = \frac{1}{2}$, $P(X = 2) = \frac{1}{4}$.

(ii) $P(X = 0) = \frac{4}{25}$, $P(X = 1) = \frac{13}{25}$, $P(X = 2) = \frac{9}{25}$.

(iii) $P(X = 0) = \frac{1}{3}$, $P(X = 1) = \frac{1}{3}$, $P(X = 2) = \frac{1}{3}$.

(iv) $P(X = 0) = 0$, $P(X = 1) = 0$, $P(X = 2) = 1$.

N 1993

4 Write down whether or not there is anything wrong with the following probability distributions. If there is something wrong, explain what it is.

a)

x	1	2	3
$P(X = x)$	0.2	0.6	0.2

b) $P(X = x) = \begin{cases} \dfrac{4 - x}{5} & x = 1, 2, 3, 4, 5 \\ 0 & \text{otherwise} \end{cases}$

L 1994

5 (i) Jill has a hand of 10 playing cards, which includes two aces. After shuffling, she places the cards in a pile face downwards on the table. She takes the top card and then the next card. On a copy of this tree diagram, insert in each branch the relevant probability.

Hence, or otherwise, find (in fraction form) the probabilities that Jill takes:

a) no aces,

b) one ace,

c) two aces.

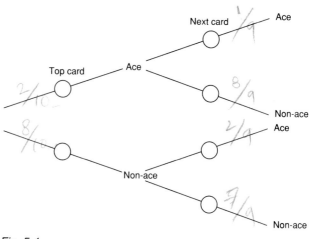

Fig. 5.4

(ii) Jill now gives the cards to Jim, but he plays differently. After taking the top card, he replaces it in the hand, shuffles, places the cards back on the table, and takes the top card again. Find (in fraction form) the probabilities that Jim takes:

   a) no aces, **b)** one ace, **c)** two aces.

(iii) Show that, although the methods are different, the expected (mean) number of aces is the same for both players.

SMP 1994

6 The discrete random variable X has the probability distribution specified in the following table.

x	-1	0	1	2
$P(X = x)$	0.25	0.10	0.45	0.20

a) Find $P(-1 \le X \le 1)$. **b)** Find $E(2X + 3)$

L 1993

Summary and key points

5.1 A discrete random variable X takes values $x_1, x_2, \dots, x_i, \dots$ with probabilities $p_1, p_2, \dots, p_i, \dots$ respectively. Each p_i is non-negative and their sum is 1.

5.2 The mean, expectation or expected value of X is given by:

$$E(X) = \Sigma \, x_i p_i$$

When using this formula to find the expected value of a variable which takes n values, do not divide by n.

The variance of X is given by:

$$\mathrm{Var}(X) = E((X - \overline{X})^2) = E(X^2) - (E(X))^2$$

Here the expression $E(X^2)$ means $\Sigma \, x_i^2 p_i$. Note that you square the values of X, not the probabilities. Note also that you square before doing the summation, not afterwards.

5.3 A uniform variable X takes n values with probabilities each equal to $\dfrac{1}{n}$. If the values are 1, 2, up to n the expected value and variance of X are given by:

$$E(X) = \tfrac{1}{2}(n + 1) \qquad \mathrm{Var}(X) = \tfrac{1}{12}(n^2 - 1)$$

5.4 Techniques of probability and of permutations and combinations can be used to find discrete probability distributions.

Continuous random variables

A continuous random variable is one which can take any value within a certain fixed interval. It is used to model continuous data, as defined in Chapter 1. Examples of quantities which can be modelled by continuous random variables are:

- *temperature* – the temperature of water can take any value from 0 to 100 °C.
- *time* – the time that elapses until a bus arrives at a stop can take any positive value.
- *mass* – the mass of rainwater that falls on a field over a year can take any non-negative value.

Other quantities that could be modelled by continuous variables are distance, area and energy. We shall also model money and population by continuous variables. Strictly, money is discrete. But the profit of a large company is equivalent to several billion pennies, and it would be absurd to analyse it in terms of a discrete random variable. Instead, we model profit as a continuous random variable. Similarly, we could not analyse the population of a large country in terms of the individual citizens.

A continuous distribution provides a statistical model of reality – i.e. a situation that may occur in real life. For example, it might be found that the heights of adult males have a distribution shown by the histogram of Fig. 6.1. We might find a mathematical formula for a curve which has a very similar shape. A clothing manufacturer could then use the formula to predict the proportions of clothes that should be made for customers in different height ranges.

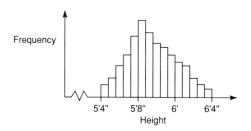

Fig. 6.1

The formula will not be a perfect fit of the histogram. It might be found, for example, that the formula gives a small but non-zero probability that an adult male is over ten feet tall, or even has negative height. That does not necessarily matter. The formula provides a mathematical model for the distribution of heights and, provided that it is accurate for the large majority of people, then it is a successful model.

In our models, we shall assume that measurements can be made with complete accuracy. For example, we shall not be worried by the fact that the time a runner takes for a race can only be measured to an accuracy of 0.01 of a second.

In our models, the variable will be able to take *any* real value within a certain range. It follows that the probability that the variable takes a particular value is zero. For example, the probability that the temperature is *exactly* 20 °C is zero. We shall not be able to calculate probabilities by adding up particular probabilities, as we did in the previous chapter. Instead we shall have to use integration to find probabilities.

In this chapter we see how calculus is necessary for the study of statistics.

6.1 Probability density functions

Let X be a continuous random variable. The probability that X takes a particular value is zero. However, there may be a non-zero probability that X lies within a particular range. For example, the probability that a randomly chosen apple weighs *exactly* 50 grams is zero. The probability that its weight lies between 49 and 51 grams is non-zero.

We describe the distribution of X by a function which gives the density of the probability. Actual probabilities are then found by integrating the function over the appropriate region.

The **probability density function (p.d.f.)** of X is a function f(x) such that:

$$P(a \le X \le b) = \int_a^b f(x)dx$$

The probability corresponds to the shaded region in Fig. 6.2.

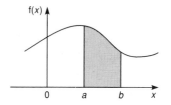

Fig. 6.2

In order for a function f(x) to be a probability density function, it must obey the following conditions. It must be greater or equal to 0 for all x, and its integral over all values of x must be 1.

$$f(x) \ge 0 \text{ for all } x$$

$$\int_{-\infty}^{\infty} f(x)dx = 1$$

Finite and infinite range

If the range of X is restricted, say between 0 and 1, then we only need to integrate between 0 and 1. So in this case the condition can be written as:

$$\int_0^1 f(x)dx = 1$$

If the range of x is infinite, then we take the limit as x tends to ∞ or $-\infty$. For example, suppose the p.d.f. of X is:

$$f(x) = \frac{1}{x^2} \quad \text{for } 1 \le x$$

$$= 0 \quad \text{elsewhere}$$

The probability that X is greater than 2 is given by:

$$\int_2^\infty \frac{1}{x^2}\, dx = \left[-\frac{1}{x}\right]_2^\infty$$

When x tends to ∞, $\frac{1}{x}$ tends to 0. At $x = 2$, $\frac{1}{x} = \frac{1}{2}$. Hence the value of the integral is:

$$(0 - (-\tfrac{1}{2})) = \tfrac{1}{2}.$$

Mode and median

The mode of a continuous random variable occurs at the highest point of the graph of $y = f(x)$, i.e. at the **maximum** of the curve.

For the median m of a continuous random variable X, there is a probability of $\frac{1}{2}$ that X is less than m. It can be found from the equation:

$$\int_{-\infty}^m f(x)\, dx = \tfrac{1}{2}$$

EXAMPLE 6.1
A continuous random variable X has p.d.f. given by:

$$f(x) = kx(2 - x) \quad \text{for } 0 \le x \le 2$$

$$= 0 \quad \text{elsewhere.}$$

a) Sketch the graph of $y = f(x)$ and show that $k = \frac{3}{4}$. What is the mode of X?

b) Find $P(1 \le X \le 1.5)$.

Solution
a) The graph of $y = f(x)$ is a parabola, crossing the x-axis at $(0, 0)$ and $(2, 0)$. The graph is shown in Fig. 6.3. Note that this verifies that $f(x) \ge 0$ for all x.

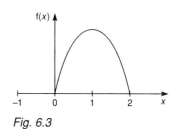

Fig. 6.3

In order for f(x) to be a p.d.f. its integral over its range must be 1.
Hence:

$$\int_0^2 kx(2 - x)\,dx = 1$$

$$k\int_0^2 (2x - x^2)\,dx = k\left[x^2 - \tfrac{1}{3}x^3 \right]_0^2 = k(1\tfrac{1}{3})$$

$$1 = 1\tfrac{1}{3}k$$

$$k = \tfrac{3}{4}$$

The mode occurs at the highest point of the graph, which by symmetry is at $x = 1$.

The mode is 1.

b) The probability that X lies between 1 and 1.5 is the area under the p.d.f. curve between these values.

$$P(1 \le X \le 1.5) = \int_1^{1.5} \tfrac{3}{4}x(2 - x) = \tfrac{3}{4}\left[x^2 - \tfrac{1}{3}x^3 \right]_1^{1.5} = 0.343\,75$$

P(1 ≤ X ≤ 1.5) = 0.344

EXAMPLE 6.2
The random variable X has p.d.f. given by:

$$f(x) = 3x^2 \quad \text{for } 0 \le x \le 1$$

$$= 0 \quad \text{elsewhere}$$

Find the median value of X.

Solution
The cumulative frequency of the probability at the median m is $\tfrac{1}{2}$,
i.e. $P(X \le m) = \tfrac{1}{2}$. Put this in terms of the p.d.f.

$$P(X \le m) = \int_0^m 3x^2\,dx = \left[x^3 \right]_0^m = m^3$$

Hence $m^3 = \tfrac{1}{2}$, giving $m = \sqrt[3]{\tfrac{1}{2}} = 0.794$.

The median is 0.794.

EXERCISE 6A

1 The p.d.f. of X is given by:

$$f(x) = k(1 - x) \quad \text{for } 0 \le x \le 1$$

$$= 0 \quad \text{elsewhere}$$

a) Find k.   **b)** Find the median value of X.   **c)** Find $P(\tfrac{1}{2} < X \le 1)$.

2 The p.d.f. of X is given by:

$$f(x) = \sin x \quad \text{for } 0 \le x \le \tfrac{1}{2}\pi$$

$$= 0 \qquad \text{elsewhere}$$

a) Show that $f(x)$ is a p.d.f.　　　　**b)** Find the median of X.　　　　**c)** Find $P(X < \tfrac{1}{4}\pi)$.

3 The p.d.f. of X is given by:

$$f(x) = \frac{k}{x^2} \quad \text{for } 1 \le x$$

$$= 0 \quad \text{for } x < 1$$

a) Find k.　　　　**b)** Find the interquartile range of X.　　　　**c)** Find $P(X \le 2)$.

4 When a boy puts a shot, the distance, X m, it travels has a continuous probability distribution with p.d.f. given by:

$$f(x) = k(9 - x^2) \quad \text{for } 0 \le x \le 3$$

$$= 0 \qquad \text{elsewhere}$$

a) Show that $k = \tfrac{1}{18}$, and sketch the graph of $y = f(x)$.

b) Find the probability he puts the shot further than 2 m.

c) For an athletic competition, only the best 20 per cent of his puts are included. Verify that these puts will be over about 1.825 m.

5 At a garage the weekly demand for petrol is $1000X$ litres, where X is a continuous random variable with p.d.f. given by:

$$f(x) = kx^2(2 - x) \quad \text{for } 0 \le x \le 2$$

$$= 0 \qquad \text{elsewhere.}$$

a) Find k.　　　　**b)** Find the modal demand.

c) Find the probability that more than 1000 litres are demanded.

6 The p.d.f. of X is given by:

$$f(x) = x(k - x) \quad \text{for } 0 \le x \le k$$

$$= 0 \qquad \text{elsewhere}$$

a) Find k.　　　　**b)** Find $P(\tfrac{1}{4}k \le X \le \tfrac{3}{4}k)$.

7 The p.d.f. of X is given by:

$$f(x) = k|1 - x| \quad \text{for } 0 \le x \le 2$$

$$= 0 \qquad \text{elsewhere}$$

Sketch the graph of $y = f(x)$. Use the formula for the area of a triangle to find k.

8 The p.d.f. of X is given by:

$$f(x) = k \qquad \text{for } 0 \le x \le 1$$
$$\quad = k(2 - x) \quad \text{for } 1 < x \le 2$$
$$\quad = 0 \qquad \text{elsewhere}$$

Sketch the graph of $y = f(x)$. Use the formula for the area of a trapezium to find k.

9 A canteen serves Meat and Potato Pie in 10 oz. helpings. The amount, X oz, of potato in a helping is a continuous random variable with p.d.f. given by:

$$f(x) = 0.0012x(10 - x)^2 \quad \text{for } 0 \le x \le 10$$
$$\quad = 0 \qquad \text{elsewhere.}$$

Show that f(x) is a p.d.f. Find the proportion of helpings which are more than three-quarters potato.

What is the modal amount of potato?

10 The length, X cm, of certain worms has a probability distribution with the following p.d.f.

$$f(x) = kx^2(15 - x) \quad \text{for } 0 \le x \le 15$$
$$\quad = 0 \qquad \text{elsewhere.}$$

a) Find k. **b)** Find the proportion of worms under 10 cm in length.

c) Find the proportion of worms between 7 cm and 8 cm in length.

11 A scientist investigates the time it takes people to react to a signal. The reaction time, T seconds, can be modelled by a continuous random variable with p.d.f. given by:

$$f(t) = k(t - \tfrac{1}{2})(1\tfrac{1}{2} - t)^2 \quad \text{for } \tfrac{1}{2} \le t \le 1\tfrac{1}{2}$$
$$\quad = 0 \qquad \text{elsewhere}$$

a) Find k. **b)** Find the proportion of people who react in less than 1 second.

c) Find the modal reaction time.

12 The annual profit of a company, in millions of pounds, can be modelled by a continuous random variable X with p.d.f. given by:

$$f(x) = \frac{k(x - 50)}{x^4} \quad \text{for } x \ge 50$$
$$\quad = 0 \qquad \text{elsewhere.}$$

a) Show that $k = 15\,000$. **b)** What is the probability that the profit is greater than £80 000 000?

c) Show that the median profit is £100 000 000.

6.2 Expectation and variance

Suppose we are modelling the height of adult males, using a continuous random variable. We might want to find the mean height. We can use a process similar to that for discrete random variables, except that instead of summing we shall integrate.

Let X be a continuous random variable with p.d.f. $f(x)$. Then its expected value, $E(X)$, is given by:

$$E(X) = \int_{-\infty}^{\infty} x f(x) \, dx$$

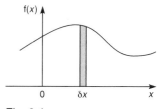

$f(x)$

Fig. 6.4

Justification

Divide the range of values of X into small intervals of length δx. The probability that X lies within the interval $(x, x + \delta x)$ is approximately $f(x)\delta x$. Multiply this probability by the x-value and sum.

The expected value is approximately $\Sigma \, x f(x) \delta x$.

Now let δx tend to 0. The summation becomes an integral, and in the limit the approximation becomes exact.

$$E(X) = \int_{-\infty}^{\infty} x f(x) \, dx$$

The variance of X is given by

$$\mathrm{Var}(X) = E((X - E(X))^2)$$

This is equivalent to:

$$E(X^2) - (E(X))^2$$

The proof is in the Mathematical appendix on page 330.

Here $E(X^2)$ is the expected value of X^2. It is found by multiplying x^2 by the p.d.f. and integrating the product over the range of X.

$$E(X^2) = \int x^2 f(x) \, dx$$

Expectation of a function of X

The expectation of any function of X is defined similarly. Multiply the function by the p.d.f. and integrate over the range. The expected value of $(2X + 7)$, for example, will be given by:

$$E(2X + 7) = \int (2x + 7) f(x) \, dx$$

EXAMPLE 6.3

Let X be the continuous random variable defined in Example 6.1 above. Find $E(X)$ and $\mathrm{Var}(X)$.

Solution

Here $f(x) = \frac{3}{4}x(2 - x)$, for $0 \le x \le 2$. Apply the formula.

$$E(X) = \int_0^2 \frac{3}{4}x^2(2 - x)\,dx = \frac{3}{4}\int_0^2 (2x^2 - x^3)\,dx$$

$$= \frac{3}{4}\left[\frac{2}{3}x^3 - \frac{1}{4}x^4\right]_0^2 = 1$$

For the variance, we first find $E(X^2)$.

$$E(X^2) = \int_0^2 \frac{3}{4}x^3(2 - x)\,dx = \frac{3}{4}\int_0^2 (2x^3 - x^4)\,dx$$

$$= \frac{3}{4}\left[\frac{1}{2}x^4 - \frac{1}{5}x^5\right]_0^2 = 1.2$$

$$\text{Var}(X) = E(X^2) - (E(X))^2 = 1.2 - 1^2 = 0.2$$

The mean is 1 and the variance is 0.2.

Note

The graph of $y = f(x)$ is symmetric about $x = 1$. This is confirmed by the fact that the mean of X is 1.

EXAMPLE 6.4

With X as defined in Example 6.3, find the expected value of $8X^3$.

Solution

The p.d.f. of X is $\frac{3}{4}x(2 - x)$. Multiply this by $8x^3$ and integrate.

$$E(8X^3) = \int_0^2 8x^3 \times \frac{3}{4}x(2 - x)\,dx$$

$$= \int_0^2 6x^4(2 - x)\,dx = \int_0^2 (12x^4 - 6x^5)\,dx$$

$$= \left[\frac{12}{5}x^5 - x^6\right]_0^2 = \frac{384}{5} - 64 = 12.8$$

The expected value is 12.8.

EXERCISE 6B

1 Find the mean and variance of X as defined in Question 1 of Exercise 6A.

2 Find the mean and variance of X as defined in Question 2 of Exercise 6A.

3 Show that the mean and variance do not exist, for the distribution given in Question 3 of Exercise 6A.

4 The p.d.f. of X is given by:

$$f(x) = \frac{k}{x} \quad \text{for } 1 \le x \le 10$$
$$= 0 \quad \text{elsewhere}$$

Find the value of k and sketch the p.d.f. of $y = f(x)$. Without any calculation, state which of the mean or median will be greater. Calculate the mean and the median.

5 The p.d.f. of X is given by:

$$f(x) = 12x^2(1 - x) \quad \text{for } 0 \le x \le 1$$
$$= 0 \quad \text{elsewhere}$$

Find $E(X)$ and $\text{Var}(X)$.

6 The lifetime of a certain electrical component is X hours, where X is a continuous random variable with p.d.f. given by:

$$f(x) = kx^2(100 - x) \quad \text{for } 0 \le x \le 100$$
$$= 0 \quad \text{elsewhere}$$

Find k. Find the mean lifetime μ hours, and find the probability that X will be less than μ.

7 The p.d.f. of X is given by:

$$f(x) = \frac{k}{x} \quad \text{for } 1 \le x \le 2$$
$$= 0 \quad \text{elsewhere}$$

Find k and $E(X)$. Find $P(X < E(X))$.

8 The p.d.f. of X is given by:

$$f(x) = 3x^2 \quad \text{for } 0 \le x \le 1$$
$$= 0 \quad \text{elsewhere}$$

Find $E(X)$ and the median of X.

9 The p.d.f. of X is given by:

$$f(x) = 2(1 - x) \quad \text{for } 0 \le x \le 1$$
$$= 0 \quad \text{elsewhere}$$

Sketch the graph of this function. State which of the expectation or median will be greater. Calculate $E(X)$ and the median of X.

10 The height, X cm, of a type of plant is modelled by a continuous random variable with p.d.f. given by:

$$f(x) = kx^2(10 - x) \quad \text{for } 0 \le x \le 10$$
$$= 0 \quad \text{elsewhere}$$

Find k. Find the expected height.

11 The temperature, X °F, at midday in August at a resort can be modelled by a continuous random variable with p.d.f. given by:

$$f(x) = k(x - 70)(90 - x)^2 \quad \text{for } 70 \le x \le 90$$

$$= 0 \qquad\qquad\qquad \text{elsewhere}$$

Show that $k = \frac{3}{40\,000}$. Find the expected temperature.

12 The time, T minutes, that you will have to wait for a bus can be modelled by a continous random variable with p.d.f. given by:

$$f(t) = \frac{k}{(10 + t)^3} \quad \text{for } 0 \le t$$

$$= 0 \qquad\qquad \text{elsewhere}$$

Show that $k = 200$. Find E(T).

*13 The p.d.f. of X is given by

$$f(x) = kx^{-n} \quad \text{for } 1 \le x$$

$$= 0 \qquad \text{elsewhere}$$

where n is greater than 1. Find k in terms of n. For what values of n does E(X) exist? For what values of n does Var(X) exist?

*14 A particle travels a distance of 10 m, with a constant speed S m s^{-1}, where S is a continuous random variable with p.d.f. given by:

$$f(s) = 2s \quad \text{for } 0 \le s \le 1$$

$$= 0 \quad \text{elsewhere}$$

Find E(S).

Write the time, T seconds, taken in terms of S, and hence find the expected time taken. Show that the expected time is not the same as the distance divided by the expected speed.

*15 A sphere of uniform gas has a radius of 1 unit. Find the mean distance of a particle of gas from the centre of the sphere. (**Hint:** Find the approximate probability that a particle lies between r and $r + \delta r$ from the centre.)

16 With X defined as in Question 4, find:

a) E(X^3) **b)** E($2X + 3$) **c)** E($X(X - 1)$)

17 With X defined as in Question 5, find

a) E($2X^3$) **b)** E$\left(\dfrac{1}{X}\right)$ **c)** E$\left(\dfrac{1}{X^2}\right)$

6.3 Cumulative frequency

Suppose we are using a continuous random variable to model the heights of adult males. The proportion of males whose heights are less than 170 cm, say, can be approximated by integrating the p.d.f. up to 170. This process gives rise to another function to describe the probability distribution.

The p.d.f. of a continuous random variable does *not* give actual probabilities. It gives the density of probability, so that actual probabilities can be found by integrating the p.d.f. over an interval. A function which *does* give probabilities is the **cumulative distribution function** (c.d.f.). In some texts the function is called the **distribution function**.

Suppose X is a continuous random variable with p.d.f. $f(x)$. The cumulative distribution function $F(x)$ is given by

$$F(x) = P(X \leq x) = \int_{-\infty}^{x} f(x)\, dx$$

This corresponds to the shaded region in Fig. 6.5.

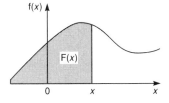

Fig. 6.5

In other words, $F(x)$ is obtained from $f(x)$ by integrating. Conversely, $f(x)$ is obtained from $F(x)$ by differentiating.

$$f(x) = \frac{d}{dx} F(x)$$

In order for a function $F(x)$ to be a c.d.f., it must obey the following rule.

$F(x)$ tends to 0 as x tends to $-\infty$, and to 1 as x tends to ∞.

$F(x)$ is an increasing function.

In particular, if the range of X is limited to $a \leq X \leq b$, then we have:

$F(a) = 0$ and $F(b) = 1$

EXAMPLE 6.5
Let X be a continuous variable with p.d.f. $f(x) = \dfrac{1}{x^2}$, for $1 \leq x$. Find the c.d.f. of X.

Solution
Apply the rule for obtaining the c.d.f. from the p.d.f.

$$F(x) = \int_{1}^{x} \frac{1}{x^2}\, dx = \left[-\frac{1}{x} \right]_{1}^{x} = 1 - \frac{1}{x}$$

The c.d.f. is $F(x) = 1 - \dfrac{1}{x}$.

Note

When $x = 1$, $F(x) = 0$. As x tends to ∞, $F(x)$ tends to 1. $F(x)$ is an **increasing** function. This verifies that $F(x)$ obeys the conditions for a c.d.f.

EXAMPLE 6.6

The amount of coffee dispensed by an automatic machine lies between 100 ml and 110 ml. The probability that the amount is less than x ml, for $100 \leq x \leq 110$, is $0.01(x - 100)^2$. Find the mean amount dispensed.

Solution

Let X ml be the amount dispensed. The information gives us the c.d.f. of X.

$$F(x) = P(X < x) = 0.01(x - 100)^2 \quad \text{for } 100 \leq x \leq 110$$

Differentiate to find the p.d.f.

$$f(x) = 0.02(x - 100) \quad \text{for } 100 \leq x \leq 110$$

To find the mean amount, multiply $f(x)$ by x and integrate.

$$\int_{100}^{110} x0.02(x - 100)dx$$

$$= \left[\tfrac{1}{3} \times 0.02x^3 - \tfrac{1}{2} \times 0.02 \times 100x^2 \right]_{100}^{110}$$

$$= 106\tfrac{2}{3}$$

The mean amount dispensed is $106\tfrac{2}{3}$ ml.

EXERCISE 6C

1 The p.d.f. of X is given by:

$$f(x) = \tfrac{1}{2}(2 - x) \quad \text{for } 0 \leq x \leq 2$$
$$= 0 \qquad \text{elsewhere}$$

Find the c.d.f. of X.

2 The p.d.f. of X is given by:

$$f(x) = 4x^3 \quad \text{for } 0 \leq x \leq 1$$
$$= 0 \quad \text{elsewhere}$$

Find the c.d.f. of X.

3 The p.d.f. of X is given by:

$$f(x) = \tfrac{1}{2} \sin x \quad \text{for } 0 \leq x \leq \pi$$
$$= 0 \qquad \text{elsewhere}$$

Find the c.d.f. of X.

4   The c.d.f. of X is given by:

$$F(x) = 0 \quad \text{for } x < 0$$
$$F(x) = x \quad \text{for } 0 \leq x \leq 1$$
$$F(x) = 1 \quad \text{for } x > 1$$

Check that $F(x)$ is a c.d.f. Find the p.d.f. of X.

5   The c.d.f. of X is given by:

$$F(x) = 0 \quad \text{for } x < 0$$
$$F(x) = x^2 \quad \text{for } 0 \leq x \leq 1$$
$$F(x) = 1 \quad \text{for } x > 1$$

Check that $F(x)$ is a c.d.f. Find the p.d.f. of X. Find the median and mean of X.

6   The c.d.f. of X is given by:

$$F(x) = 0 \qquad \text{for } x < 1$$
$$F(x) = 1 - \frac{1}{x^2} \quad \text{for } 1 \leq x$$

Check that $F(x)$ is a c.d.f. Find the p.d.f. of X. Find the mean of X and show that the variance of X does not exist.

7   The p.d.f. of X is given by:

$$f(x) = 3(\sqrt{x} - x^2) \quad \text{for } 0 \leq x \leq 1$$
$$= 0 \qquad\qquad \text{elsewhere}$$

Find the c.d.f. of X. Show that the median, m, of X satisfies the equation:

$$2m^3 - 4m^{1\frac{1}{2}} + 1 = 0$$

Hence show that the median lies between 0.4 and 0.5.

8   The lifetime, X hours, of a battery is a continuous random variable with p.d.f. given by:

$$f(x) = \frac{k}{(x + 20)^2} \quad \text{for } 0 \leq x \leq 20$$
$$= 0 \qquad\qquad \text{elsewhere}$$

Show that $k = 40$. Find the c.d.f. of X. If a battery has lasted ten hours, what is the probability it will last a further five hours?

9   When I go to the bus stop, the probability that I shall wait more than t minutes is $\dfrac{1000}{(t + 10)^3}$.

Let T minutes be the time I wait until a bus comes. Find the c.d.f. and hence the p.d.f. of T. Hence find the median and mean time that I wait.

10 A car insurance company finds that the probability that one of their customers will drive more than $10\,000x$ miles without an accident is $\dfrac{16}{(2+x)^4}$.

Letting X be the distance in tens of thousands of miles before an accident, find the p.d.f. of X. find the median and mean values of X.

6.4 Rectangular and exponential distributions

There are many special continuous distributions. We shall consider the most important one, the **normal** distribution, in Chapter 9. Here we deal with the **rectangular** and the **exponential** distributions.

Rectangular distribution

The rectangular distribution is the continuous equivalent of the discrete uniform distribution. In it the probability density is constant over a fixed interval, i.e. the p.d.f. is constant.

Suppose X is a continuous variable with range $a \le X \le b$. Then if X has a rectangular distribution, its p.d.f. is given by:

$$f(x) = \frac{1}{b-a} \quad \text{for } a \le x \le b$$

$$= 0 \qquad \text{elsewhere}$$

The graph of the p.d.f. is shown in Fig. 6.6. Notice that the region under the graph is a rectangle with area 1.

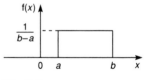

Fig. 6.6

A random number generator, such as the one on a scientific calculator, should deliver values whose distribution is rectangular in the region $0 \le X \le 1$.

EXAMPLE 6.7
Suppose X has a rectangular distribution in the region $1 \le X \le 3$. Find the mean and variance of X.

Solution
The p.d.f. of X is $f(x) = \frac{1}{2}$, for $1 \le x \le 3$. Apply the formula for mean distribution.

$$E(X) = \int_1^3 \tfrac{1}{2}x \, dx = \left[\tfrac{1}{4}x^2\right]_1^3 = 2$$

For the variance, first find $E(X^2)$.

$$E(X^2) = \int_1^3 \tfrac{1}{2}x^2 \, dx = \left[\tfrac{1}{6}x^3\right]_1^3 = 4\tfrac{1}{3}$$

$$\text{Var}(X) = 4\tfrac{1}{3} - 2^2 = \tfrac{1}{3}$$

The mean is 2 and the variance is $\tfrac{1}{3}$.

EXERCISE 6D

1   X is a rectangular distribution in the region $1 \le x \le 2$. Find the c.d.f. of X.

2   The c.d.f. of X is given by

$\qquad F(x) = 0 \qquad$ for $x < 0$

$\qquad F(x) = \tfrac{1}{4}x \quad$ for $0 \le x \le 4$

$\qquad F(x) = 1 \qquad$ for $x > 4$

Show that X has a rectangular distribution.

3   I know that trains leave from a railway station every ten minutes. I arrive at the station at a time which has a rectangular distribution between 8 a.m. and 9 a.m. Show that the time I shall have to wait for a train also has a rectangular distribution, and find its mean.

4   A needle is spun round on the ground. Show that when the needle halts the bearing towards which it is pointing has a rectangular distribution, and find its mean and variance.

5   The Big Wheel at a funfair has radius 10 m. When it comes to a halt, the angle which a spoke makes with the vertical has a rectangular distribution. Write down the p.d.f. of the angle.

Find the expected height above the ground of a particular point on the wheel.

6   The weights of the male and females of a certain species of bird are X grams and Y grams respectively, where X is rectangular between 150 and 160, and Y is rectangular between 170 and 190. Write down the p.d.f.s of X and Y.

A bird is picked at random. Assuming that it is equally likely to be male or female, find its expected weight.

7   The variable X has a rectangular distribution between 0 and $\tfrac{1}{2}\pi$. Find $E(X)$ and $\text{Var}(X)$.

8   X has a rectangular distribution in the range $a \le X \le b$. Verify that the mean of X is $\tfrac{1}{2}(a + b)$ and find its variance.

*9   The random number generated by a computer has a rectangular distribution between 0 and 1. Two numbers X_1 and X_2 are generated, and X is the value of the greater. By considering the c.d.f.s of X_1, X_2 and X, find the p.d.f. of X. Find $E(X)$.

Exponential distribution

The exponential distribution provides a useful model for waiting times, or for the lifetimes of components. The range of values extends up to infinity, but with rapidly decreasing probability density.

Suppose X has range $0 \le X$, and p.d.f. given by:

$$f(x) = \lambda e^{-\lambda x} \quad \text{for } 0 \le x$$

$$= 0 \qquad \text{elsewhere } (\lambda \text{ is a positive constant.})$$

Then X has an exponential distribution. The mean and variance of X are given by:

$$E(X) = \frac{1}{\lambda} \qquad \text{Var}(X) = \frac{1}{\lambda^2}$$

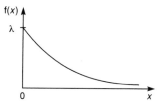

The proofs of these results are in the Mathematical appendix, on page 330.

The graph of the p.d.f. of X is shown in Fig. 6.7.

Fig. 6.7

EXAMPLE 6.8
The probability that a light bulb will still be working after t hours of use is $e^{-t/1000}$. Show that the lifetime of the bulb has an exponential distribution, and find its mean.

Solution
Let T be the lifetime of the bulb. The probability that T is greater than t is $e^{-t/1000}$.

$$P(T > t) = e^{-t/1000}$$

Hence the c.d.f. of T is given by:

$$F(t) = P(T \le t) = 1 - e^{-t/1000}$$

Differentiate to find the p.d.f.

$$f(t) = \tfrac{1}{1000} e^{-t/100} \quad \text{for } 0 \le t$$

This is the p.d.f. of an exponential distribution, with $\lambda = \tfrac{1}{1000}$. The mean is $\dfrac{1}{\lambda}$, i.e. 1000.

The distribution is exponential, with mean 1000 hours.

EXERCISE 6E

1 The p.d.f. of X is given by:

$$f(x) = \tfrac{1}{4} e^{-\frac{1}{4}x} \quad \text{for } 0 \le x$$

$$= 0 \qquad \text{for } x < 0$$

Find the median value of X. Find the interquartile range of X.

2 When I arrive at a bus stop, the time, *T* minutes, I have to wait has an exponential distribution with mean 10. Write down the p.d.f. of *T*. Find the probability I shall have to wait more than 20 minutes.

3 The lifetime, *X* hours, of certain electrical components has a probability distribution with p.d.f.

$$f(x) = \lambda e^{-\lambda x} \quad \text{for } 0 \le x$$
$$= 0 \qquad \text{elsewhere}$$

Half these components fail within 20 hours. Find λ.

4 The time, *T* days, between infection with a certain disease and the appearance of its first symptoms has an exponential distribution with mean 20. Write down the distribution of *T*.

Find the probability that the symptoms will appear within five days.

If symptoms have not appeared within ten days, find the probability that they will not appear within a further 20 days.

5 The time, *T* days, that a local council takes to reply to a complaint has an exponential distribution with mean 30. Write down the distribution of *T*.

What is the probability that I shall have to wait more than 40 days for a reply to my complaint?

If I have waited 40 days without a reply to my complaint, what is the probability that I shall have to wait a further 40 days?

The council wishes to claim that 99 per cent of all complaints will receive a reply within a certain period. What is the least period for which the council could truthfully make this claim?

*6 The exponential distribution is said to be 'memoryless'; that is, if *X* is greater than *k*, the probability that *X* is greater than $k + m$ is equal to the probability that *X* is greater than *m*. Prove this property. Why do you think the distribution is called 'memoryless'?

*7 I can travel to work by either blue or green buses. The waiting times for these buses are both exponential, with means 10 minutes and 15 minutes respectively. The arrivals of these buses are independent of each other. When I arrive at the bus stop, what is the probability that I shall have to wait more than 20 minutes for a bus?

LONGER EXERCISE

Buffon's needle

Imagine a floor with floorboards *d* units apart. A needle of length *d* units is thrown at random onto the floor. What is the probability that it will cross a crack between boards? Buffon showed in 1730 that this probability is $\dfrac{2}{\pi}$.

To simplify the calculation, let $d = 2$. The centre of the needle lands at a point a distance *X* from the nearest crack. What is the distribution of *X*?

The needle makes an acute angle θ with the direction of the crack. What is the distribution of θ?

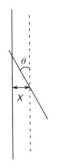

Fig. 6.8

If the needle crosses a crack, find a relationship between X and θ.

Figure 6.9 shows the possible values of X and θ. Copy the diagram, putting in the limits of X and θ. On your diagram indicate the region within which the relationship holds.

By consideration of area, find the probability that the needle will cross a crack.

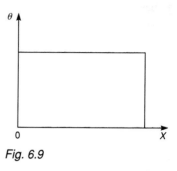

Fig. 6.9

EXAMINATION QUESTIONS

1 The continuous random variable Y has a rectangular distribution

$$f(y) = \frac{1}{\pi} \quad -\tfrac{1}{2}\pi \le y \le \tfrac{1}{2}\pi$$
$$= 0 \quad \text{otherwise.}$$

a) Find the mean of Y **b)** Find the variance of Y

L 1992

2 For a continuous random variable define the probability density function f, and the (cumulative) distribution function F.

Give an example of a continuous random variable that has occurred in your work, and draw a suitable diagram to illustrate its distribution.

A random variable X has probability density function f given by:

$$f(x) = \frac{1}{b - a}, \quad a \le x \le b,$$

$$f(x) = 0, \qquad \text{otherwise.}$$

Find $E(X)$ and $\text{Var}(X)$. Draw a sketch of the (cumulative) distribution function F.

A chain is made of 12 links. When the chain is loaded each link is equally likely to break at any value between 20 kg and 25 kg. Find, to 3 decimal places, the probability that the chain will break when loaded with 21 kg, measured to the nearest kg.

L 1990

3 The continuous random variable X has probability density function f given by:

$$f(x) = k\left(\frac{2}{x^2} - \frac{1}{2}\right), \quad \text{for } 1 \le x \le 2$$

$$= 0, \qquad \text{otherwise,}$$

where k is a constant.

Show that $k = 2$.

Find the cumulative distribution function, F, of X, and hence or otherwise find the value of t for which $F(t) = \frac{2}{3}$.

Find the mean of X and show that the variance of X is approximately 0.0472.

C 1992

4 The number of hours of sunshine per day in Fuengirola in June (of any year) may be described by a continuous random variable, X_1 whose distribution is given by the probability density function:

$$f(x) = \tfrac{1}{4}, \qquad 8 \le x \le 12.$$

(i) State the mean and calculate the standard deviation of hours of sunshine per day during the month of June in Fuengirola.

The number of hours of sunshine per day in Barcelona in June (of any year) may be described by a continuous random variable, X_2 whose distribution is given by the probability density function:

$$f(x) = \tfrac{1}{4}, \qquad 6 \le x \le 10.$$

(ii) Assuming the random variables X_1 and X_2 to be independent of each other, find the probability that for any one day in June the number of hours of sunshine in Barcelona is greater than 8 and the number of hours of sunshine in Fuengirola is greater than 11.

NI 1992

5 A continuous random variable X has probability density function f given by:

$$f(x) = k(1 + \cos x), \quad 0 \le x \le \pi,$$

$$f(x) = 0, \qquad\qquad \text{otherwise.}$$

(i) Show that $k = \dfrac{1}{\pi}$.

(ii) Find, to four decimal places, the mean, μ, of the distribution.

[You may use, without proof, the result $\displaystyle\int_0^\pi x \cos x \, dx = -2.$]

(iii) Find the distribution function of X for all values of x. Hence determine $P(X \le \mu)$ and verify that μ is between the 55th and 56th percentiles.

N June 91 p2 q13

6 The average speed, X m.p.h., of a bus on a certain journey of 5 miles is a continuous random variable with probability density function f given by:

$$f(x) = \frac{k}{x^2}, \quad 10 \le x \le 20,$$

$$f(x) = 0, \quad \text{otherwise.}$$

(i) Show that $k = 20$.

(ii) Find, correct to two decimal places, the mean and variance of X.

(iii) Given that $P(X < m) = 0.5$, find the value of m.

(iv) Find the probability that the time for the journey is less than 25 minutes.

W AS 1992

7 The probability density function f of a continuous random variable X is given by:

$$f(x) = kx(2 - x), \quad 0 \le x \le 1,$$

$$f(x) = 0, \qquad\qquad \text{otherwise.}$$

Show that $k = \frac{3}{2}$ and calculate

(i) the mean and the variance of X,

(ii) $P(X < \frac{1}{2})$,

(iii) The probability that all of three independently observed values of X will be less than $\frac{1}{2}$,

(iv) $P(X > \frac{1}{4} | X < \frac{1}{2})$.

W AS 1991

8 Workers on a large industrial estate have journey times to work, in hours, which are modelled by the random variable X with probability density function:

$$f(x) = 20x^3(1 - x), \quad 0 \le x \le 1.$$

(i) Sketch the graph of the probability density function.

(ii) Hence state, with an explanation, the likely location of the industrial estate in relation to local housing.

(iii) Find the expectation and the standard deviation of the workers' journey times *in minutes*.

(iv) Obtain the cumulative distribution function, and use it to verify that the median journey time is a little over 41 minutes.

MEI 1994

9 In this question you may use, without proof, the result that:

$$\int_0^\infty x^n e^{-x} \, dx = n! \quad n \ge 0.$$

The quarterly incomes, in thousands of pounds, of working adults in Britain are modelled by the random variable X with probability density function:

$$f(x) = kx^3 e^{-x} \quad 0 \le x < \infty.$$

(i) Show that $k = \frac{1}{6}$.

(ii) Find the modal quarterly income.

(iii) Sketch the graph of the probability density function. Explain, **without doing any calculations**, whether the median income is greater than, equal to, or less than the mode.

(iv) Find the mean and standard deviation of the quarterly incomes.

MEI 1993

Summary and key points

6.1 A continuous random variable X takes any value within a given range. Probabilities can be found from the probability density function $f(x)$ by:

$$P(a \leq X \leq b) = \int_a^b f(x)\,dx$$

Note that $f(x)$ does not provide actual probabilities.

6.2 If X has p.d.f. $f(x)$, then its mean and variance are given by:

$$E(X) = \mu = \int xf(x)\,dx$$

$$\mathrm{Var}(X) = E((X - E(X))^2) = E(X^2) - (E(X))^2$$

Here $E(X^2)$ is $\int x^2 f(x)\,dx$. Note that $f(x)$ is not squared.

6.3 The cumulative distribution function is given by:

$$F(x) = P(X \leq x) = \int_{-\infty}^x f(x)\,dx$$

Note that $f(x) = F'(x)$.

6.4 A rectangular distribution in the range $a \leq X \leq b$ has p.d.f.

$$f(x) = \frac{1}{b - a} \quad \text{for } a \leq x \leq b$$

The mean of this distribution is $\frac{1}{2}(a + b)$.

An exponential distribution has p.d.f.

$$f(x) = \lambda\, e^{-\lambda x} \quad \text{for } 0 \leq x$$

Here λ is a positive constant. The mean is $\dfrac{1}{\lambda}$ and the variance is $\dfrac{1}{\lambda^2}$.

Binomial and geometric distributions

In Chapter 5 we considered discrete random variables. There are some special discrete distributions which provide suitable models for many natural situations. In this chapter we shall consider two of these special distributions.

Suppose a weekly lottery is set up so that one in twenty of the tickets will win prizes. Non-mathematicians often think that they will be certain to win a prize, provided that they buy a ticket every week for twenty weeks. After studying probability you know that this is not the case. You can buy 20 tickets and fail to win a prize. It is possible, though unlikely, that all your tickets will win prizes. The number of prizes that you win is a random variable, determined by chance. This sort of random variable occurs so often that its distribution has a special name, the **binomial** distribution.

Another strategy might be as follows. You might decide to buy a lottery ticket each week, and continue to do so until you win a prize. You might be lucky, and win a prize within 20 weeks. You might be unlucky, and have to wait a lot longer than 20 weeks before winning. The number of tickets you buy has a **geometric** distribution.

7.1 The binomial distribution

Suppose three fair coins are spun. There are eight possible ways in which they could land heads (H) or tails (T).

HHH   HHT   HTH   HTT   THH   THT   TTH   TTT

As the coins are fair, each of these arrangements is equally likely. In three of the arrangements, there is exactly one head. Hence the probability there will be exactly one head is $\frac{3}{8}$.

A similar listing procedure will be possible even when the coins are not fair.

EXAMPLE 7.1
For a biased coin, the probability of landing heads up is $\frac{1}{4}$. The coin is tossed three times. List the ways in which there could be one head (H) and two tails (T). Find the probability that there will be exactly one head.

Solution
The single head could come on the first, second or third toss. The possible arrangements are:

    HTT   THT   TTH

The probability of the first arrangement is:

$$P(HTT) = \tfrac{1}{4} \times \tfrac{3}{4} \times \tfrac{3}{4} = \tfrac{9}{64}$$

Each of the other two arrangements has the same probability. Hence the probability of exactly one head is three times $\frac{9}{64}$, that is $\frac{27}{64}$.

The probability of exactly one head is $\frac{27}{64}$.

EXERCISE 7A

1   For the coin described in Example 7.1, find the probability that there will be exactly two heads in the three tosses.

2   Assuming that equal numbers of boys and girls are born, what is the probability that a family of three children will contain exactly one girl?

3   Three fair dice are rolled. What is the probability that there will be exactly two 6s?

4   Four fair coins are tossed. What is the probability there will be exactly one head?

5   Three seeds are planted in a plot. Each seed has probability $\frac{3}{4}$ of germinating. What is the probability that exactly two will germinate?

6   An archer shoots four arrows at a target. Each arrow has probability $\frac{1}{3}$ of hitting the gold (the centre), and the shots are independent of each other. What is the probability that exactly one gold will be scored?

7   Assuming that boys and girls are equally likely, what is the probability that a family of four children will consist of two boys and two girls?

8   If 40 per cent of the electorate supports the Labour Party, what is the probability that, out of three voters selected at random, exactly one will support Labour?

9 An astrologer claims that she can tell people's birth sign (of which there are 12). If in fact she is guessing, what is the probability she gets exactly one right out of three guesses?

10 A machine has four components, and will work provided that at least three of them are functioning. If each component has probability 0.1 of breaking down before the end of the day, what is the probability that the machine will still be working at the end of the day?

The general formula

In Example 7.1 above we evaluated the probability of 'exactly one head in three tosses' by listing all the possible outcomes. We can do this for a small number of tosses. If the coin were tossed 20 times, though, it would be very tedious to list all the ways that we could get seven heads and thirteen tails. We need a more efficient method.

Consider again the lottery example. Every week you buy a ticket, and you have probability $\frac{1}{20}$ of winning a prize. The process of buying a ticket is repeated 20 times, and in each case the probability that you win is independent of whether or not you won the previous times. The number, X, of prizes you win is a discrete random variable, and we say that X has a binomial distribution. The key features are:

- an event (buying a ticket) has a fixed probability of being a success (in this case, $\frac{1}{20}$).

- the event is repeated a number of times (in this case 20). The repetitions are independent of each other.

In general, suppose an event or experiment has two possible outcomes, which we shall call 'success' and 'failure'. Let the probability of 'success' be p. Suppose the experiment is repeated n times, and that each trial is independent of the others. The number of successes has a **binomial distribution**.

If X is the number of successes, we often write $X \sim B(n, p)$ to show that X is a random variable with a binomial distribution, where n is the number of trials and p is the probability of success. For our lottery example above, the number of prizes won is X, where $X \sim B(20, \frac{1}{20})$. For the coin of Example 7.1, the number of heads is X, where $X \sim B(3, \frac{1}{4})$.

Notes
1 We have used the word 'success' to describe one of the two outcomes. This outcome does not have to be desirable.
2 It is important to emphasise that these trials must be independent of each other. For example, even if we get a run of 19

successes, this does not alter the probability that the 20th trial will also be a success.

3 The distribution is determined by two numbers – n the number of trials, and p the probability of success in each trial. These are called the **parameters** of the distribution.

Formula

Suppose that $X \sim B(n, p)$. Then X takes values from 0 (all failures) to n (all successes). Let the probability of failure be q, where $q = 1 - p$. The probability that X takes a particular value i is given by:

$$P(X = i) = \binom{n}{i} p^i q^{n-i}$$

Proof

Suppose that we have a string of i successes, followed by a string of $(n - i)$ failures. Since each trial is independent of the others, the probability of this happening is

$$\underbrace{p \times p \times p \times ... \times p}_{i \text{ successes}} \times \underbrace{q \times q \times q \times ... \times q}_{n-i \text{ failures}} = p^i q^{n-i}$$

This is the probability of i successes followed by $(n - i)$ failures. There would be the same probability if we had all the failures followed by the successes, or if the successes and failures were intermingled.

There are n trials. The number of ways the i successes could be arranged is the number of ways of choosing i places out of n. This is ^nC_i or $\binom{n}{i}$. Hence we multiply the probability of one fixed arrangement by the number of possible arrangements.

$$P(X = i) = \binom{n}{i} p^i q^{n-i}$$

Note

The expression $\binom{n}{i} p^i q^{n-i}$ may be familiar. It is the ith term in the binomial expansion of $(q + p)^n$. This is where the phrase 'binomial distribution' comes from.

$$(q + p)^n = q^n + \binom{n}{1} q^{n-1} p + ... + \binom{n}{i} q^{n-i} p^i + ... + p^n$$
$$= P(X = 0) + P(X = 1) + ... + P(X = i) + ...$$
$$+ P(X = n)$$

As $(q + p)^n = 1^n = 1$, this verifies that the sum of all the probabilities is 1.

Bar charts

Bar charts of various binomial distributions are shown here.

Figure 7.1 shows bar charts for B(10, p), for different values of p. Note that if $p = \frac{1}{2}$ the chart is symmetric about the mode. If $p < \frac{1}{2}$ it is skewed to the left, and if $p > \frac{1}{2}$ it is skewed to the right.

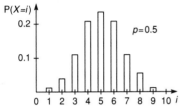 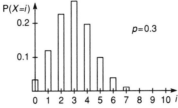 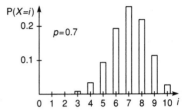

Fig. 7.1

Figure 7.2 shows bar charts for B(n, 0.5), for different values of n. Note that for larger n, the bars are clustered more closely round the mode. For $n = 100$, the chart has a 'bell' shape.

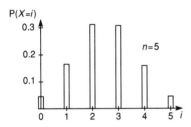 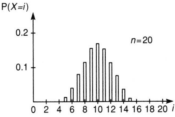 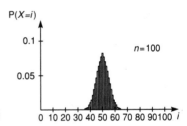

Fig. 7.2

EXAMPLE 7.2

Suppose that X is a random variable, with $X \sim B(10, 0.3)$. Find the probability that $X = 2$.

Solution

Apply the formula, with $n = 10$ and $p = 0.3$.

$$P(X = 2) = \binom{10}{2} 0.3^2 0.7^8 = 0.233$$

The probability is 0.233.

EXAMPLE 7.3

In the lottery example at the beginning of the chapter, each ticket has probability $\frac{1}{20}$ of winning a prize. If you buy 20 tickets in succession, what is the probability that you win exactly one prize?

Solution

If X is the number of winning tickets, then $X \sim B(20, 0.05)$. The probability that you win exactly one prize is:

$$P(X = 1) = \binom{20}{1} 0.05 \times 0.95^{19} = 0.377$$

The probability you will win exactly one prize is 0.377.

EXAMPLE 7.4

There are 1000 students in a college, and it is known that 200 of them study mathematics. Ten students are picked at random. Use a binomial distribution to find the approximate probability that the sample of ten contains four maths students.

Solution

The probability that a student studies maths is $\frac{200}{1000} = \frac{1}{5}$. If we have chosen one maths student, this reduces slightly the probability that the next student also studies maths. Hence the events are not strictly independent. But as the sample of ten is small in comparison with the student body of 1000, we shall ignore this difference.

The number of maths students is approximately $B(10, \frac{1}{5})$.

Let X be the number of maths students. Use the formula:

$$P(X = 4) \simeq \binom{10}{4}(\tfrac{1}{5})^4(\tfrac{4}{5})^6 = 0.088$$

The probability is approximately 0.088.

EXERCISE 7B

1 In each of the following distributions, find the probability required.

a) $X \sim B(10, 0.4)$, $P(X = 3)$

b) $X \sim B(20, 0.1)$, $P(X = 2)$

c) $X \sim B(15, 0.7)$, $P(X = 7)$

d) $X \sim B(25, 0.2)$, $P(X = 5)$

2 A fair die is rolled ten times. Find the probability that exactly three 6s are scored.

3 A regular tetrahedron has the numbers 1, 2, 3, 4 on its faces. It is tossed seven times. Find the probability that it lands three times on the face labelled 4.

4 A roulette wheel has holes labelled 1 to 36. The wheel is spun 20 times. Assuming that the wheel is fair, find the probability that for exactly four spins the ball lands in a hole whose number is divisible by 3.

5 Assume that 51 per cent of all births are boys. Find the probability that out of ten births four will be boys.

6 The probability that a certain type of bulb will flower is $\frac{3}{4}$. If six are bought find the probability that five flower.

7 A supermarket finds that 4 per cent of its eggs are cracked. If a customer buys a dozen, find the probability that two are cracked.

8 A rifleman fires eight shots at a target. With each shot he has a probability 0.8 of hitting the target, and each shot is independent of the others. What is the probability that he hits the target five times?

9 A motorist has to pass through twelve sets of traffic lights. At each set, the probability that the car will have to stop is $\frac{2}{3}$, and the sets are not linked in any way. Find the probability that the car will have to stop at nine sets.

10 The proportion of the electorate which supports the Reactionary Party is 28 per cent. Find the probability that a random sample of 16 voters contains four supporters of the party.

11 A kettle manufacturer maintains the quality of its product by testing a random sample of 20 kettles. If the proportion of defective kettles produced by the factory is 0.04, find the probability that the sample contains two defectives.

12 Assuming that 15 per cent of the population are left-handed, find the probability that a random sample of 12 people contains three left-handers.

13 A bag contains 100 red beans and 200 black beans. If five beans are drawn out, use the binomial distribution to find the approximate probability that there will be two red beans.

14 In a school there are 600 girls and 500 boys. If ten are chosen at random to go on a trip, estimate the probability that seven of them will be girls.

15 A library contains 2000 fiction books and 3000 non-fiction books. If eleven books are picked at random estimate the probability that four will be fiction.

16 Four letters are written, and four envelopes are addressed for them. The letters are put into the envelopes at random. If X is the number of letters in the correct envelopes, explain why X does *not* have a binomial distribution.

17 In the card game of *Bridge*, 13 cards are dealt to each player. Let X be the number of spades contained in a Bridge hand. Explain why X does not have a B$(13, \frac{1}{4})$ distribution.

18 An urn contains 14 blue balls and 16 white balls. Six balls are taken out in succession. Letting X be the number of blue balls drawn, state whether or not X has a binomial distribution in the following cases.

  a) The balls are returned to the urn after being drawn.

  b) The balls are not returned to the urn after being drawn.

Mean and variance

We can find the mean and variance of a binomial distribution. For the lottery example, as the probability that an individual ticket will win a prize is $\frac{1}{20}$, we would anticipate one prize for every 20 tickets we buy. We shall see that this is the case.

Suppose $X \sim B(n, p)$.

Then $E(X) = np$ and $\mathrm{Var}(X) = npq$

The proofs of these results are in the Mathematical appendix on page 330.

Note

If $X \sim B(20, \frac{1}{20})$, then $E(X) = 20 \times \frac{1}{20} = 1$. This verifies that if you

buy 20 lottery tickets, each with probability $\frac{1}{20}$ of winning a prize, your expected number of winning tickets is 1.

EXAMPLE 7.5

A man plants ten saplings. For each sapling the probability that it will grow into a mature tree is 0.25, and each sapling is independent of the others. Find the mean and variance of the number of mature trees he obtains.

Solution

Let X be the number of mature trees he gets. Then $X \sim B(10, 0.25)$. Apply the formulae from above.

$$E(X) = 10 \times 0.25 = 2.5$$

$$\mathrm{Var}(X) = 10 \times 0.25 \times 0.75 = 1.875$$

The mean is 2.5 and the variance is 1.875.

EXERCISE 7C

1 Find the mean and variance of each of the following distributions.

a) B(10, 0.4) b) B(20, 0.3) c) $B\left(n, \dfrac{1}{n}\right)$ d) B(20, 1)

2 An archer shoots arrows at a target. For each arrow the probability that she will strike the target is 0.8. If she shoots twelve arrows, find the mean and variance of the number of times she hits the target.

3 The probability that an egg is cracked is 0.05. Find the mean and variance of the number of cracked eggs in a carton of six.

4 The proportion of defective items produced by a factory is 10 per cent. If a sample of 20 items is taken, find the mean and variance of the number of defective items in the sample.

5 A school contains 1000 pupils, of whom 450 are girls. If a group of ten pupils is picked at random, estimate the mean and variance of the number of girls in the group.

6 At a local election 3500 people voted, of whom 2000 people voted for the Labour candidate. An exit poll asked 30 people how they had voted. Estimate the mean and variance of the number of people who stated that they had voted Labour.

7 The mean of the distribution $B(12, p)$ is 4. Find p.

8 The mean of the distribution $B(n, 0.3)$ is 12. Find n.

9 The variance of the distribution $B(n, 0.4)$ is 120. Find n.

10 The variance of the distribution $B(50, p)$ is 8. Find the possible values of p.

11 The distribution $B(n, p)$ has mean 60 and variance 24. Find p and n.

12 The distribution $B(n, p)$ has mean μ and variance σ^2. Express p and n in terms of μ and σ^2.

13 Complete the following table for $B(5, 0.4)$.

i	0	1	2	3	4	5
$P(X = i)$	0.07776		0.3456			0.01024

From the table find $E(X)$ and $Var(X)$. Check that your results agree with the formulae for the binomial distribution.

14 The number of passengers in 100 cars were counted. The results are shown in the table below.

Number of passengers	0	1	2	3	4
Frequency	43	24	16	12	5

Find the mean and variance of these figures. Do these figures fit a binomial distribution $B(5, p)$, for some p? Find p from your results, and comment.

7.2 Cumulative probabilities

We often need to know the probability that a random variable takes values within a certain range. For example, we might want to know the probability that, if we buy 20 lottery tickets, we shall win fewer than three prizes. We find the probability by adding individual probabilities.

$$P(X < 3) = \sum_{0}^{2} P(X = i) = P(X = 0) + P(X = 1) + P(X = 2)$$

If we wanted to find the probability of winning *at least three* prizes, we should need to evaluate:

$$P(X \geq 3) = \sum_{3}^{20} P(X = i)$$

This would involve working out 18 probabilities. It is easier to look at the probability of *not* winning at least three prizes, i.e. of winning fewer than three prizes. To find the probability of winning at least three, subtract the probability of winning fewer than three from 1.

$$P(X \geq 3) = 1 - P(X < 3)$$
$$= 1 - (P(X = 0) + P(X = 1) + P(X = 2))$$

Now there are only three probabilities to calculate.

Calculator tips

When there are several binomial probabilities to calculate, it often helps to factorise as much as possible. The sum of the three probabilities above is:

$$P(X = 0) + P(X = 1) + P(X = 2)$$

$$= 0.95^{20} + \binom{20}{1}0.95^{19}0.05 + \binom{20}{2}0.95^{18}0.05^2$$

$$= 0.95^{18}(0.95^2 + 20 \times 0.95 \times 0.05 + 190 \times 0.05^2)$$

Work out the sum of the three terms inside the brackets, then multiply by 0.95^{18}. You should obtain 0.925.

It is also useful to put the probability p into the memory of your calculator; if you have more than one memory, store q in one of the extra memories.

EXAMPLE 7.6

A marksman fires ten shots at a target. For each shot, the probability he will hit the bull's-eye is 0.7. Each shot is independent of the others. Find the probability that he will obtain *at most eight* bull's-eyes.

Solution

Let X be the number of bull's-eyes. Then $X \sim B(10, 0.7)$. The probability we want is:

$$P(X \leq 8) = \sum_{0}^{8} P(X = i)$$

There are nine probabilities to work out here. Turn the problem round.

$$P(X \leq 8) = 1 - (P(X = 9) + P(X = 10))$$

$$= 1 - \left(\binom{10}{9} 0.7^9 0.3 + 0.7^{10} \right)$$

$$= 1 - 0.7^9 (10 \times 0.3 + 0.7)$$

$$= 0.851$$

The probability of at most eight bull's-eyes is 0.851.

EXERCISE 7D

1 In each of the following distributions, find the probability indicated.

    a) $X \sim B(10, 0.2)$, $P(X \le 2)$ **b)** $X \sim B(20, 0.3)$, $P(X < 2)$

    c) $X \sim B(15, 0.5)$, $P(X \ge 14)$ **d)** $X \sim B(10, 0.4)$, $P(X > 7)$

    e) $X \sim B(10, 0.45)$, $P(X \le 8)$ **f)** $X \sim B(20, 0.1)$, $P(X \ge 2)$

    g) $X \sim B(15, 0.85)$, $P(X < 13)$ **h)** $X \sim B(30, 0.12)$, $P(X > 2)$

2 A multiple choice test contains 20 questions, each of which has five possible answers. A candidate is completely ignorant of the subject of the test, and picks the answers at random. Find the probability that the candidate gets fewer than three answers right.

3 Consider again the lottery example, in which a gambler buys 20 tickets, each of which has probability $\frac{1}{20}$ of winning a prize. Find the probabilities that:

    a) at least one prize is won,   **b)** at least three prizes are won.

4 In a certain batch of tulip bulbs, $\frac{3}{4}$ of them will flower. Find the probability that if I buy 15 at least 12 will flower.

5 The probability that Mrs Williams will be late for work is 0.1. What is the probability that on 30 days she will be late more than three times? What assumptions are you making?

6 When Mary and Jane play squash, the probability that Mary wins a point is 0.4. Find the probability that Mary will win fewer than three of the first twelve points.

7 In the game of *Cameroons* (or *Yahtsee*) five dice are rolled. At the beginning of the game it is a good thing to get as many 6s as possible. Find the probability that with one roll at least three 6s are obtained.

8 The New Progressive Party is supported by 5 per cent of the population. Find the probability that a random sample of 30 people contains at most two supporters of the party.

9 A factory produces silicon chips, of which 12 per cent are defective. Find the probability that a random sample of 20 contains more than two defective chips.

10 A tennis player finds that his first serve is good on 60 per cent of attempts. Assuming that the attempts are independent of each other, find the probability that in ten serves at least eight will be good.

Use of tables

If we have more than a few probabilities to add up, the process takes time and we are liable to make errors. If $X \sim$ B(30, 0.4), and we want to find $P(X \leq 14)$, there would be 15 probabilities to add up. There are three ways we could find the probability without having to do excessive amounts of arithmetic.

Using a computer   This will be discussed in the Computer investigations section on page 157.

Approximating the binomial distribution by a certain continuous distribution. This will be discussed in Chapter 9 on page 176.

By use of tables   We shall discuss this now.

The tables on pages 335–337 give cumulative binomial probabilities for certain values of n, for certain values of p. Suppose, as above, $X \sim$ B(30, 0.4) and we want to find $P(X \leq 14)$. Look at the part of the table below where $n = 30$. Look down the column headed 0.4, until you reach the row labelled 14. The figure here is the required probability, 0.8246.

$n = 30$

$p = 0.05$	0.1	0.15	1/6	0.2	0.25	0.3	1/3	0.35	0.4	0.45	0.5
$i =$											
0 0.2146	0.0424	0.0076	0.0042	0.0012	0.0002	0.0000	0.0000	0.0000	0.0000	0.0000	0.0000
1 0.5535	0.1837	0.0480	0.0295	0.0105	0.0020	0.0003	0.0001	0.0000	0.0000	0.0000	0.0000
2 0.8122	0.4114	0.1514	0.1028	0.0442	0.0106	0.0021	0.0007	0.0003	0.0000	0.0000	0.0000
3 0.9392	0.6474	0.3217	0.2396	0.1227	0.0374	0.0093	0.0033	0.0019	0.0003	0.0000	0.0000
4 0.9844	0.8245	0.5245	0.4243	0.2552	0.0979	0.0302	0.0122	0.0075	0.0015	0.0002	0.0000
5 0.9967	0.9268	0.7106	0.6164	0.4275	0.2026	0.0766	0.0355	0.0233	0.0057	0.0011	0.0002
6 0.9994	0.9742	0.8474	0.7765	0.6070	0.3481	0.1595	0.0838	0.0586	0.0172	0.0040	0.0007
7 0.9999	0.9922	0.9302	0.8863	0.7608	0.5143	0.2814	0.1668	0.1238	0.0435	0.0121	0.0026
8 1.0000	0.9980	0.9722	0.9494	0.8713	0.6736	0.4315	0.2860	0.2247	0.0940	0.0312	0.0081
9 1.0000	0.9995	0.9903	0.9803	0.9389	0.8034	0.5888	0.4317	0.3575	0.1763	0.0694	0.0214
10 1.0000	0.9999	0.9971	0.9933	0.9744	0.8943	0.7304	0.5848	0.5078	0.2915	0.1350	0.0494
11 1.0000	1.0000	0.9992	0.9980	0.9905	0.9493	0.8407	0.7239	0.6548	0.4311	0.2327	0.1002
12 1.0000	1.0000	0.9998	0.9995	0.9969	0.9784	0.9155	0.8340	0.7802	0.5785	0.3592	0.1808
13 1.0000	1.0000	1.0000	0.9999	0.9991	0.9918	0.9599	0.9102	0.8737	0.7145	0.5025	0.2923
14 1.0000	1.0000	1.0000	1.0000	0.9998	0.9973	0.9831	0.9565	0.9348	(0.8246)	0.6448	0.4278
15 1.0000	1.0000	1.0000	1.0000	0.9999	0.9992	0.9936	0.9812	0.9699	0.9029	0.7691	0.5722
16 1.0000	1.0000	1.0000	1.0000	1.0000	0.9998	0.9979	0.9928	0.9876	0.9519	0.8644	0.7077
17 1.0000	1.0000	1.0000	1.0000	1.0000	0.9999	0.9994	0.9975	0.9955	0.9788	0.9286	0.8192
18 1.0000	1.0000	1.0000	1.0000	1.0000	1.0000	0.9998	0.9993	0.9986	0.9917	0.9666	0.8998
19 1.0000	1.0000	1.0000	1.0000	1.0000	1.0000	1.0000	0.9998	0.9996	0.9971	0.9862	0.9506

The tables give the probability that X is less than or equal to certain values. They are not given for values of p greater than $\frac{1}{2}$. Adjustment may be necessary, as follows.

< or ≤

Suppose you are asked for the probability that X is less than 14. This is the same as X being less than or equal to 13.

$$P(X < 14) = P(X \leq 13)$$

In general, $P(X < i) = P(X \leq i - 1)$

> and ≥

Suppose you are asked for the probability that X is greater than 15. This is the same as X *not* being less than or equal to 15. Subtract this second probability from 1.

$$P(X > 15) = 1 - P(X \leq 15)$$

In general, $P(X > i) = 1 - P(X \leq i)$

$$P(X \geq i) = 1 - P(X < i) = 1 - P(X \leq i - 1)$$

Values of p greater than $\frac{1}{2}$

Suppose you are asked for the probability that X is greater than 15, where $X \sim B(20, 0.7)$. Here X is the number of successes. If we let Y be the number of failures, then $Y \sim B(20, 0.3)$. The probability that X is greater than 15 is the same as the probability that Y is less than 5.

$$P(X > 15) = P(Y < 5)$$

In general, $P(X > i) = P(Y < n - i)$

When the cumulative probability reaches a given level

The tables can also be used to find the value where the cumulative probability exceeds a certain level. Suppose that $X \sim B(30, 0.4)$, and we want to find the least i such that $P(X \leq i)$ is at least 0.95. Look down the $p = 0.4$ column of the $n = 30$ table opposite, until we reach a value greater than 0.95. This occurs at $i = 16$. This is our least value of i.

EXAMPLE 7.7

Three-quarters of the population of a town are over 18. If a random sample of 30 people is taken, find the probability that it will contain at least 20 people over 18.

Solution

Let X be the number of people over 18 in the sample. Then $X \sim B(30, 0.75)$. We want to find the probability that X is at least 20, i.e. $P(X \geq 20)$.

Turn to the $n = 30$ table of cumulative binomial probabilities. There is no entry for $p = 0.75$. Instead consider the number Y of people who are *under* 18. Then $Y \sim N(30, 0.25)$. The probability that X is at least 20 is the same as the probability that Y is less than or equal to 10.

$$P(X \geq 20) = P(Y \leq 10)$$

Now we have a form for which we can use the table. Look down the $p = 0.25$ column until we reach the 10 row. The entry is 0.8943.

The probability is 0.8943.

EXAMPLE 7.8

Certain silicon chips are sold in batches of 40. The manufacturers want to be able to claim that more than 90 per cent of the batches contain at most i faulty chips. What is the least value of i for which they can make this claim, if it is known that 5 per cent of the chips are faulty?

Solution

Let X be the number of faulty chips. Then $X \sim B(40, 0.05)$. We want to find the least i such that:

$$P(X \leq i) > 0.9$$

Turn to the $n = 40$ table of cumulative binomial probabilities. Look down the $p = 0.05$ column until 0.9 is exceeded. This first happens at $i = 4$.

The value of i is 4.

EXERCISE 7E

1 Use tables to find the probability in each of the following distributions.

a) $X \sim B(10, 0.2)$, $P(X \leq 4)$ b) $X \sim B(20, 0.4)$, $P(X \leq 8)$

c) $X \sim B(20, 0.35)$, $P(X < 7)$ d) $X \sim B(30, 0.5)$, $P(X < 12)$

e) $X \sim B(20, 0.45)$, $P(X < 14)$ f) $X \sim B(20, 0.5)$, $P(X < 15)$

g) $X \sim B(30, 0.45)$, $P(X \leq 20)$ h) $X \sim B(40, 0.5)$, $P(X \leq 25)$

i) $X \sim B(20, 0.7)$, $P(X > 15)$ j) $X \sim B(10, 0.8)$, $P(X \geq 6)$

k) $X \sim B(20, 0.6)$, $P(X \leq 7)$ l) $X \sim B(30, 0.65)$, $P(X < 16)$

2 A marksman fires 20 shots at a target. Each shot has probability 0.1 of hitting the bull's-eye. Use tables to find the probability that he scores at most five bull's-eyes.

What is the smallest value of i for which he has less than 0.1 chance of obtaining at least i bull's-eyes?

3 It is thought that 45 per cent of the electorate supports the Purple Party. An opinion poll of 40 people is taken. What is the probability that at least 20 of the people asked will support the Purple Party?

What is the greatest value of i for which we can be 95 per cent sure that the sample will contain at least i Purple Party supporters?

4 A railway company runs 40 trains a day. Each train has probability 0.2 of being late, and each train is independent of the others. The company wishes to claim that, on 95 per cent of days, at least i of its trains will be on time. What is the greatest value of i for which it can make this claim?

*5 (*Drunkard's walk*)   A drunkard leaves a pub, and steps to right or left with equal probability 0.5. What is the probability that after 30 steps he will be within five steps of the pub door?

What is the least number i of steps so that we can be 90 per cent sure that he will be within i steps of the pub door?

7.3 The geometric distribution

In many games each player rolls a die, and cannot start until a 6 has been thrown. The number of times the die is rolled is not fixed – the player may be lucky and get a 6 on the first roll, or may be unlucky and have to roll it ten times or more. In theory, there is no limit to the number of times the die may have to be rolled.

The probability that a 6 is first obtained on the first try is $\frac{1}{6}$.

If a 6 is first obtained on the second try, then a 6 *wasn't* obtained on the first try (with probability $\frac{5}{6}$) and *was* obtained on the second. Hence:

The probability that a 6 is first obtained on the second try is $\frac{5}{6} \times \frac{1}{6}$.

The probability that a 6 is first obtained on the third try is $\frac{5}{6} \times \frac{5}{6} \times \frac{1}{6}$.

Following this pattern, the probability that a 6 is first obtained on the nth try is $(\frac{5}{6})^{n-1} \times \frac{1}{6}$.

These probabilities form a geometric progression, with first term $\frac{1}{6}$ and common ratio $\frac{5}{6}$. Hence the distribution from which the probabilities come is called the **geometric distribution**.

General formula
Suppose a trial or experiment has two possible outcomes, 'success' and 'failure'. The probability of success is p, and of failure is $q = 1 - p$.

The experiment is repeated independently until a 'success' is obtained. Letting X be the number of trials necessary, we say that X has a geometric distribution.

X takes whole numbered values from 1 upwards. The probabilities are given by:

$$P(X = i) = pq^{i-1}$$

Proof

If $X = i$, then the first success occurred on the ith try. There has been a run of $(i - 1)$ failures, followed by a single success. The probability of this is:

$$\underbrace{q \times q \times ... \times q}_{i - 1 \text{ times}} \times p = pq^{i-1}$$

Notes

1 We can use the formula for the sum of an infinite geometric progression, to find the sum of all these probabilities.

$$\sum_{1}^{\infty} pq^{i-1} = p + pq + pq^2 + ... = \frac{p}{1 - q} = \frac{p}{p} = 1.$$

This confirms that the sum of the probabilities is 1.

2 The geometric distribution is determined by p, the probability of success. This probability is the parameter of the distribution.

EXAMPLE 7.9

At each attempt, a candidate has probability $\frac{1}{3}$ of passing the driving test. Find the probability that the third attempt will be successful, assuming that each attempt is independent of the previous attempts.

Solution

As each attempt is independent of the others, the number of attempts, X, has a geometric distribution with $p = \frac{1}{3}$. Apply the formula.

$$P(X = 3) = \frac{1}{3}\left(\frac{2}{3}\right)^{3-1} = \frac{4}{27}$$

The probability that the third attempt will be successful is $\frac{4}{27}$.

EXERCISE 7F

1 In each of the following X has a geometric distribution with parameter p. Find the probabilities indicated.

a) $p = 0.3$, $P(X = 2)$ b) $p = 0.6$, $P(X = 1)$

c) $p = 0.5$, $P(X = 8)$ d) $p = 0.1$, $P(X = 3)$

2 A fair die is rolled until a 6 appears. Find the probability that five rolls are required.

3 A fair coin is spun until a head is scored. Find the probability that three spins are required.

4 Michael has probability 0.2 of passing his Maths GCSE. He continues to take the exam, and each attempt is independent of the others. What is the probability he passes on his fourth attempt?

5 A janitor has a key ring with ten similar keys. He tries to open a door in the dark, and picks a key at random. If that key doesn't work another key is tried. In which of the following cases is a geometric distribution appropriate?

 a) The janitor holds onto the ring, and never tries the same key twice.

 b) The janitor drops the ring on the floor after each attempt.

 In the situation for which a geometric distribution is appropriate, find the probability that six attempts will be needed.

6 Three people want to play squash (which requires only two players). Each person spins a coin. If one coin is different from the other two then that person 'sits out'. Otherwise the coins are spun again. Find the probability that four rounds of spinning will be required.

7 Two coins are spun. Find the probability that the first double head will occur on the tenth go.

*8 A box contains a large number of black socks and white socks, in the ratio 2:1. Socks are drawn singly in the dark, until two socks with different colours have been obtained. Find the probability that five socks will be drawn.

9 X has a geometric distribution with parameter $p > 0$. What is the most likely value of X?

*10 Two people, Alan and Beatrice, take turns to roll a die, Alan starting. The winner is the first person to roll a 6. Find the probability that Alan wins.

*11 Gwendolyn and Madeleine shoot arrows at a target. Gwendolyn's chance of hitting the gold (the centre) is $\frac{1}{10}$, and Madeleine's chance is $\frac{1}{8}$. They shoot alternately, Gwendolyn starting, and the winner is the first person to hit the gold. What is the probability that Gwendolyn wins?

Mean and variance

Suppose X has a geometric distribution with probability p at each try. The mean and variance of X are given by:

$$E(X) = \frac{1}{p} \qquad Var(X) = \frac{q}{p^2}$$

The proofs of these results are in the Mathematical appendix, on page 331.

Cumulative probabilities

We do not have tables for the cumulative probabilities of the geometric distribution. These are comparatively easy to work out. Suppose X has a geometric distribution with parameter $\frac{1}{4}$. Suppose we are looking for the probability that success is achieved within eight trials, i.e. for the probability that X is less than or equal to 8.

This can be obtained by subtracting from 1 the probability that X is *greater* than 8.

$$P(X \leq 8) = 1 - P(X > 8)$$

X will be greater than 8 if the first eight trials are all failures. This has probability $(\frac{3}{4})^8$.

$$P(X \leq 8) = 1 - (\tfrac{3}{4})^8$$

In general, $P(X \leq i) = 1 - P(X > i) = 1 - q^i$

EXAMPLE 7.10
Find the mean and variance of the number of driving tests taken by the candidate of Example 7.9.

Solution
Here $p = \frac{1}{3}$ and $q = \frac{2}{3}$. Apply the formulae.

$$E(X) = \frac{1}{\frac{1}{3}} = 3$$

$$\text{Var}(X) = \frac{\frac{2}{3}}{(\frac{1}{3})^2} = 6$$

The mean is 3 and the variance is 6.

EXAMPLE 7.11
Find the probability that the candidate of Example 7.9 will take fewer than ten tests before passing.

Solution
Letting X be the number of tests, we want $P(X < 10)$ or $P(X \leq 9)$. Use the formula above.

$$P(X \leq 9) = 1 - P(X > 9) = 1 - (\tfrac{2}{3})^9 = 0.974$$

The probability of fewer than ten tests is 0.974.

EXERCISE 7G

1 Find the mean and variance of the geometric distributions with the following parameters.

   a) $p = \frac{1}{2}$ **b)** $p = \frac{2}{3}$ **c)** $p = 0.05$

2 Variable X has a geometric distribution and $E(X) = 15$. Find the parameter of the distribution of X. Find $\text{Var}(X)$.

3 Variable X has a geometric distribution and $\text{Var}(X) = 12$. Find $E(X)$.

*4 Variable X has a geometric distribution. Show that $E(X)$ can take any value greater or equal to 1. Show that $\text{Var}(X)$ can take any value greater or equal to 0.

5 In each of the following X has a geometric distribution with the parameter given. Find the required probability.

a) $p = 0.3$, $P(X > 4)$ **b)** $p = 0.6$, $P(X > 3)$ **c)** $p = 0.1$, $P(X < 10)$

d) $p = 0.8$, $P(X < 4)$ **e)** $p = 0.25$, $P(X \le 5)$ **f)** $p = 0.45$, $P(X \ge 7)$

6 A fair die is rolled until a 6 appears. Find the probabilities that this will take:

a) more than ten rolls   **b)** fewer than 20 rolls.

7 A fair coin is spun until a head appears. Find the probabilities that this will take:

a) at least three spins,   **b)** at most five spins.

8 An insurance salesman finds that 1 per cent of the calls he makes result in a sale. Find the probability that, in a week, he will make fewer than 50 calls before his first sale.

9 A fair coin is spun until two successive results are different. Find the probability that this will require more than four spins.

10 In a particularly vandalised area only 10 per cent of the public telephones work. Find the probability that a caller will have to try more than 12 telephones before finding one that works.

11 It is thought that 8 per cent of motorists drive with inadequate insurance. The police investigate motorists at random to see whether their insurance is adequate. Find the probability that the police will check at least 15 people before finding someone with inadequate insurance.

12 At a fairground game the punter rolls a die and hopes to get a 6. The game ends when a 6 is first rolled or after three rolls, whichever is the sooner. Letting X be the number of rolls, set up a table showing the distribution of X. From your table find $E(X)$ and $Var(X)$.

LONGER EXERCISE

Binomial machine

In 1889 the geneticist Sir Francis Galton devised a machine to simulate binomial probability. Figure 7.3 shows such a machine.

A stream of small spheres like lead shot or mustard seed is poured in at the funnel at A. B is a wedge placed symmetrically below A, and C and D are wedges placed below B, on either side. The spheres then collect in partitions at the bottom. The proportion of the spheres in each partition is found.

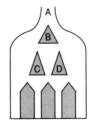

Show that these proportions should have the distribution $B(3, \frac{1}{2})$.

How would you extend the machine to simulate $B(4, \frac{1}{2})$?   *Fig. 7.3*

If you are practically minded, you could construct such a machine, using wedges of thick cardboard or wood glued onto a backing. How closely does your machine simulate the binomial distribution?

In 1895 the statistician Karl Pearson made a machine which could simulate B(4, p), for any probability p. How was this done?

EXAMINATION QUESTIONS

1 Jim has four shots at a target. On any shot the probability that he hits the target is 0.3, and the results of the shots are independent of each other. Let X be the number of times Jim hits the target. Complete the table. *binomial distribution.*

X	0	1	2	3	4
Probability	0.2401	0.4116	.2646	0.0756	0.0081

Calculate the mean and variance of X directly from the table.

Check your results by another method. *1.2 and 0.84*

SMP 1992

2 State the conditions under which the binomial distribution may be used for the calculation of probabilities.

The probability that a girl chosen at random has a weekend birthday in 1993 is 2/7. Calculate the probability that, among a group of ten girls chosen at random,

(i)   none has a weekend birthday in 1993,

(ii) exactly one has a weekend birthday in 1993.

Among 100 groups of ten girls, how many groups would you expect to contain more than one girl with a weekend birthday in 1993?

C AS 1993

3 a) A class of 16 pupils consists of 10 girls, 3 of whom are left-handed, and 6 boys, only one of whom is left-handed. Two pupils are to be chosen at random from the class to act as monitors. Calculate the probabilities that the chosen pupils will consist of

(i)   one girl and one boy

(ii) one girl who is left-handed and one boy who is left-handed,

(iii) two left-handed pupils,

(iv) at least one pupil who is left-handed.

b) The probability of a manufactured item being defective is 0.1. A batch consisting of a very large number of the items is inspected as follows. A random sample of five items is chosen. If this sample contains no defective item then the batch is accepted, while if the sample includes 3 or more defectives it is rejected. If the sample contains either 1 or 2 defectives then a second random sample of five items is chosen from the batch. The batch will be accepted if this second sample contains no defective item and will be rejected otherwise. Calculate, correct to three decimal places, the probabilities that

(i)   the first sample will result in the batch being accepted,

(ii) the first sample will result in the batch being rejected,

(iii) the second sample will be necessary and will result in the batch being accepted.

W AS 1990

4 A loaded die is such that when it is thrown the probability of obtaining a score of 6 is 0.25. In five independent throws of the die calculate, correct to three decimal places, the probabilities that

(i)   a 6 will be obtained exactly once,

(ii)   a 6 will be obtained for the first time on the fifth throw,

(iii) a 6 will be obtained for the second time on the fifth throw.

W 1992

5 What is a necessary condition for two events A and B to be described as *statistically independent?*

The Geometric probability distribution arises in circumstances that are decidedly similar to those required for the Binomial distribution. In what way is the random variable for the Geometric different from that for the Binomial?

a) A random variable, X, follows the Geometric distribution with probability $p = 0.3$.

(i)   Write down the probability $P(X = 4)$.

(ii)   Carefully describe why $P(X = n)$ is $0.7^{n-1}0.3$.

(iii) Describe in words a situation that has probability 0.7^{n-1}.

b) A sixth-former is waiting for a bus to take him to town. He passes the time by counting the number of buses, up to and including one that he wants, that come along his side of the road. If 30% of the buses travelling on that side of the road go to town, what is:

(i)   the most likely count he makes to the arrival of one that will take him to town;

(ii)   the probability that he will count at most 4 buses?

O 1991

Summary and key points

7.1 Suppose an experiment has probability p of success and q of failure. If the experiment is repeated independently n times, the number X of successes has a binomial distribution, $B(n, p)$. The probability distribution is:

$$P(X = i) = \binom{n}{i} p^i q^{n-i} \quad \text{for } 0 \le i \le n.$$

The experiments must be independent of each other. The value of p must be the same for each trial.

The mean and variance of X are given by:

$$E(X) = np$$

$$Var(X) = npq$$

7.2 When working out the probability that X lies within a range of values, it is sometimes easier to change the problem as below.

$$P(X \geq i) = 1 - P(X < i)$$

For some values of n and p, there are tables to give the sums of probabilities.

7.3 Suppose an experiment has probability p of success and q of failure. The experiment is repeated independently until a success has occurred. The number, X, of trials has a geometric distribution. The probability distribution is:

$$P(X = i) = pq^{i-1} \quad \text{for } 1 \leq i$$

The experiments must be independent of each other. The value of p must be the same for each trial.

The mean and variance of X are given by:

$$E(X) = \frac{1}{p} \text{ and } Var(X) = \frac{q}{p^2}.$$

The cumulative probabilities of X are given by:

$$P(X \leq i) = 1 - q^i$$

CHAPTER **8**

Poisson distribution

When people speak of random events they often mean things that happen unpredictably, such as traffic accidents or bolts of lightning. There is a statistical model which sometimes fits these events, called the Poisson distribution.

8.1 The Poisson distribution

It is often easy to see when a binomial distribution is a useful model for a random variable. The Poisson distribution is also useful in many situations, but these are less obvious.

Suppose the rate of traffic accidents along a stretch of road is monitored. In some months there are no accidents at at all, in others there are many. The mean number of accidents per month might be two. A bar chart of the number of accidents over a period of 40 months might look like Fig. 8.1.

A statistical model for the number of accidents per month is provided by the Poisson distribution. This gives the probability that there will be i accidents along the stretch of road, for each value of i. For example, the probability of no accidents will be given as 0.135.

The notion of a probability model is important. When we use the Poisson distribution to describe a random variable, we do not claim that the variable must take each value with exactly the probability predicted by the Poisson distribution. The distribution is a model, from it we predict the probabilities of the situation and hope that they are reasonably close to the ones found by experiment. A graph showing the probabilities of this Poisson distribution is shown in Fig. 8.2. Note that it is roughly the same shape as the bar chart of Fig. 8.1.

To indicate that a random variable X has a Poisson distribution with mean λ we write:

$$X \sim \text{Po}(\lambda)$$

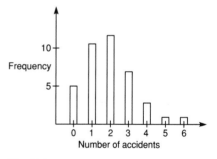

Fig. 8.1

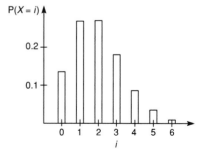

Fig. 8.2

Formula

If X has a Poisson distribution with mean λ, then X takes whole numbered values from zero upwards. The probabilities are given by the following formula.

$$P(X = i) = \frac{e^{-\lambda}\lambda^i}{i!}$$

Note that we do not *prove* this formula. A Poisson variable is *defined* as one with this distribution. The proof that this is a proper distribution and that its mean is λ is in the Mathematical appendix on page 332.

The Poisson distribution $Po(\lambda)$ is useful to model the following sort of situation. Suppose occurrences of some phenomena occur randomly, and that:

1 The occurrences are distributed through time or space so that they are equally likely to occur in any interval of a fixed length.
2 The occurrences are independent of each other.
3 The mean number of occurrences in a unit interval of time or space is λ.
4 Two occurrences cannot occur at the same point of time or space.

Let us see how these conditions could be satisfied by the traffic accident example above, i.e. how the number of accidents per month could have a $Po(2)$ distribution.

1 The accidents are distributed through time, and it is reasonable to assume that they are as likely to occur in one period of time as in another.
2 Accidents occur randomly, independently of each other.
3 We have assumed that there is a mean number of two accidents per month.
4 It is extremely unlikely that there would be two accidents occurring simultaneously.

Examples of phenomena which can usefully be modelled by a Poisson distribution are:

- the number of telephone calls received per hour
- the number of meteorites falling in a square mile during one year
- the number of goals scored by one side in a soccer match
- the number of flaws in a length of cloth.

Examples of phenomena for which a Poisson distribution is *not* appropriate are:

- the number of cases of an infectious disease in a town (Occurrences are not independent of each other.)

- the number of spades held in a hand of 13 cards. (There is a maximum of 13 spades in any pack.)

Calculator tips

When adding several Poisson probabilities, it is a good idea to factorise as far as possible. Suppose $X \sim$ Po(λ) and we are asked for P($X \le 2$).

$$P(X = 0) + P(X = 1) + P(X = 2) = e^{-\lambda} + \frac{e^{-\lambda}\lambda^1}{1!} + \frac{e^{-\lambda}\lambda^2}{2!}$$

$$= e^{-\lambda}(1 + \lambda + \tfrac{1}{2}\lambda^2)$$

If λ is not an integer, it is useful to keep it in the memory of your calculator.

EXAMPLE 8.1

The number of daisies on a square metre of lawn has a Poisson distribution with mean 5. Find the probability there are four daisies in a square metre.

Solution

Letting X be the number of daisies, $X \sim$ Po(5). Apply the formula.

$$P(X = 4) = \frac{e^{-5}5^4}{4!} = 0.175$$

The probability of four daisies is 0.175.

EXAMPLE 8.2

The number of taxis that arrive at a hotel in each period of five minutes is modelled by a Poisson distribution with mean 3. Find the probability that at least two taxis will arrive in a given five-minute period.

Solution

Letting X be the number of taxis that arrive, $X \sim$ Po(3). We want to find P($X \ge 2$). The Poisson distribution provides a model of the situation, *not* an exact description. For example, the distribution will give a non-zero – though very small – probability that X is greater than the total number of taxis in the world. As there are infinitely many probabilities to consider, we find the probability that there are fewer than two taxis, and subtract this from 1.

$$P(X \ge 2) = 1 - P(X < 2) = 1 - (P(X = 0) + P(X = 1))$$

$$= 1 - \left(e^{-3} + \frac{e^{-3}3^1}{1!}\right)$$

$$= 1 - e^{-3}(1 + 3)$$

$$= 0.801$$

The probability of at least two taxis is 0.801.

EXERCISE 8A

1 Find the required probability in each of the following.

 a) $P(X = 2)$, where $X \sim Po(3)$ b) $P(X = 0)$, where $X \sim Po(1)$

 c) $P(X = 1)$, where $X \sim Po(0.1)$ d) $P(X = 5)$, where $X \sim Po(4)$

2 Find the required probability in each of the following.

 a) $P(X < 2)$, where $X \sim Po(2)$ b) $P(X \leq 2)$, where $X \sim Po(4)$

 c) $P(X \geq 2)$, where $X \sim Po(2.5)$ d) $P(X > 4)$, where $X \sim Po(1.7)$

3 The number of goals scored during a football match can be modelled by a Poisson distribution with mean 2. Find the probability that during a match:

 a) three goals are scored,   b) at least two goals are scored.

4 The number of dandelions on a square yard of lawn has a Poisson distribution with mean 2.3. Find the probabilities that in a square yard:

 a) there are four dandelions   b) there are fewer than four dandelions.

5 The number of people who win the jackpot in the National Lottery per week has a Poisson distribution with mean 2.7. Find the probabilities that in a given week:

 a) no one wins the jackpot,   b) more than one person wins the jackpot.

6 The number of accidents in the night shift at a factory has a Poisson distribution with mean 3. Find the probabilities that:

 a) there are two accidents   b) there are at least three accidents.

7 The number of fish present in a given stretch of river has a Poisson distribution with mean 3.8. Find the probabilities that in this stretch there are:

 a) four fish,   b) at most three fish.

8 A violinist finds that the number of strings which break per month has a Poisson distribution with mean 2.4. Find the probability that in a month:

 a) three strings break,   b) fewer than two strings break.

9 The daily demand for a certain book in a bookshop follows a Poisson distribution with mean 3.8. Find the probability that in a day:

 a) two copies are requested,   b) at least two copies are requested.

10 A motorist finds that on average his car has 1.5 punctures every year. Assuming that the number of punctures follows a Poisson distribution, find the probability that in a year:

 a) there are no punctures,   b) there are more than two punctures.

11 The number of misspellings in a page of a newspaper has a Poisson distribution with mean 2.7. Find the probability that in a page:

a) there are three misspellings,   **b)** there are fewer than two misspellings.

12 If X has a Poisson distribution with mean λ, find the value of λ which will give the greatest value of $P(X = 1)$.

Expected value and variance

Suppose X has a Poisson distribution with mean λ. Then the expected value of X is λ, i.e. $E(X) = \lambda$. It is also true that $Var(X) = \lambda$.

The proofs are in the Mathematical appendix on page 332.

EXAMPLE 8.3

It is thought that the number of flaws on a metre of cloth produced by a machine follows a Poisson distribution. The proportion of flaw-free metres is 0.3. Find the mean number of flaws.

Solution

Letting X be the number of flaws, we have $X \sim Po(\lambda)$, where λ is the mean. From the information given:

$P(X = 0) = 0.3$

Hence $e^{-\lambda} = 0.3$, giving $\lambda = 1.20$.

The mean number of flaws is 1.20.

EXERCISE 8B

1   It is known that X has a Poisson distribution, and $P(X = 0)$ is 0.75. Find the mean of X.

2   You are given that X has a Poisson distribution and that the probability that X is greater than zero is 0.6. Find the mean of X.

3   The number of times per night the fire brigade is called out has a Poisson distribution. The probability they are not called out is 0.15. Find the mean number of times they are called out.

4   The number of incorrectly dialled numbers made per hour by a telephone sales representative has a Poisson distribution. The probability she dials all the numbers correctly is 0.82. Find the mean number of incorrectly dialled numbers per hour.

5   For the number of cases per year, X, of a certain disease, $X \sim Po(\lambda)$. The probability that there are no cases is 0.467. Find λ and calculate the probability that there will be more than one case.

6 The number of times per week that a computer breaks down has a Poisson distribution. The probability that it doesn't break down is 0.106. Find the probability that it breaks down twice in a week.

7 The number of arrivals per hour at a hotel has a Poisson distribution, and the probability that no one comes in any hour is 0.528. Find the probability that more than one person comes.

8 The number of applications for a course at a college has a Poisson distribution. The probability that no one applies for it is 0.012. Find the probability that more than two people apply.

9 Over a period of 1000 days, the deaths columns in a newspaper were examined to see how many people over 90 were mentioned. The results are shown in the table below.

Number	0	1	2	3	4	5	6	7	8+
Frequency	250	310	202	142	66	21	8	1	0

Find the mean of these figures. Find the corresponding frequencies for the Poisson distribution with the same mean. Does it seem that the Poisson distribution is a good model for the number of deaths?

10 It is known that X has a Poisson distribution, and the probability that X is greater than 1 is 0.75. Show that the mean, λ, of X obeys the equation:

$$4 + 4\lambda = e^{\lambda}$$

Show that, correct to two decimal places, $\lambda = 2.69$. Find the probability that X is 0.

8.2 Poisson as approximation to binomial

A famous example of a Poisson distribution was given in the nineteenth century. It was found that the number of Prussian soldiers killed each year by a horse kick followed a Poisson distribution with mean 0.61. This could not be an exact Poisson distribution, as the number of Prussian soldiers was finite. If each soldier had an equal probability of being killed by a horse kick, and these events were independent of each other, then the number killed had a binomial distribution. However, if the probability is small and the number of soldiers large, then the distribution *approximately* obeys the conditions for a Poisson distribution, as follows.

- The fatal horse kicks are spread throughout the year, with equal probability in equal periods.
- The occurrences are independent of each other.
- The mean number is found by multiplying the number of soldiers by the probability.
- It is very unlikely that two fatal horse kicks would happen simultaneously.

In general, suppose we have a binomial distribution, $X \sim B(n, p)$. Then if n is very large and p very small, the distribution of X is approximately $Po(np)$.

EXAMPLE 8.4

A typist is copying a list of 1000 numbers. For each number, the probability that she will type it wrongly is 0.002. Use the Poisson approximation to the binomial to find the probability that there will be fewer than two mistakes in the whole list.

Solution

Letting X be the number of mistakes, we have that $X \sim B(1000, 0.002)$. Here n is large and p is small. Hence we can use the Poisson approximation, and say that the distribution of X is approximately $Po(np)$, which is $Po(2)$.

$$P(X < 2) = P(X = 0) + P(X = 1)$$

$$= e^{-2} + 2e^{-2}$$

$$= 0.4060$$

The probability of fewer than two mistakes is 0.406.

Note

The binomial distribution gives the value of the probability as 0.4057. Hence the approximation is correct to three decimal places.

EXERCISE 8C

1 Suppose that $X \sim B(2000, 0.0003)$. Find the mean of X. Use the Poisson approximation to the binomial distribution to find $P(X = 2)$.

2 In each of the following use the Poisson approximation to the binomial to find the required probability.

a) $X \sim B(500, 0.003)$, $P(X = 1)$ b) $X \sim B(800, 0.005)$, $P(X = 3)$

c) $X \sim B(1200, \frac{1}{3000})$, $P(X = 0)$ d) $X \sim B(2000, 0.001)$, $P(X = 4)$

e) $X \sim B(600, 0.003)$, $P(X < 2)$ f) $X \sim B(1000, 0.0025)$, $P(X > 1)$

g) $X \sim B(1600, 0.0007)$, $P(X \leq 2)$ h) $X \sim B(1300, 0.0015)$, $P(X \geq 3)$

3 The chances of winning the jackpot on the National Lottery are about 1 in 14 000 000. Find the probability that in 10 000 000 entrants there will be exactly one winner.

4 Assuming that birthdays are evenly spread throughout the year, find the probability that in a school of 600 pupils exactly two were born on 1 April.

5   A medical treatment gives damaging side effects for one in 1000 of the patients treated by it. If 3000 people are given the treatment, find the probability that fewer than three will show the side effects.

6   A machine for packing eggs cracks 0.01 per cent of them. Find the probability that in a group of 4000 eggs packed by this machine none will be cracked.

7   The proportion of the population with blood group Z is 0.5 per cent. Find the probability that in 1000 donors there will be at least two people with blood group Z.

8   A chain is made out of 1000 links, each of which has probability 0.0006 of breaking under tension. Find the probability that at least one link will break under tension.

9   A woman writes a novel, and sends copies to 100 publishers. If each publisher has probability 0.002 of accepting the novel, find the probability that at least one will accept it. Find the probability that more than one will accept it.

10   A firm sends out letters to 2000 customers. Each letter has probability 0.002 of being incorrectly addressed. Find the probability that at least two are incorrectly addressed.

8.3 Combinations of Poisson variables

A Poisson distribution gives a model for the number of occurrences of a random event in a fixed period of time or space. If the period is altered, then a Poisson distribution will still be a good model, but the mean will be altered. For example, suppose that the number of customers arriving in a shop every hour has a Poisson distribution with mean 12. The number of customers arriving during a half-hour period will have a Poisson distribution with mean 6. The number arriving over a four-hour period will have a Poisson distribution with mean 48.

EXAMPLE 8.5
The number of weeds in a lawn of area 20 square metres has a Poisson distribution with mean 16. Find the probability that a particular square metre will have no weeds on it.

Solution
Let X be the number of weeds on the square metre. Then X has a Poisson distribution with mean $\frac{16}{20}$, i.e. 0.8. We can write this as $X \sim$ Po(0.8).

There will be no weeds if X is zero.

$$P(X = 0) = e^{-0.8} = 0.449$$

The probability of no weeds is 0.449.

EXERCISE 8D

1 The number of buses, X, which arrive at a bus stop per hour satisfies $X \sim$ Po(4). Find the probabilities of:

   a) 1 bus in half an hour,   **b)** no buses in 15 minutes.

2 The number of cars which stop at a petrol station per minute has a Poisson distribution with mean 1.7. Find the probabilities of:

   a) no cars in half a minute,   **b)** six cars in five minutes.

3 The number of stones in ten 1-kg packs of lentils has a Poisson distribution with mean 5. Find the probability that a 1-kg pack will be stone free.

4 A motorist finds that the number of times, X, he is stopped by the police per year satisfies $X \sim$ Po(1.8). Find the probabilities that:

   a) he will be stopped once in six months,   **b)** he will be stopped at least three times in two years.

5 The number of trees struck by lightning in a square mile of woodland per year has a Poisson distribution with mean 2.7. Find the probabilities of:

   a) four trees struck in one year in three square miles,   **b)** three trees struck in two years in one square mile,
                                                c) seven trees struck in three years in two square miles

6 *Chocoball Cookies* are made from a dough and chocolate mixture containing 350 small spheres of chocolate (the chocoballs) per kg. Assuming that the number of chocoballs in a 20-gram cookie follows a Poisson distribution, find the probabilities that:

   a) a cookie contains no chocoballs,   **b)** a cookie contains more than three chocoballs.

7 A doctor sees, on average, three cases of Brod's syndrome per year. Making a suitable assumption about the distribution of the number of cases seen, find the probabilities that:

   a) she sees one case in three months,   **b)** she sees four cases over a two-year period.

8 On average, 0.8 messages per hour are left on an answering machine. Making suitable assumptions about the distribution of the number of messages, find the probabilities of:

   a) there are no messages in half an hour,   **b)** there are seven messages in eight hours.

9 For the number, X, of misprints on each page of a newspaper, $X \sim$ Po(1.3). Assuming that the pages are independent of each other, find the probabilities that:

   a) there are no misprints on the first three pages,

   b) there are no misprints on the first page, given that there are two misprints on the first two pages.

10 The number of injuries, X, which occur per shift in a factory satisfies $X \sim$ Po(0.4). The shifts are independent of each other. Find the probabilities that:

a) there are two accidents in the three shifts of a day,

b) there was one accident in the first shift, given that there were two accidents in the three shifts.

*11 Cloth is made in 20 m lengths. On average there are five flaws per length. The lengths are then cut into 1 m strips, which are discarded if they contain any flaws. Criticise the following argument.

There are five flaws in 20 m, hence $\frac{5}{20}$, i.e. $\frac{1}{4}$, of the strips will have to be discarded.

Find the correct proportion of strips which are discarded.

Sums of Poisson variables

Suppose X and Y are independent Poisson variables, with means λ and μ respectively. Then $X + Y$ has a Poisson distribution with mean $\lambda + \mu$.

The mathematical proof appears in the Mathematical appendix on page 333.

EXAMPLE 8.6
The number of fax messages an office worker receives in an hour has a Poisson distribution with mean 3.1. The number of telephone messages received also has a Poisson distribution, with mean 5.7. Fax messages and telephone messages are independent of each other. Find the probability that a total of four messages will be received in an hour.

Solution
Let X and Y be the numbers of fax and telephone messages respectively. We are told that $X \sim$ Po(3.1) and $Y \sim$ Po(5.7). The distribution of the total number of messages is given by:

$$X + Y \sim \text{Po}(8.8)$$

$$P(X + Y = 4) = \frac{e^{-8.8}8.8^4}{4!} = 0.038$$

The probability of a total of four messages is 0.038.

EXERCISE 8E

1 If X and Y are independent variables such that $X \sim$ Po(2) and $Y \sim$ Po(3), find $P(X + Y = 4)$.

2 If X and Y are independent variables such that $X \sim$ Po(3.2) and $Y \sim$ Po(2.8), find $P(X + Y = 6)$.

3 If X and Y are independent variables such that $X \sim$ Po(0.5) and $Y \sim$ Po(0.6), find $P(X + Y < 3)$.

4 If X and Y are independent variables such that $X \sim$ Po(1.2) and $Y \sim$ Po(1.7), find $P(X + Y \geq 4)$.

5 The number of vehicles per minute, X, passing a point going north is such that $X \sim$ Po(3), and the number going south, Y, is such that $Y \sim$ Po(4). Assuming that the distributions are independent, find the probability that a total of five vehicles pass in a given minute.

6 A cafeteria sells tea and coffee: the numbers of cups sold in any five-minute period have Poisson distributions with means 2 and 3.7 respectively. Assuming independence of the distributions, find the probability that a total of four cups will be sold in five minutes. Find the probability that no tea or coffee will be sold in one minute.

7 The numbers of letters arriving by first and second deliveries have the distributions Po(5) and Po(4) respectively. Assuming that the numbers arriving are independent of each other, find the probability that there will be a total of ten letters arriving in one day. Find the probability that there will be fewer than four letters arriving during one day.

8 The number of jobs completed per week by a service engineer has a Poisson distribution with mean 7. The mean for another engineer is 6.5. Find the probability that between them they complete 12 jobs in a week.

9 When team A plays team B, the numbers of goals scored by the teams have Poisson distributions with means 1.2 and 1.3 respectively. Assuming that the numbers of goals scored are independent, find the probabilities that:

a) there will be a total of four goals scored,   **b)** no goals will be scored.

8.4 Practice in Poisson distributions

Truncated distributions

The Poisson distribution is a useful model for the *demand* for certain commodities. Only a limited amount of the commodity can be stocked, however, and once that has run out the supply will have to be cut off. The *supply* will then have a Poisson distribution which is cut off, i.e. **truncated**.

EXAMPLE 8.7

At a video rental shop, the daily demand for *Crazy Axeman III* has a Poisson distribution with mean 1.2. The shop keeps three copies in stock. Find the probability that all three copies will be out on loan at any one time. Find the mean number of copies out on loan.

Solution

Let X be the demand. All copies will be out if X is three or greater. To find this, subtract from 1 the probability that the demand is less than three.

$$P(X < 3) = e^{-1.2}\left(1 + 1.2 + \frac{1.2^2}{2}\right) = 0.879$$

$$1 - 0.879 = 0.121$$

The probability that all are out is 0.121.

To find the mean number out on loan, multiply each number by its probability.

$$\begin{aligned}
\text{Mean number} &= 0 \times P(X = 0) + 1 \times P(X=1) \\
&\quad + 2 \times P(X = 2) + 3 \times P(X \ge 3) \\
&= 1.16
\end{aligned}$$

The mean number out on loan is 1.16.

Note
The mean number loaned is slightly less than the mean number requested. This is to be expected.

EXAMPLE 8.8
How many copies of *Crazy Axeman III* should the video shop of Example 8.7 stock, to ensure that it is 99 per cent sure of meeting demand?

Solution
As above, let X be the demand. The shop needs to find n such that $P(X \le n)$ is at least 0.99. Evaluate the probabilities. We have already found $P(X < 3)$, i.e. $P(X \le 2)$.

$$P(X \le 2) = 0.879 \quad P(X \le 3) = 0.966 \quad P(X \le 4) = 0.992$$

Four copies should be stocked.

Some situations involve both the binomial and the Poisson distributions.

EXAMPLE 8.9
The probability that a man is late for work is 0.1. Assuming that each day is independent of every other, find the probability that he will be late for work on at least three days during a week of five days.

Estimate the probability that, in a year of 50 weeks, there will be two weeks during which he is late on at least three days.

Solution
Let X be the number of days in a week in which he is late. Then $X \sim B(5, 0.1)$. Find the probability that X is at least 3.

$$\begin{aligned}
P(X \ge 3) &= 10 \times 0.1^3 \times 0.9^2 + 5 \times 0.1^4 \times 0.9 + 0.1^5 \\
&= 0.008\,56
\end{aligned}$$

The probability he is late at least three times is 0.008 56.

Now let Y be the number of weeks in a year in which he is late at least thrice. We have that $Y \sim B(50, 0.008\,56)$. This distribution has a large n and a small p, and hence can be approximated by the Poisson distribution with mean $50 \times 0.008\,56$. Then Y is approximately $Po(0.428)$.

$$P(Y = 2) = \frac{e^{-0.428}0.428^2}{2} = 0.060$$

The probability is approximately 0.06.

EXERCISE 8F

1 A DIY store hires out steam wallpaper strippers. The daily demand has a Poisson distribution with mean 0.9. If two machines are kept in stock, find the probability that both will be out on loan. Find the mean number out on loan.

   How many should the store keep in stock to be 99 per cent sure of meeting demand?

2 The ambulance department at a hospital receives calls at a rate per hour which has a Poisson distribution with mean 2.3. Assume that each call takes exactly one hour to answer. If there are four ambulances available, find the probability that there will be calls which are unanswered.

   How many ambulances should be available to ensure that the probability of calls being unanswered is less than 0.01?

3 During a squash game, the number of balls that burst has a Poisson distribution with mean 0.8. If the players take two balls to the game, find the probability that their game will have to end early because both balls are burst.

   How many balls should they take, to be 99 per cent sure of being able to finish their game properly?

4 The number of flaws in a length of cloth has a Poisson distribution with mean 0.3. Any length with more than one flaw is discarded.

   Find the proportion of lengths of cloth that are discarded. Find the mean number of flaws in the lengths that are not discarded.

5 A vending machine sells *Chockie* bars, and is restocked at the beginning of each hour. The demand per hour for these bars has a Poisson distribution with mean 1.6. If the machine is stocked with three bars, find the mean number sold per hour.

   How many should the machine hold, if the probability of demand being unsatisfied is to be less than 0.01?

6 The probability that any egg is cracked is 0.1. Find the probability that a carton of six eggs contains more than two cracked eggs.

   Use the Poisson approximation to the binomial to find the probability that, in a batch of 200 cartons, none contains more than two cracked eggs.

7 When Val and Jill play a tennis match of three sets, the probability that Val wins a set is 0.9. Assuming that the results are independent of each other, find the probability that Val wins the match.

Estimate the probability that in 50 matches Jill will win five.

8 An electrical device contains ten components. Each component has probability 0.01 of being faulty. The device will work provided that at most one component is faulty. Find the probability that the device will work.

Estimate the probability that, of 200 such devices, all but one will work.

9 Each day, a factory which produces computer chips tests a sample of 20 chips. If at least two chips are defective then the whole day's production is tested. If the probability that an individual chip is defective is 0.01, find the probability that there will be at least two defective in the batch of 20.

Use the Poisson distribution to find the probability that, in 200 days, the whole day's production will be tested on more than one occasion.

10 A psychologist investigates the learning ability of rats by sending them through a maze. There are seven junctions in the maze, at which a rat can turn right or left, only one of which is the correct decision. Assuming that the rat is equally likely to choose to turn right or left, find the probability that it will make the correct decision at each junction.

A rat goes through the maze 50 times. Assuming that it has no learning ability, use the Poisson approximation to find the probability that it will make no mistakes on more than two occasions.

LONGER EXERCISE

Predicting football matches

One of the situations which we modelled using a Poisson distribution was the number of goals scored by a football team. How good a model is it? Can you use it to predict the result of a football match, even to win the football pools?

Select a team, and find the mean number of goals it has scored for the first few games of the season. Do the number of goals fit a Poisson distribution? If so, predict the number of goals scored over the next few games. You might find it better to separate the goals scored at home from those scored away.

If you have done the analysis for two teams, can you predict the actual result of the game? Can you predict which game is most likely to end in a score-draw?

EXAMINATION QUESTIONS

1 The number of accidents per week at a factory is a Poisson random variable with parameter 2.

   a) Find the probability that in any week chosen at random exactly 1 accident occurs.

   The factory is observed for 100 weeks.

   b) Determine the expected number of weeks in which 5 or more accidents occur.

L 1992

2 A shop sells a particular make of radio at a rate of 4 per week on average. The number sold in a week has a Poisson distribution.

a) Find the probability that the shop sells at least 2 in a week.

b) Find the smallest number that can be in stock at the beginning of a week in order to have at least a 99% chance of being able to meet all demands during the week.

L 1993

3 State the conditions under which the binomial distribution B(n, p) may be approximated by a Poisson distribution and write down the mean of this Poisson distribution. Describe, briefly, from your projects if possible, an example to illustrate either a binomial distribution or a Poisson approximation to a binomial distribution.

Samples of blood were taken from 250 children in a region in India. Of these children, 4 had blood type A2B. Write down an unbiased estimate of p, the proportion of all children in this region having blood type A2B.

Consider a group of n children from this region and let X be the number with blood type A2B. Assuming that X is distributed B(n, p) and that p has the value estimated above, calculate, to 3 decimal places, the probability that number of children of blood type A2B in a group of 6 children from the region will be (a) zero, (b) more than one.

Use a Poisson approximation to calculate, to 4 decimal places, the probability that, in a group of 800 children from this region, there will be fewer than 3 children of blood type A2B.

L 1988

4 Independently for each page, the number of typing errors per page in the first draft of a novel has a Poisson distribution with mean 0.4.

a) Calculate, correct to five decimal places, the probabilities that:

   (i) a randomly chosen page will contain no error,

   (ii) a randomly chosen page will contain 2 or more errors,

   (iii) the third of three randomly chosen pages will be the first to contain an error.

b) Write down an expression for the probability that each of n randomly chosen pages will contain no error. Hence find the largest n for which there is a probability of at least 0.1 that each of the n pages contain no error.

Independently for each page the number, Y, of typing errors per page in the first draft of a Mathematics textbook also has a Poisson distribution.

c) Given that P($Y = 2$) = 2P($Y = 3$):

   (i) find E(Y),   (ii) show that P($Y = 5$) = 4P($Y = 6$).

d) One page is chosen at random from the first draft of the novel and one page is chosen at random from the first draft of the Mathematics textbook. Calculate, correct to three decimal places, the probability that exactly one of the two chosen pages will contain no error.

W 1991

5 Fanfold paper for computer printers is made by putting perforations every 30 cm in a continuous roll of paper. A box of fanfold paper contains 2000 sheets. State the length of the continuous roll from which the box of paper is produced.

The manufacturers claim that faults occur at random and at an average rate of 1 per 240 metres of paper. State an appropriate distribution for the number of faults per box of paper. Find the probability that a box of paper has no faults and also the probability that it has more than 4 faults.

Two copies of a report which runs to 100 sheets per copy are printed on this sort of paper. Find the probability that there are no faults in either copy of the report and also the probability that just one copy is faulty.

MEI 1991

6 An insurance company has 40 000 clients covered for 'severe industrial accident'. Such accidents are estimated to affect 1 in 200 000 of the population in any year, and they are assumed to occur independently of one another. Let X be the number of claims for severe industrial accident received by the company in a randomly chosen year.

(i) State the distribution of X, and explain why an appropriate Poisson distribution would give a good approximation.

(ii) Find the probability that the number of claims received by the company in a year is:

(A) 0,　　　　(B) 1,　　　　(C) 2 or more.

A second insurance company offers cover on the same terms for severe industrial accident, and it receives an average of 1.25 claims per year.

(iii) Estimate the number of clients insured for severe industrial accident with the second company.

(iv) The two companies merge. Find the probability that the number of claims received in a year by the merged company is:

(A) 0,　　　　(B) 2.

MEI 1993

7 A polytechnic offers a short course on advanced statistical methods. As the course involves a large amount of practical work only 8 places are available. Advertising starts two months before the course and if, at the end of one month, 3 or fewer places have been taken the course is cancelled. If 4 or more places have been taken by the end of one month the course is run regardless of the number of applications received in the second month. If the number of applications per month follows a Poisson distribution with mean 3.6, and places are allocated on a first come first served basis, what is the probability that at the end of one month the course will be:

a) cancelled,　　　**b)** full?

What is the probability that:

c) a place will be available at the start of the second month,

d) the course will run with 8 students?

If the course is offered on four separate occasions, what is the probability that it will

e) run once and be cancelled three times,

f) run with 8 students on 2 or more occasions?

AEB 1990

Summary and key points

8.1 The Poisson distribution gives a good model for events which are randomly scattered throughout space or time. If X has a Poisson distribution with mean λ:

$$P(X = i) = \frac{e^{-\lambda}\lambda^{i}}{i!}$$

The mean and variance of this distribution are both λ.

8.2 If X has the binomial distribution $B(n, p)$, where n is large and p is small, then the distribution of X is approximately Poisson with mean np.

8.3 If X and Y are independent Poisson variables with means λ and μ, then $X + Y$ has a Poisson distribution with mean $\lambda + \mu$.

Practical investigations I

Statistics is a practical subject. A statistical investigation involves the collection as well as the analysis of data. So far we have only dealt with the analysis. This section contains suggestions for investigations in which you collect your own data. The best project is one that you are interested in yourself, but be careful not to let your own opinions sway the way you carry out the investigation.

It is up to you to obtain the data. This might be obtained directly from a questionnaire or experiment, or from published statistics. However you obtain the information, make sure it isn't biased.

Throwing a disc

Mark out a grid of squares. Onto it throw a disc such as a coin which is small enough to fit entirely into a square. Repeat many times. For what proportion of times does the coin:

a) lie entirely within a square,   **b)** cross exactly one line,   **c)** cross two lines,
d) cover a corner of a square?

Here you are finding experimental probabilities. The probabilities of the events above can also be found theoretically. How close are the probabilities which you found experimentally to those you calculated theoretically?

Buffon's needle

Imagine a floor is laid with floorboards d units apart. A needle of length d units is thrown onto it. What is the probability that the needle will cross a crack between floorboards? Find this probability experimentally.

In the Longer exercise at the end of Chapter 6, you found the probability theoretically. How close was your experimental probability?

Binomial and Poisson distributions

Many questions in Chapters 7 and 8 asked you to model a particular situation using a binomial or Poisson distribution. Was this justified? You can collect data and then see whether the distribution fits by plotting graphs for the data and for the theoretical distribution, and checking how close they are. You can also see whether the variances of the data and the distribution are close.

Football scores   Is a Poisson distribution a good model for the number of goals scored in football matches? Obtain data and find out.

Bull's-eyes   When three darts are thrown at a dartboard, can the number of bull's-eyes obtained be modelled by a $B(3, p)$ distribution? Investigate by practical experiment.

Share values

In many newspapers there are pages giving statistics about leading companies. The share value for each company is shown and the paper may also show the yield, which is the amount paid to shareholders, expressed as a percentage of the share value.

Find some data from a newspaper. You could follow the fortunes of a particular company, and compare its performance with that of the stock market as a whole. How close is the connection between share value and yield? Can you make any predictions?

Life expectancy

Do women live longer than men? Many newpapers contain death notices. Is the usual age at death greater for women than for men? Are the data biased?

Elections

General elections are rich sources of statistics. Details can be obtained from public libraries. You could investigate the levels of support for a particular party, either in one single election or over several elections, and either in one constituency or across the country. Do results vary according to the region? Are they affected by the sex of the candidate?

Evaluating education

Schools are required by law to publish their examination results. These 'league tables' have been heavily criticised for providing too crude an indication of a school's standards. In particular, they do not take account of the standards of pupils when they enter the school.

Measuring the effectiveness of a school involves sophisticated statistical techniques. Educationalists argue heatedly about the correct way to do it. One simple way to measure a school or college's sixth form is to compare exam results of pupils on entry and on exit.

The standard at entry can be measured by the number and grades of GCSEs obtained. Similarly, the standard at exit can be found from the A-levels obtained. From these you can find the 'value added'. Is the 'value added' for one particular school greater or less than for others?

Alternatively, you could plot a scatter diagram of results on entry and exit for several schools and colleges and draw a line of best fit. A school with results that lie far from the line is an **outlier**, and may be doing either better than the average or worse.

Computer investigations I

These computer investigations involve the use of a spreadsheet program. It is assumed that you are familiar with the process of entering numbers, text and formulae, and with the technique of copying groups of cells.

The spreadsheets have been tested on *Lotus 123* and on *Quattro Pro*, and it is hoped they will work for many other spreadsheet packages. It may be necessary to change the formulae in some cases, and in particular the notation for describing a range of cells may have to be changed from (A1..A10) to (A1:A10).

Fair means or foul

In Chapter 1 we defined two sorts of mean as well as the ordinary arithmetic mean. They are the geometric mean G and the harmonic mean H. They are defined as:

$$G = \sqrt[n]{(x_1 x_2 ... x_n)} \qquad H = \frac{n}{\dfrac{1}{x_1} + \dfrac{1}{x_2} + ... + \dfrac{1}{x_n}}$$

Now investigate the behaviour of the three means, using a spreadsheet. In cells A1, A2 up to A10 enter the ten numbers:

23 27 19 32 14 26 29 33 18 30

In cell A13 enter the ordinary mean, i.e. 1/10*@SUM(A1..A10). You should see 25.1 appear.

Use column B for the geometric mean. In B1 enter +A1, in B2 enter +B1*A2, then copy down the column to B10. This cell will now hold the product of all the numbers. In B13 enter +B10^0.1. You should see 24.27 appear.

Use column C for the harmonic mean. In C1 enter 1/A1, then copy this down to C10. In C13 enter 10/@sum(C1..C10). You should see 23.37 appear.

Now you are ready to investigate. What happens when you change the data? Is one of the means always larger than another? What happens if one number is very large, or very small?

Gambler's ruin

Two people, A and B, play a sequence of games. After each game the loser pays £1 to the winner. The sequence ends when one player has no more money, i.e. is ruined. When will this happen? If A starts with £3 and B with £6, what is the probability that A loses the whole sequence? In this investigation you create a spreadsheet to find out.

Enter 3 in A1 and 6 in B1. We simulate the game by the random number generator. Enter @RAND in C2. If this is less than 0.5 A wins, and otherwise B wins. In A2 and B2 enter respectively

@IF(C2<.5,A1+1,A1−1)   @IF(C2>.5,B1+1,B1−1)

Copy the row A2–C2 down as far as you like. Is there a zero in either column? After how many games does this happen?

Repeat the process. If the spreadsheet is set on automatic recalculation, then new random numbers are generated each time you change a value. The whole experiment can be repeated by entering different values in D1.

The game can be varied by altering the initial capital of A and B, or by altering the probability that A wins.

Random versus stratified sampling

Does a stratified sample give more reliable results than a purely random sample? In this model you set up a spreadsheet for a simplified model of opinion polling.

Suppose that the electorate is evenly divided between men and women. Suppose that the proportion of support for the Purple Party is p for men and q for women. The overall support for the party is $\frac{1}{2}(p + q)$. Here you compare a random sample of 100 people with a stratified sample of 50 men and 50 women.

Initially, let $p = 0.3$ and $q = 0.4$. Enter these in A1 and A2. In A3 enter their average, 1/2*(A1+A2). You should see 0.35 appear. In the E column enter 100 random numbers, by entering @RAND in E1 and copying it down to E100.

The B column will give the random sample. A random number less than $\frac{1}{2}(p + q)$ will correspond to a Purple Party supporter. Enter @IF(E1<A$3,1,0) in B1, and copy it down to B100. (The $ sign is there to prevent the proportion changing as the formula is copied down.) Put the proportion of Purple supporters in A5, by entering @SUM(B1..B100)/100. You should then see the result of the random sample. How close is it to 0.35?

For the stratified sample, enter @IF(E1<A$1,1,0) in C1. Copy down to C50. This will provide the sample of 50 men. For the 50 women, enter @IF(E51<A$2,1,0) in D51, and copy down to D100. To get the proportion obtained from this sample, enter @SUM(C1..D100)/100 in A7.

Which result is closer to the overall proportion of 0.35? The sampling can be repeated, by recalculating the spreadsheet. You can alter the support by altering p and q, i.e. by changing the entries in A1 and A2. What happens if men and women differ more widely? In particular, what happens if the party is supported by virtually all men and virtually no women?

You can vary the situation by considering what happens if the electorate isn't evenly split between men and women, or by splitting the electorate into more than two groups.

Binomial probability

A computer can do all the involved calculation connected with the binomial distribution. Here you can set up a spreadsheet for this. It is suggested that you label the spreadsheet and save it, so that you can use it to check some of your answers to questions in Chapter 7.

The spreadsheet will find probability and cumulative probability for B(n, p), for any n and any p. In A1, B1 and C1 enter 'n value', 'p value' and 'q value' respectively. For the time being, enter 10 in A2 and 0.4 in B2. The q and p values add up to 1, so enter $1 - B2$ in C2.

The values that X can take will be entered in the E column. Enter 'i' in E1, and fill the E column with the numbers 0, 1, 2, up as far as you like.

The F column will hold the probabilities. Enter 'P($X=i$)' in F1. The probability that $X = 0$ is q^n, so enter $+C2\char`\^A2$ in F2. You should see 0.006047 appearing.

The probabilities that $X = i$ and that $X = i + 1$ are given by:

$$P(X = i) = \frac{n!}{i!(n - i)!} p^i q^{n-i}$$

$$P(X = i + 1) = \frac{n!}{(i + 1)!(n - i - 1)!} p^{i+1} q^{n-i-1}$$

In going from one probability to the next, we multiply by p and divide by q. We multiply by $(n - i)$ and divide by $(i + 1)$. In other words:

$$P(X = i + 1) = P(X = i)\frac{p(n - i)}{q(i + 1)}$$

The formula to enter in F3 is:

$+F2*B\$2/C\$2*(A\$2 - E2)/(E2+1)$

You should see 0.040311 appear. The $ signs are put in as you will be copying the formula down the column. Do this, and you will see the probabilities appearing. Check that they are correct.

The G column will hold the cumulative probabilities. In G1 enter 'P($X<=i$)', and enter $+F2$ in G2. In G3 enter $+G2+F3$. Copy this formula down the column. Check that these agree with the cumulative probabilities given in the table on page 335. By changing the entries in A2 and B2 you can find any binomial probability.

See if you can set up a spreadsheet to calculate Poisson probabilities.

Consolidation section B

Chapter 5

1 A random variable, X, takes values 1, 2, 3 and 4 with probabilities given by:

$$P(X = i) = \frac{k}{i},$$

where k is a constant. Find k.

2 Two fair dice are rolled. The variable, X, is defined as the score on the first die if the second die does not give a six, and twice the score on the first die if the second die does give a six. Find the distribution of X.

3 Find the mean and variance of the variable X of Question 1.

4 Find the mean and variance of the variable X of Question 2.

5 At a fairground game, the player is dealt three cards from a standard pack. If an ace first comes up on the first, second or third card the player wins £1, 50p, 20p respectively. If no ace comes up then the player loses. What is a fair amount to pay for this game?

6 A box contains counters labelled 1, 2, ..., n. One is drawn at random. If the variance of the number obtained is 30, find n.

7 A fair spinner is in the form of an equilateral triangle with the numbers 1, 2 and 3 on its sides. It is spun twice, and X is the product of the two numbers obtained. Find the distribution of X, and find its mean and variance.

8 Two people are picked at random from a group containing eight Conservative voters and ten Labour voters. Let X be the number of Labour voters picked. Find the distribution of X, and find its mean and variance.

Chapter 6

9 It is given that X is a continuous random variable, with p.d.f. as below. Find the constant k.

$$f(x) = kx^2(2 - x) \quad \text{for } 0 \le x \le 2$$
$$= 0 \qquad\qquad \text{elsewhere}$$

10 Find the mean and standard deviation of the variable X of Question 9.

11 Find the cumulative distribution function of the variable X of Question 9.

12 In a game a coin is thrown at a wall. The probability that it lands more than x m from the wall is $(1 - \frac{1}{4}x^2)$ for $0 \leq x \leq 2$. Let X be the distance from the wall at which it lands.

    a) Find the c.d.f. and p.d.f. of X.   **b)** Find the mean and variance of X.

    The player will win £$(10 - 2.5X^2)$. Find the expected gain of the player.

13 When a minicab is ordered, the probability that it will arrive within x minutes is $(1 - e^{-x/30})$. Find the median and mean of the arrival time.

Chapter 7

14 The random variable, X, has a distribution given by $X \sim B(11, \frac{1}{4})$. Find $P(X = 3)$. Find $P(X \geq 4)$.

15 In a fairground game an arrow on a board is spun and comes to rest pointing at one of five equal sectors. A player bets on one particular sector ten times. Find the probability that:

    a) he wins three times,   **b)** he wins fewer than three times.

16 Find the mean and variance of the variable X of Question 14.

17 Find the mean and variance of the number of wins of the player of Question 15.

18 It is thought that, out of an electorate of 25 million, 11 million support the Purple Party. If 30 people are picked at random, find the probability that ten of them will be Purple Party supporters.

19 A player bets on the game of Question 15 until she wins, and then stops. Find the probabilities that:

    a) she plays four games,   **b)** she plays fewer than ten games.

20 Find the mean and variance of the number of games played by the player of Question 19.

Chapter 8

21 The variable X has a Poisson distribution with mean 1.7. Find the probability that X is equal to 3. Find the probability that X is less than 4.

22 The number of items handed in per day at a lost property office has a Poisson distribution. The probability that none are handed in is 0.23. Find the probability that exactly two are handed in.

23 The probability that a lottery entry will contain the correct number is one in a million. Use the Poisson approximation to the binomial distribution to find the probability that in half a million entries:

    a) none will contain the correct number,   **b)** at least two will contain the correct number.

24 The number of drinks consumed by a man in an evening has a Poisson distribution with mean 2. Each evening is independent of the others. Find the probabilities that:

a) in two evenings he will consume five drinks,

b) in five evenings he will consume more than four drinks.

25 A newsagent finds that the weekly demand for the magazine *Paperclip Collector* has a Poisson distribution with mean 1.3. The newsagent orders two copies each week.

a) Find the probability that both copies are sold.

b) Find the mean number of copies sold.

How many copies should the newsagent order to be 95 per cent confident of meeting demand?

MIXED QUESTIONS

1 What are the expectation and variance for the following distributions? Give explanations.

a) $B(n, 0)$ b) $B(n, 1)$ c) $Po(0)$

d) a geometric distribution with $p = 1$ e) a geometric distribution with $p = 0$

2 What would be appropriate distributions for the following?

a) the number of boys among 50 babies born in a hospital

b) the number of cases of triplets born in a hospital over a year

3 Suppose you draw the p.d.f. of a function on uniform cardboard, and then cut out the region between the curve and the x-axis. The region is to be balanced on a knife edge perpendicular to the x-axis. Where would the knife edge go?

4 Suppose a die is rolled until *two* sixes have appeared. Letting X be the number of rolls, what is the distribution of X? What is the distribution of the number of rolls to obtain n sixes?

5 A man throws a dart at a target which is 20 m away. The distance that the dart travels is X m. The probability that $X = 20$, i.e. that the dart reaches the target, is $\frac{1}{4}$. For $X < 20$, the probabilities are given by:

$$P(X < x) = \frac{1}{400}(x^2 - 100) \text{ for } 10 \le x < 20$$
$$= 0 \qquad\qquad \text{for } x < 10$$

Is X a discrete or continuous variable? Check that the distribution of X is properly defined. What are the mean and median of X?

6 When an item is sent by the Royal Mail's 'Guaranteed Delivery' service, the probability that it will be delayed or lost is 0.05. If 100 items are sent by this service, calculate the probability that fewer than three are delayed or lost:

a) exactly,   b) using a Poisson approximation.

The extra fee for this service is £2.70 per item. If an item is not delivered on time, the sender is repaid twice this fee, i.e. £5.40. Calculate the amount per item the Royal Mail expects to gain from the service.

7 If a car is put through the MOT test, the number of points on which it fails the test can be modelled by a B(5, 0.1) distribution. Calculate the probability that the car will pass the MOT test.

If a car fails the test, find the mean number of points on which it fails.

Is the binomial distribution a good model for this situation? Give reasons.

8 A supermarket sells apples in packs of four. The number of bruised apples per pack has a B(4, 0.1) distribution. Any pack with more than one bruised apple is withdrawn from sale. Find the expected number of bruised apples in the packs which are on sale.

9 A discrete variable, X, takes the values 1, 2, ..., 100 with equal probability. Find $E(X)$ and $Var(X)$.

X is to be approximated by a continuous rectangular variable Y. Suggestions for the range of Y are:

a) $0 \le Y \le 100$ **b)** $1 \le Y \le 100$ **c)** $0.5 \le Y \le 99.5$ **d)** $0.5 \le Y \le 100.5$

In each case find $E(Y)$ and $Var(Y)$. Which is most suitable?

10 A positive whole number is to be picked at random, i.e. a random variable X is to have range 1, 2, 3, ...

a) Show that we cannot have $P(X = i) = p$ for all i, for a constant p.

b) Suppose a geometric distribution is used, i.e. $P(X = i) = pq^{i-1}$ for some p. Find p, if the probability of picking a single-digit number is to be $\frac{1}{2}$.

c) Suppose a truncated Poisson distribution is to be used, i.e. $P(X = i) = \dfrac{ke^{-\lambda}\lambda^i}{i!}$. Find k in terms of λ. If $\lambda = 10$ find the probability of picking a single-digit number.

d) Suppose $P(X = i) = \dfrac{k}{i^2}$. Find k, given that $\displaystyle\sum_{i=1}^{\infty}\frac{1}{i^2} = \frac{\pi^2}{6}$. Find the probability of picking a single-digit number.

*e) By comparing $\displaystyle\sum_{i=1}^{\infty}\frac{1}{i}$ with $\displaystyle\int_1^{\infty}\frac{1}{x}\,dx$, show that we cannot have $P(X = i) = \dfrac{k}{i}$ for a constant k.

DISCUSSION QUESTIONS

1 (*The Petersburg paradox*)

A coin is spun until it shows heads. You gain one rouble if the first spin gives heads, two roubles if the second gives heads, four roubles if the third gives heads and so on, the number of roubles doubling each time. How much should you pay for the privilege of playing this game?

2 (*The wager*)

God is, or he is not. At the far end of an infinite distance a coin is being spun which will come down heads or tails. How will you wager?

You must wager. It is not optional. There is an infinitely happy life to gain, and a chance of gain against a finite number of chances of loss, and what you stake is finite. It is no good saying that whether we gain is uncertain, while what we risk is certain ...

Adapted from the *Pensées*, Blaise Pascal, 1660

3 If X is a continuous random variable, then for every value of x, $P(X = x) = 0$. Does this not mean that X cannot equal x? What values can X have?

4 You can enter data into a scientific calculator, and it can then work out the mean and standard deviation. What if you are given the data in the form of the number of values, the sum of the values and the sum of their squares, i.e. you are given n, Σx and Σx^2? Can you still use your calculator?

LONGER EXERCISES

Bridge hands

In *Bridge*, the 52 cards are dealt to four players, each getting 13. The number of cards in each suit is very important for the subsequent play.

1 Let X be the number of spades in a *Bridge* hand. Find the distribution of X. Find $E(X)$.

*2 The length of the longest suit is very important when measuring the strength of the hand. Let Y be this length. Find the distribution of Y. Find $E(Y)$.

There is a lot of calculation involved here, and you might like to share the labour among several people. For each possible value of Y, write down the ways in which the hand could be divided between the different suits. For example, if $Y = 5$, then the hand could be divided among the suits in the following ways.

      5 5 3   5 5 2 1   5 4 4   5 4 3 1   5 4 2 2   5 3 3 2

Actuaries

When you take out a life assurance policy, you pay a fixed amount each year (the **premium**) and a fixed amount (the **sum assured**) is paid out when you die or when you reach a certain age. **Actuaries** are people who work out the complicated mathematics involved with life assurance. Here you construct a very simplified model of life assurance.

Suppose that the sum assured is £x, and that the premium is £100 per annum. Suppose that the policy will be paid out when the client either dies or reaches the age of 65. Suppose for simplification that the client is equally likely to die in any year up to the age of 65. Make an estimate for the probability that the client will die before reaching 65.

Find the value of x. You may find it helpful to consider 1000 clients, all taking out policies at age 20. In order to balance their books, the actuaries must ensure that when the policies mature after 45 years, the total value of the premiums they have received is equal to the total of the amounts they have to pay out, taking into account those clients who die before reaching 65.

You may also find it simpler first to ignore interest, and then to extend your model by considering interest at 5 per cent.

EXAMINATION QUESTIONS

1 The discrete random variable, X, has probability function:

$$P(X = x) = \begin{matrix} kx & x = 1, 2, \dots, 5 \\ 0 & \text{otherwise.} \end{matrix}$$

a) Show that $k = \frac{1}{15}$.

Find the value of:

b) $E(X + 3)$,   **c)** $\text{Var}(2X - 4)$.

L 1995

2 Independently for each page of a printed book the number of errors occurring has a Poisson distribution with mean 0.2. Find, correct to three decimal places, the probabilities that:

(i)   the first page will contain no error,

(ii) four of the first five pages will contain no error,

(iii) the first error will occur on the third page.

W 1990

3 At a stall in a charity fair, a card is selected at random from a set of 13 different cards and placed face down. The player has up to 3 guesses to say which card it is. Let X be the number of guesses made. (For example, if the player guesses incorrectly at the first attempt and correctly at the second attempt, then $X = 2$.)

(i)   Write down the values of $P(X = 1)$ and $P(X = 2)$; show that $P(X = 3) = \frac{11}{13}$.

(ii) Find $E(X)$ and $\text{Var}(X)$.

If the player guesses correctly at the first attempt he wins 50 pence; a correct guess at the second attempt wins 25 pence; a correct guess at the third attempt wins 15 pence; otherwise he wins nothing. Let Y pence be the amount won.

(iii) Write down the probability distribution for Y, and use it to find the expected amount won.

Players pay 10 pence to play the game, and the stall hopes to attract about 200 players during the day.

(iv) Approximately what profit is the stall likely to make?

MEI 1994

4 The amount, X kg, of impurities per 10 kg of mineral ore is a continuous random variable with probability density function f given by:

$$f(x) = \tfrac{1}{8}(x - 5) \quad 5 \leq x \leq 9$$

$$f(x) = 0 \qquad\qquad \text{otherwise}$$

(i) Show that the mean, μ, of X is $7\frac{2}{3}$.

(ii) Show that, in the interval $5 \le x \le 9$, the distribution function F of X is given by:

$$F(x) = \tfrac{1}{16}(x - 5)^2$$

Hence find the median, m, of X.

(iii) Show that $P(\mu < X < m) = \frac{1}{18}$.

N 1993

5 A car hire firm has three vehicles A, B and C, each of the same model. Whenever a car is ordered, one is chosen at random from the ones available, so that over a long period of time all the cars are used equally. The number of cars requested on a day may be regarded as having a Poisson distribution with mean 1.5.

(i) Find the probability that on a given day the firm is unable to meet the demand for cars, giving your answer to three decimal places.

(ii) Show that on a given day the probability that car A will be used is approximately 0.47.

(iii) Given that on a given day car A is used, find the probability that it is the only car used, giving your answer to two decimal places.

N 1992

6 a) The random variable, X, has a Poisson distribution with mean a. Given that:

$$P(X = 1) = 3P(X = 0)$$

find the value of a, and hence calculate $P(X > 2)$, giving 3 decimal places in your answer.

b) The random variable S is the number of successes in 5 independent trials in which the probability of success in any trial is $\frac{1}{3}$, so that S has a binomial distribution with $n = 5$ and $p = \frac{1}{3}$. The random variable D is the difference (taken always as positive) between the number of successes and the number of failures in 5 such trials; hence D can take the values 1, 3, 5 only.

(i) Show that $P(D = 1) = \frac{40}{81}$, and find $P(D = 3)$ and $P(D = 5)$.

(ii) Find $E(D^2)$.

It can be shown that $D^2 = 4S^2 - 20S + 25$. Use standard results concerning the mean and variance of a binomial distribution to obtain the values of $E(S)$ and $E(S^2)$, and hence check the value of $E(D^2)$ found in part (ii).

C Nov 1994

7 The total number of inquiries (in hundreds) per week received by a Belfast insurance broker regarding the launch of a new pension plan may be described by a random variable, X, which has the following probability density function.

$$f(x) = ax \qquad \text{for } 0 \le x \le 1$$

$$= a(2 - x) \quad \text{for } 1 \le x \le 2$$

$$= 0 \qquad \text{otherwise}$$

(i)   Find the constant, a.

(ii) Sketch the probability density function over the interval $0 \le x \le 2$.

(iii) Calculate the interquartile range of X.

(iv) Using your sketch, or otherwise, obtain the mean of X.

(v)   If the broker received over 50 inquiries during a particular week, calculate the probability that at least 150 inquiries were received during that week.

NI 1992

8 For any random variable, X, the cumulative distribution function is defined as $F(x) = P(X \le x)$ and $\dfrac{d}{dx} F(x) = f(x)$ where $f(x)$ is the probability density function of X.

The time, X, in hours before failure of a component used in a safety system is exponentially distributed with parameter λ. Thus $f(x) = \lambda e^{-\lambda x}$, $x \ge 0$.

a) Find $E(X)$ and $F(x)$.

A particular safety system has two identical components and will work provided either one or both of the components works. The time in hours before failure of either one is independent of the other.

b) If T is the time to failure of the system, calculate the probability that the system will have failed within t hours and hence calculate $G(t)$, the cumulative distribution function of T.

c) Show that $\dfrac{dG(t)}{dt} = \begin{array}{ll} 2\lambda e^{-\lambda t}(1 - e^{-\lambda t}) & t \ge 0 \\ 0 & \text{otherwise} \end{array}$

d) Find the expected value of T.

e) Give an interpretation to your values of $E(X)$ and $E(T)$.

A 1990

Normal distribution

In recent chapters we have discussed several special distributions, such as the binomial, geometric and Poisson distributions, and the rectangular and exponential distributions. There is one distribution which stands out from the rest in importance, the normal distribution.

This distribution was first discovered by de Moivre in 1733, in his work on the binomial distribution. It was later rediscovered by Gauss, who used it to model errors in measurement. The curve is also known as the **Gaussian** curve or as the **error** curve.

The normal distribution can be used as a model for very many naturally occurring phenomena. It also arises as the limit distribution of many other distributions.

9.1 The standard normal distribution

The normal distribution is a continuous probability distribution. It is so important that there are several special features for its notation. We use Z rather than X for the random variable itself, and for the probability density function (p.d.f.) we use φ rather than f.

A variable Z has a standard normal distribution if its p.d.f. is given by:

$$\varphi(z) = \frac{1}{\sqrt{2\pi}} e^{-\frac{1}{2}z^2} \quad \text{for all } z$$

Clearly $\varphi(z) \geq 0$ for all z. The proof that $\int_{-\infty}^{\infty} \varphi(z)\, dz = 1$ is beyond the scope of this book.

The graph of the p.d.f. is shown in Fig. 9.1. Notice that it has a distinctive bell-shape, giving rise to yet another name, the **bell curve**.

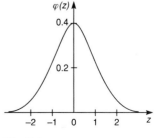

Fig. 9.1

The mean of Z is 0, and the variance (and hence the standard deviation) is 1. The graph is symmetric about the mean $Z = 0$, and the distances from the two points of inflection to the centre are both 1.

To indicate that Z has a standard normal distribution we write $Z \sim N(0, 1)$.

Calculating probabilities

If $Z \sim N(0, 1)$, the probability that Z lies between a and b is:

$$\int_a^b \varphi(z) \, dz$$

Unfortunately this integral cannot be evaluated exactly. There is no elementary function whose derivative is $\varphi(z)$. So the values of the integral have to be found numerically.

The cumulative distribution function (c.d.f.) of Z is written $\Phi(z)$. In Fig 9.2, $\Phi(-1)$ is shown shaded.

$$\Phi(z) = P(Z \leq z) = \int_{-\infty}^z \varphi(z) \, dz$$

We noted above that $\varphi(z)$ cannot be integrated exactly. Hence $\Phi(z)$ cannot be found exactly. However, the values of $\Phi(z)$ can be evaluated numerically, and tables giving these values appear at the end of this book on page 338.

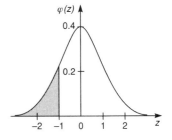

Fig. 9.2

Use of tables

As an example, use the extract below to find $\Phi(0.375)$, go to the row numbered 0.3, and look down the column headed 0.07. They meet at 0.6443 as shown. The column headed 5 on the right gives the adjustment for the third digit as 19, so add that to 0.6443 to obtain 0.6462.

z	0.00	0.01	0.02	0.03	0.04	0.05	0.06	0.07	0.08	0.09	1	2	3	4	5	6	7	8	9
0.0	0.5000	0.5040	0.5080	0.5120	0.5160	0.5199	0.5239	0.5279	0.5319	0.5359	4	8	12	16	20	24	28	32	36
0.1	0.5398	0.5438	0.5478	0.5517	0.5557	0.5596	0.5636	0.5675	0.5714	0.5753	4	8	12	16	20	24	28	32	35
0.2	0.5793	0.5832	0.5871	0.5910	0.5948	0.5987	0.6026	0.6064	0.6103	0.6141	4	8	12	15	19	23	27	31	35
0.3	0.6179	0.6217	0.6255	0.6293	0.6331	0.6368	0.6406	0.6443	0.6480	0.6517	4	8	11	15	19	23	26	30	34
0.4	0.6554	0.6591	0.6628	0.6664	0.6700	0.6736	0.6772	0.6808	0.6844	0.6879	4	7	11	14	18	22	25	29	32
0.5	0.6915	0.6950	0.6985	0.7019	0.7054	0.7088	0.7123	0.7157	0.7190	0.7224	3	7	10	14	17	21	24	27	31
0.6	0.7257	0.7291	0.7324	0.7357	0.7389	0.7422	0.7454	0.7486	0.7517	0.7549	3	6	10	13	16	19	23	26	29
0.7	0.7580	0.7611	0.7642	0.7673	0.7704	0.7734	0.7764	0.7794	0.7823	0.7852	3	6	9	12	15	18	21	24	27

Note that the table only gives values for positive z. To find values for negative z, use the symmetry of the $\varphi(z)$ graph. The probability that Z is less than -1.3, for example, is equal to the probability that Z is greater than $+1.3$. Hence to find $\Phi(-1.3)$, use the following.

$$\Phi(-1.3) = 1 - \Phi(1.3)$$

$$= 1 - 0.9032 = 0.0968$$

Figure 9.3 indicates the required region.

To find the probability that Z lies within the range $a \le Z \le b$, evaluate Φ at a and b and subtract.

$$P(a \le Z \le b) = \Phi(b) - \Phi(a)$$

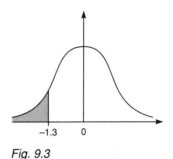

Fig. 9.3

Notes

1   The normal distribution is continuous. It doesn't matter whether we consider $Z < a$ or $Z \le a$, i.e. $P(Z < a) = P(Z \le a)$.
2   It is often a good idea to sketch the normal curve, and shade in the area required, as in Fig. 9.3. This is particularly helpful when negative values of z are involved.
3   This and some of the other tables in this book were obtained from a spreadsheet. In the Pure Mathematics book of this series there is a computer investigation on page 505 to evaluate $\Phi(z)$.

EXAMPLE 9.1

The variable, Z, has the standard normal distribution, i.e. $Z \sim N(0, 1)$. Find the probability that Z lies between -0.142 and 2.037.

Solution

We need to find $\Phi(-0.142)$ and $\Phi(2.037)$. The second probability can be found directly from the tables, as 0.9791. For the first probability we need to use the technique for negative values of z.

$$\Phi(-0.142) = 1 - \Phi(0.142) = 1 - 0.5565 = 0.4435$$

Subtract, to obtain 0.5356.

$$0.9791 - 0.4435 = 0.5356$$

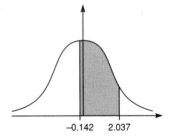

Fig. 9.4

The probability that Z lies between -0.142 and 2.037 is 0.5356.

EXERCISE 9A

Throughout this exercise $Z \sim N(0, 1)$.

1   Evaluate these functions.

   a) $\Phi(2)$ **b)** $\Phi(1.72)$ **c)** $\Phi(1.636)$ **d)** $\Phi(1.524)$

   e) $\Phi(-1.341)$ **f)** $\Phi(-2.031)$ **g)** $\Phi(-0.329)$ **h)** $\Phi(-1.038)$

2 Find the following probabilities.

a) $P(Z < 2.145)$ b) $P(Z \leq 0.672)$ c) $P(Z < 1.972)$

d) $P(Z < -1.482)$ e) $P(Z \leq -0.283)$ f) $P(Z \leq -2.005)$

g) $P(Z \geq 0.283)$ h) $P(Z > 1.943)$ i) $P(Z \geq 2.179)$

j) $P(Z \geq -1.749)$ k) $P(Z > -0.471)$ l) $P(Z \geq -2.046)$

m) $P(1.25 < Z < 2.07)$ n) $P(0.125 < Z < 1.076)$

o) $P(-2.581 < Z < -1.354)$ p) $P(-1.671 \leq Z \leq -0.927)$

q) $P(-1.38 < Z < 1.47)$ r) $P(-0.481 \leq Z \leq 0.366)$

s) $P(-2.478 \leq Z < 2.146)$ t) $P(-1.472 < Z \leq 1.673)$

u) $P(|Z| < 1.652)$ v) $P(|Z| < 0.687)$ w) $P(|Z| < 2.354)$

x) $P(|Z| > 0.729)$ y) $P(|Z| \geq 1.643)$ z) $P(|Z| \geq 2.563)$

3 The IQ scores of the population are standardised so that their distribution is $N(0, 1)$. Find the probability that the score of a person picked at random will be:

a) less than 1.245,   b) less than -0.746,   c) between -1.2 and 1.3.

The high intelligence quotient (IQ) organisation Sedile restricts membership to people whose standardised score is over 2.32. What proportion of the population are eligible to join?

4 Verify the following for the standard normal distribution.

a) About $\frac{2}{3}$ of the probability lies within one standard deviation of the mean.

b) About $\frac{19}{20}$ of the probability lies within two standard deviations of the mean.

c) About $99\frac{3}{4}$ per cent of the probability lies within three standard deviations of the mean.

Finding the z-value

So far we have used the tables to find probabilities. They can also be used in the opposite direction – to find the z-value which gives a certain probability.

Suppose we want to find the value of Z for which $\Phi(z) = 0.95$. In the extract from the tables on page 171 look for the entry which is just below 0.95. This is 0.9495, at $z = 1.64$. We need an extra 0.0005 to bring the probability up to 0.95. Look at the columns on the right to find a 5. This is in the column headed 5. Hence the value of z which corresponds to a probability of 0.95 is 1.645.

Note

We may not always be able to find the z-value exactly. Like so much else in statistics, the use of these tables is only an approximate procedure.

z	0.00	0.01	0.02	0.03	0.04	0.05	0.06	0.07	0.08	0.09	1	2	3	4	5	6	7	8	9
0.0	0.5000	0.5040	0.5080	0.5120	0.5160	0.5199	0.5239	0.5279	0.5319	0.5359	4	8	12	16	20	24	28	32	36
0.1	0.5398	0.5438	0.5478	0.5517	0.5557	0.5596	0.5636	0.5675	0.5714	0.5753	4	8	12	16	20	24	28	32	35
0.2	0.5793	0.5832	0.5871	0.5910	0.5948	0.5987	0.6026	0.6064	0.6103	0.6141	4	8	12	15	19	23	27	31	35
0.3	0.6179	0.6217	0.6255	0.6293	0.6331	0.6368	0.6406	0.6443	0.6480	0.6517	4	8	11	15	19	23	26	30	34
0.4	0.6554	0.6591	0.6628	0.6664	0.6700	0.6736	0.6772	0.6808	0.6844	0.6879	4	7	11	14	18	22	25	29	32
0.5	0.6915	0.6950	0.6985	0.7019	0.7054	0.7088	0.7123	0.7157	0.7190	0.7224	3	7	10	14	17	21	24	27	31
0.6	0.7257	0.7291	0.7324	0.7357	0.7389	0.7422	0.7454	0.7486	0.7517	0.7549	3	6	10	13	16	19	23	26	29
0.7	0.7580	0.7611	0.7642	0.7673	0.7704	0.7734	0.7764	0.7794	0.7823	0.7852	3	6	9	12	15	18	21	24	27
0.8	0.7881	0.7910	0.7939	0.7967	0.7995	0.8023	0.8051	0.8078	0.8106	0.8133	3	6	8	11	14	17	19	22	25
0.9	0.8159	0.8186	0.8212	0.8238	0.8264	0.8289	0.8315	0.8340	0.8365	0.8389	3	5	8	10	13	15	18	20	23
1.0	0.8413	0.8438	0.8461	0.8485	0.8508	0.8531	0.8554	0.8577	0.8599	0.8621	2	5	7	9	11	14	16	18	21
1.1	0.8643	0.8665	0.8686	0.8708	0.8729	0.8749	0.8770	0.8790	0.8810	0.8830	2	4	6	8	10	12	14	16	19
1.2	0.8849	0.8869	0.8888	0.8907	0.8925	0.8944	0.8962	0.8980	0.8997	0.9015	2	4	5	7	9	11	13	15	16
1.3	0.9032	0.9049	0.9066	0.9082	0.9099	0.9115	0.9131	0.9147	0.9162	0.9177	2	3	5	6	8	10	11	13	14
1.4	0.9192	0.9207	0.9222	0.9236	0.9251	0.9265	0.9279	0.9292	0.9306	0.9319	1	3	4	6	7	8	10	11	13
1.5	0.9332	0.9345	0.9357	0.9370	0.9382	0.9394	0.9406	0.9418	0.9429	0.9441	1	2	4	5	6	7	8	10	11
1.6	0.9452	0.9463	0.9474	0.9484	(0.9495)	0.9505	0.9515	0.9525	0.9535	0.9545	1	2	3	4	(5)	6	7	8	9
1.7	0.9554	0.9564	0.9573	0.9582	0.9591	0.9599	0.9608	0.9616	0.9625	0.9633	1	2	3	3	4	5	6	7	8
1.8	0.9641	0.9649	0.9656	0.9664	0.9671	0.9678	0.9686	0.9693	0.9699	0.9706	1	1	2	3	4	4	5	6	6
1.9	0.9713	0.9719	0.9726	0.9732	0.9738	0.9744	0.9750	0.9756	0.9761	0.9767	1	1	2	2	3	4	4	5	5

EXAMPLE 9.2

Let $Z \sim N(0, 1)$. Find the tenth percentile of Z.

Solution

The tenth percentile corresponds to the value of Z which cuts off the lower 10 per cent of probability, as shown shaded in Fig. 9.5. By the symmetry of the curve, if z is the 90th percentile, then $-z$ is the tenth percentile. We look for a value of z such that $\Phi(z) = 0.9$. Following the procedure above, we find that $z = 1.281$ or 1.282. Either could be correct.

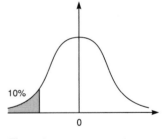

Fig. 9.5

The lower tenth percentile is −1.282.

EXERCISE 9B

Throughout this exercise $Z \sim N(0, 1)$.

1 Find the upper quartile of Z. What is the interquartile range of Z?

2 For each of the following, find the value of a which satisfies the given equation.

a) $P(Z < a) = 0.8$ b) $P(Z \leq a) = 0.732$ c) $P(Z < a) < 0.13$

d) $P(Z < a) = 0.471$ e) $P(Z > a) = 0.381$ f) $P(Z \geq a) = 0.745$

g) $P(Z > a) = 0.923$ h) $P(|Z| < a) = 0.95$ i) $P(|Z| \geq a) = 0.01$

3 In Question 3 of Exercise 9A the IQ scores of the population were standardised so that they came from a N(0, 1) distribution. What should be the minimum score of someone from the top 10 per cent of the population?

9.2 The general normal distribution

The **standard normal distribution** is one for which the mean is 0 and the variance 1. The normal distribution occurs in many contexts, and we cannot count on it always having this mean and variance. The mean could be any value, and the variance could be any positive value. Below are graphs of the normal curve for different values of μ and of σ.

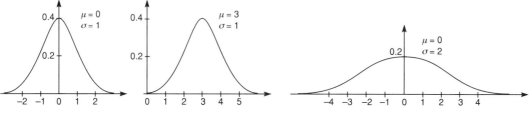

Fig. 9.6

Notes
1 Increasing μ shifts the curve to the right.
2 Increasing σ makes the curve flatter and wider.

Suppose X has a normal distribution with mean μ and variance σ^2.
Then we write $X \sim N(\mu, \sigma^2)$. The p.d.f. of X is:

$$f(x) \frac{1}{\sigma\sqrt{2\pi}} e^{-(x-\mu)^2/(2\sigma^2)}$$

It would be impossible to provide tables for every value of μ and every value of σ^2. We don't need to – any normal variable can be reduced to the standard normal variable.

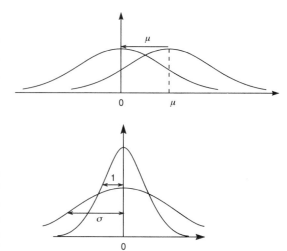

If $X \sim N(\mu, \sigma^2)$, then $\dfrac{X - \mu}{\sigma} \sim N(0, 1)$

Justification
Subtracting μ from X shifts the curve to the left by μ units. In particular, the mean is shifted μ units to the left, and hence becomes 0. Dividing by σ compresses the curve by a factor of σ. The distance from the centre to the two points of inflection is now 1, hence the standard deviation becomes 1. The effect of these transformations is shown in Fig. 9.7.

Fig. 9.7

So by applying these transformations to X, it is converted to Z, the standard normal variable. The standard normal tables can be used.

EXAMPLE 9.3

The lengths of certain snakes can be modelled by a normal distribution with mean 20 cm and variance 25 cm^2. Find the proportion of the snakes with length greater than 27 cm.

Solution

Letting X cm be the length of a randomly chosen snake, we know that $X \sim N(20, 25)$. We want the probability that X is greater than 27.

We know that $\dfrac{X - 20}{5}$ has the N(0, 1) distribution. Apply this transformation, by subtracting 20 and dividing by 5.

$$P(X > 27) = P\left(\frac{X - 20}{5} > \frac{27 - 20}{5}\right) = P(Z > 1.4).$$

By tables we find that $\Phi(1.4) = 0.9192$, and hence that $P(Z > 1.4) = 0.0808$.

8.08 per cent of the snakes are longer than 27 cm.

EXAMPLE 9.4

The marks obtained in a national mathematics examination have a distribution which is approximately normal with mean 63 and variance 256. Where should the passmark be set to ensure that 60 per cent of the candidates pass?

Solution

Let the passmark be x. We need 60 per cent of the candidates to get at least x marks, and hence for 40 per cent of the candidates to get less than x. First find the z value corresponding to a probability of 0.4, i.e. the value of z for which $\Phi(z) = 0.4$.

The value for which $\Phi(z) = 0.6$ is 0.253. Hence the value of z we require is -0.253. This corresponds to the converted value of x.

$$\frac{x - 63}{\sqrt{256}} = -0.253$$

$$x = 59$$

The passmark should be set at 59.

EXERCISE 9C

1 **a)** If $X \sim N(2, 4)$, find $P(X < 5)$.   **b)** If $X \sim N(10, 9)$, find $P(X < 12)$.

  c) If $X \sim N(2, \frac{1}{4})$, find $P(X < 2\frac{1}{2})$.   **d)** If $X \sim N(5, 3)$, find $P(X < 6)$.

  e) If $X \sim N(75, 100)$, find $P(X > 73)$.   **f)** If $X \sim N(0.2, 0.01)$, find $P(X > 0.22)$.

2 a) If $X \sim N(5, 4)$, find a such that $P(X < a) = 0.9$.

b) If $X \sim N(10, 100)$, find a such that $P(X \leq a) = 0.6$.

c) If $X \sim N(3, 1)$, find a such that $P(X > a) = 0.8$.

d) If $X \sim N(-15, 4)$, find a such that $P(X \geq a) = 0.3$.

3 The contents, X cm^3, of certain cans are such that $X \sim N(105, 20)$. Find the proportion of cans which hold less than 100 cm^3.

4 The midday temperature, $X\,°F$, at a resort is such that $X \sim N(80, 34)$. Find the probability that the temperature will be over 90 °F.

5 When asked for 1 lb of cheese, the assistant cuts off an amount which is normal with mean 1.1 lb and standard deviation 0.3 lb. What proportion of the amounts weigh more than 1.5 lb?

6 Intelligence quotient (IQ) is defined so that it is distributed normally with mean 100 and variance 225. What proportion of the population has an IQ of over 130? What is the minimum IQ of the top 1 per cent of the population?

7 The marks obtained in a national examination follow a normal distribution with mean 47 and variance 360. If the pass mark is 40, find the proportion who pass.

If the top 9 per cent of the candidates obtain a distinction, what is the least mark they get?

8 The pupils arrive at a school at X minutes before 9 a.m, where $X \sim N(10, 40)$. Find the proportion of pupils who arrive after 9 a.m.

9 Cartons of orange juice are advertised as containing 1000 cm^3. In fact, their contents have mean 1005 cm^3 and standard deviation 6 cm^3. Assuming that the distribution of the volume is normal, what proportion of the cartons contain less than 1000 cm^3?

What volume is exceeded by 99 per cent of the cartons?

10 The time, T minutes, taken to run a race is such that $T \sim N(120, 100)$. What proportion of runners take less than 115 minutes?

The organisers of the race want to pick the fastest 10 per cent of the runners to contest another event. What is the maximum time that these runners take?

11 A machine makes metal bars whose lengths are normally distributed with mean 20.01 cm and standard deviation 0.004 cm. The longest 5 per cent and the shortest 5 per cent of the production are scrapped as substandard. What are the lengths between which the satisfactory bars lie?

12 A gun is fired at a target which is 1000 m away. The shell travels X m towards the target, where $X \sim N(1000, 10)$. What proportion of shells land within 2 m of the target?

The closest 20 per cent of the shells are classed as hits. How close to the target do these shells have to land?

13 The annual profit, £X millions, of a company can be modelled by a N(4, 0.8) distribution. Find the probability that the profit exceeds £4 500 000.

The directors assure the shareholders that the profit will exceed a certain minimum value with probability 0.95. What is this minimum value?

14 A device used by the police to measure the speed of cars is liable to be inaccurate by X m.p.h., where $X \sim$ N(0, 11). What is the probability that a car travelling at 60 m.p.h. will be recorded as travelling at over 65 m.p.h.?

The speed limit on a certain stretch of road is 50 m.p.h. The police will only base a prosecution for speeding on the device if the probability that the car was speeding is greater than 0.99. What is the least speed for which the police will prosecute?

*15 The weight of certain fruit have a normal distribution with mean 30 grams and standard deviation 8 grams. A fruit is classified *large* if its weight is more than 40 grams. What proportion of the fruit are large?

A supermarket accepts only the large fruit. What is the median weight of these fruit? Sketch the p.d.f. of the weight of these large fruit, and state whether their mean weight will be greater or less than the median weight.

Finding values of μ and σ

Suppose that we know that a variable, X, has a normal distribution, but haven't been told its mean and variance. The mean and variance can be found from two probabilities concerning X. This will involve solving simultaneous equations.

EXAMPLE 9.5
It is thought that the times taken to run a 1000 m race will follow a normal distribution. It was found that 10 per cent of the entrants took less than 160 seconds, and that 20 per cent took less than 165 seconds. Find the mean time.

Solution
Let X seconds be the time. Suppose $X \sim$ N(μ, σ^2). Find the z-values corresponding to probabilities of 0.1 and 0.2, i.e. values of z_1 and z_2 for which $\Phi(z_1) = 0.1$ and $\Phi(z_2) = 0.2$. These values are

$$z_1 = -1.282 \qquad z_2 = -0.842$$

These z-values are the standardised values corresponding to the X values of 160 and 165 respectively. Hence:

$$\frac{160 - \mu}{\sigma} = -1.282 \qquad \frac{165 - \mu}{\sigma} = -0.842$$

$$\mu - 160 = 1.282\sigma \qquad \mu - 165 = 0.842\sigma.$$

Solve these equations to find that $\sigma = 11.4$ and $\mu = 174.6$.

The mean time for the race is 175 seconds.

EXERCISE 9D

1 In the following $X \sim N(10, \sigma^2)$. In each case find σ.

   a) $P(X < 12) = 0.6$ **b)** $P(X < 9) = 0.3$ **c)** $P(X \leq 20) = 0.9$

2 In the following $X \sim N(\mu, 4)$. In each case find μ.

   a) $P(X > 0) = 0.75$ **b)** $P(X \leq 10) = 0.1$ **c)** $P(X < 12) = 0.912$

3 In the following $X \sim N(\mu, \sigma^2)$. In each case find μ and σ.

   a) $P(X < 6) = 0.8$ and $P(X < 10) = 0.9$ **b)** $P(X < 25) = 0.61$ and $P(X < 35) = 0.72$

   c) $P(X < 3) = 0.17$ and $P(X < 5) = 0.65$ **d)** $P(X < -3) = 0.12$ and $P(X > 2) = 0.05$

   e) $P(X > 5.3) = 0.593$ and $P(X > 6.7) = 0.496$

4 The masses of a certain species of bird have a normal distribution with mean 50 grams. If 10 per cent of the birds weigh more than 60 grams, find the variance of their masses.

5 The heights of the female students at a university have mean 150 cm. A quarter of the students are under 140 cm. Assuming that the heights are normally distributed, find their standard deviation.

6 The annual rainfall in a town has a normal distribution with standard deviation 5 inches. If the rainfall is over 20 inches for a third of the years, find the mean rainfall.

7 Of the students at a university, it was found that 10 per cent of them had IQs over 125, and 20 per cent had IQs over 120. Find the mean and variance of the IQs of the students, assuming that this is normally distributed.

8 A large number of runners entered a race. Five per cent finished in under 120 minutes, and 15 per cent took over 160 minutes. Find the mean and variance of the time taken, assuming that this is normally distributed.

9 The height, in metres, of mature specimens of a certain tree has a normal distribution. Thirty per cent of the trees are over 20 m, and 70 per cent are over 14.8 m. Find the mean and standard deviation of the height.

10 A machine produces components. Thirty per cent of them have widths greater than 10.05 cm, and 10 per cent have width less than 10.01 cm. Assuming that the width is normally distributed, find its mean and standard deviation. What proportion of the components have widths within 0.01 cm of the mean?

9.3 The normal approximation to the binomial and Poisson distributions

In Chapters 7 and 8 we dealt with the binomial and Poisson distributions. To find cumulative probabilities we have to add up individual probabilities. For example, if $X \sim B(10, \frac{1}{2})$, to find $P(X \leq 2)$ we use the following.

$P(X < 3) = P(X = 0) + P(X = 1) + P(X = 2)$

What if $X \sim B(1000, \frac{1}{2})$? To find $P(X \leq 470)$, say, we would have to add up 471 individual probabilities. Fortunately the normal distribution provides a method of finding the approximate values of these cumulative probabilities.

Binomial

The normal distribution was originally obtained as the limit of the binomial distribution. Recall that a binomial distribution arises when we have n independent trials, each of which has the probability p of success, and q of failure. The number of successes in the trials is X, and we say that X has a binomial distribution. In symbols:

$X \sim B(n, p)$

The mean of X is np, and the variance is npq.

It can be shown that, as n tends to infinity, the distribution of X tends to that of a normal distribution with the same mean and variance.

> If n is large, the distribution of X is approximately $N(np, npq)$.

Hence the normal distribution can be used to find the approximate values of a binomial distribution, provided that the number n of trials is large.

Figure 9.8 shows the frequencies of the binomial distribution $B(30, 0.4)$, and the corresponding normal curve $N(12, 7.2)$. Notice how close together they are, even for this small value of n.

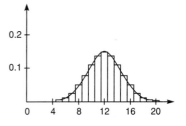

Fig. 9.8

What do we mean by large? As a rough guide, if both np and nq are at least 10, the normal distribution will provide a reasonably accurate approximation.

Continuity correction

There is a crucial difference between a binomial distribution $B(n, p)$ and the normal distribution $N(np, npq)$ with which we approximate it. The binomial distribution is discrete, restricted to whole number values. The normal distribution is continuous, able to take any value. If $X \sim B(n, p)$, then the following have the same probability.

X is at most 17, i.e. $X \leq 17$

X is less than 18, i.e. $X < 18$

For the normal distribution, however, we obtain different results from $X \leq 17$ and $X < 18$. So we compromise, by putting $X < 17.5$.

In general, whenever we use the normal distribution to find a probability of the form $X < r$, consider that it is equivalent to $X \le r - 1$, and compromise by putting $X < r - 0.5$. Similar corrections will apply to the other inequality symbols.

EXAMPLE 9.6

A multiple choice test contains 100 questions, each of which has five possible answers. Find the probability that a candidate who answers at random gets more than 24 right.

Solution

As the answers are picked at random, the number, X, correct has a binomial distribution with $n = 100$ and $p = 0.2$.

$$X \sim B(100, 0.2)$$

Here $np = 20$ and $nq = 80$. Hence the normal approximation can be used. The mean is 100×0.2, i.e. 20, and the variance is $100 \times 0.2 \times 0.8$, i.e. 16.

X is approximately N(20, 16)

We want $P(X > 24)$. This is equivalent to $P(X \ge 25)$, so we compromise by finding $P(X > 24.5)$.

$$P(X > 24.5) = 1 - P(X \le 24.5)$$

$$\approx 1 - \Phi\left(\frac{24.5 - 20}{4}\right) = 1 - \Phi(1.125) = 1 - 0.8696 = 0.1304$$

The probability of more than 24 right answers is 0.130.

EXERCISE 9E

1 If $X \sim B(100, 0.4)$, use the normal distribution to find the approximate values of the following.

   a) $P(X < 50)$ **b)** $P(X > 53)$ **c)** $P(X \le 35)$ **d)** $P(X \ge 45)$

2 A fair die is rolled 90 times. Find the probability of scoring more than 20 sixes.

3 The proportion of people supporting the Crimson Party is 0.4. Find the probability that an opinion poll of 1000 people will contain at least 430 Crimson Party supporters.

4 Anne and Belinda play squash. The probability that Anne wins a point is 0.45, and each point is independent of the others. Find the probability that Anne will win at least 50 points out of 100.

5 A machine produces computer chips, 40 per cent of which are faulty. Find the probability that there are fewer than 420 faulty chips in a batch of 1000.

6 A UK (Useless Knowledge) competition has 50 questions, each of which has three possible answers. Find the probability that a contestant who answers at random will get more than 20 right.

7   The medicine for a certain condition has probability 0.6 of success. If 80 patients are treated with the medicine, find the probability that it is successful in fewer than half the cases.

8   The time I take to drive to work has a normal distribution, with mean 30 minutes and standard deviation 12 minutes. Find the probability I shall be late, if I leave 40 minutes before I should start work.

In a working year of 250 days, find the probability that I am late more than 60 times.

9   The weight, W grams, of certain apples is such that $W \sim$ N(30, 40). An apple weighing less than 25 g is counted as *small*. Find the proportion of small apples.

In a batch of 100 apples, what is the probability that fewer than 26 will be small?

10   A fair coin is tossed 100 times. Find the smallest number of heads for which the probability of obtaining at least this number is over 0.9.

11   A fair die is rolled 200 times. Find the smallest number of sixes for which the probability of obtaining at least this many sixes is over 0.99.

12   A multiple choice examination has 50 questions, each of which has four possible answers. The examiners want to ensure that someone who answers at random should have at most a 5 per cent chance of passing. What should the pass mark be?

*13   A fair coin is tossed until 60 heads have been obtained. How many times should the coin be tossed for there to be a probability of 0.99 for this to happen?

Poisson

Suppose variable X has a Poisson distribution with mean λ, i.e. $X \sim$ Po(λ). Then provided λ is large, the distribution of X is approximately normal with the same mean and variance.

X is approximately N(λ, λ)

As a rough guide, the approximation will be reasonably accurate provided that λ is at least 30. Figure 9.9 shows the bar chart for Po(30) and the p.d.f. curve for N(30, 30).

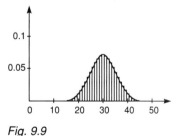

Fig. 9.9

The Poisson distribution is discrete. So when approximating it with the normal distribution, apply the continuity correction.

EXAMPLE 9.7
A woman takes a 14-day fishing holiday. For each day, the number of fish she catches has a Poisson distribution with mean 3. Each day is independent of the others. Find the probability that she catches fewer than 30 fish in total.

Solution

Each day's catch has a Po(3) distribution. If she catches X fish over 14 days, X has a Po(42) distribution. The value of 42 is greater than 30, so the normal approximation can be used.

We want $P(X < 30)$. This is equivalent to $P(X \leq 29)$, so use the continuity correction to find $P(X < 29.5)$.

$$P(X < 29.5) \simeq \Phi\left(\frac{29.5 - 42}{\sqrt{42}}\right) = \Phi(-1.929)$$

$$= 1 - \Phi(1.929) = 1 - 0.9731 = 0.0269$$

The probability she catches fewer than 30 fish is 0.027.

EXERCISE 9F

1 The variable X has a Poisson distribution with mean 40. Find the probabilities that:

   a) X is greater than 50,   b) X is at least 30.

2 The number of flaws in lengths of cloth produced by a machine has a Poisson distribution with mean 2. Find the probability that in 50 lengths there will be more than 120 flaws in total.

3 The number of misprints in a page of a newspaper has a Poisson distribution with mean 3. Find the probability that in 20 pages there will be at most 50 misprints.

4 The number of accidents per day on a certain stretch of road has a Poisson distribution with mean 0.5. Find the probability that in 200 days there will be fewer than 120 accidents.

5 The number of letters received per day by a woman has a Poisson distribution with mean 2.5. What is the probability that in 20 days she receives at least 55 letters?

   What is the least number of letters she will be 90 per cent sure of receiving in 100 days?

6 The number of cases of Brod's Syndrome seen by a hospital in a month has a Poisson distribution with mean 5. What is the probability of seeing more than 50 cases in a year?

   What is the greatest number, n, with probability 0.95 that fewer than n cases will be seen in 20 months?

*7 The number of accidents per day along a stretch of road has a Poisson distribution with mean 3. What is the least number of days, after which we shall be 95 per cent sure that there will be over 100 accidents?

LONGER EXERCISE

How good is the approximation?

In section 9.3 above, the normal distribution was used to find approximate probabilities arising from the binomial and Poisson distributions. How close are the approximations? Exact cumulative probabilities for the binomial distribution are given in the tables on pages 335 to 337. You will be able to check the accuracy using these tables.

1 Let $X \sim B(40, 0.4)$. Find $P(X < 12)$ by the normal approximation and by use of the cumulative tables. What is the percentage error in using the normal approximation?

2 Find $P(X < i)$, for some other values of n, p and i. What happens if p is close to 0, or close to 1? What happens if i is close to 0, or close to n?

3 The rule of thumb we gave was that np and nq should both be at least 10. What is the justification for this rule?

EXAMINATION QUESTIONS

1 Jam is packed in tins of nominal net weight 1 kg. The actual weight of jam delivered to a tin by the filling machine is normally distributed about the mean weight set on the machine with a standard deviation of 12 g.

The average filling of jam is 1 kg.

a) Find the probability that a tin chosen at random contains less than 985 g.

It is a legal requirement that no more than 1% of tins contain less than the nominal weight.

b) Find the minimum setting of the filling machine which will meet this requirement.

L 1992

2 One fifth of a given population has a minor eye defect. Use the normal distribution as an approximation to the binomial distribution to estimate the probability that the number of people with the defect is:

(i)   more than 20 in a random sample of 100 people

(ii)   exactly 20 in a random sample of 100 people

(iii) more than 200 in a random sample of 1000 people.

C AS 1993

3 Mass-produced pipes have internal diameters that are Normally distributed with mean 10 cm and standard deviation 0.4 cm.

(i)   Calculate, correct to three decimal places, the probability that a randomly chosen pipe will have an internal diameter greater than 10.3 cm.

(ii)   Find the value of d, correct to two decimal places, if 95% of the pipes have internal diameters greater than d cm.

W 1992

4 A class of 35 third-form pupils conduct a physics experiment in which each measures the time for one complete swing of a pendulum. The experiment is repeated until each pupil has six measurements.

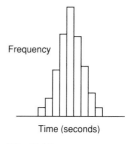

Frequency

A bar chart of their results is reproduced in Fig. 9.10. What features of this suggest that the Normal distribution may be an appropriate model?

The mean time for a complete swing was 1.015 seconds and the standard deviation of the times was 0.045. Using the Normal distribution and these values as estimates of the population parameters, calculate:

Time (seconds)

Fig. 9.10

a) the probability that a recorded time is less than 1.1 seconds,

b) the number of recordings of a time less than 1.0 seconds,

c) the number of recorded times that are more than two standard deviations away from the mean time.

O 1990

5 Sugar is sold in bags whose weights are normally distributed with mean 1000 g and standard deviation 4 g.

a) Calculate the probability, to 3 decimal places, that a bag chosen at random weighs more than 1005 g. Estimate the expected number of bags in a batch of 400 with weights greater than 1005 g.

The supplier periodically weighs the bags. She weighs a random sample of 5 bags.

b) Calculate the probability, to 3 decimal places, that all 5 bags weigh between 990 g and 1010 g.

On receipt of a large batch of these bags of sugar a retailer weighs a random sample of 10 bags.

c) Calculate the probability, to 3 decimal places, that in this sample fewer than 2 bags weigh less than 995 g.

A AS 1992

6 The quantity of milk in bottles from a dairy is normally distributed with mean 1.036 pints and standard deviation 0.014 pints.

Show that the probability of a randomly chosen bottle containing less than a pint is very nearly 0.5%.

In the rest of this question take the answer of 0.5% to be exact. A crate contains 24 bottles. Find the probability that

(i) no bottles contain less than a pint of milk,

(ii) at most 1 bottle contains less than a pint of milk.

A milk float is loaded with 150 crates (3600 bottles) of milk. State the expected number of bottles containing less than a pint of milk.

Give a suitable approximating distribution for the number of bottles containing less than a pint of milk. Use this distribution to find the probability that more than 20 bottles contain less than a pint of milk.

MEI 1992

7 Eggs are graded according to length L mm. A size 3 egg is one for which $60 < L < 65$. An egg producer finds that 37% of her eggs are larger than size 3 while 21% are smaller. Assume that L is normally distributed with mean μ and standard deviation σ.

(i) Show the information given on a sketch of the distribution of L.

(ii) Write down two equations involving μ and σ and solve them.

Further investigation shows that (A) $L > 70$ for about 7% of eggs, and (B) $L < 55$ for less than 1% of eggs.

(iii) Determine whether (A) is consistent with the distribution found in (ii).

(iv) Determine whether (B) is consistent with the distribution found in (ii).

MEI 1994

Summary and key points

9.1 The standard normal variable Z has p.d.f.

$$\varphi(z) = \frac{1}{\sqrt{2\pi}} e^{-\frac{1}{2}z^2}$$

The mean of Z is 0 and its variance is 1.

The c.d.f. of Z is $\Phi(z)$. Tables of $\Phi(z)$ are given on page 338. They are used to find the probability corresponding to a given z-value, and the z-value corresponding to a given probability. Make sure you go the correct way.

9.2 If a normal variable, X, has mean μ and variance σ^2, then we write:

$$X \sim N(\mu, \sigma^2)$$

We can convert X to the standard variable by the transformation:

$$Z = \frac{X - \mu}{\sigma}$$

We can find the mean and standard deviation of a normal distribution using two probabilities concerning it.

9.3 If n is large, then the binomial distribution $B(n, p)$ can be approximated by the normal distribution $N(np, npq)$.

If λ is large, then the Poisson distribution $P(\lambda)$ can be approximated by the normal distribution $N(\lambda, \lambda)$.

In both cases, we use the continuity correction by changing, for example, $P(X \geq 12)$ to $P(X > 11.5)$.

Combinations of random variables

In Chapter 4 we introduced the distinction between a population and a sample taken from that population. To a large extent, statistical operations consist of making inferences about a population from the sample.

Suppose the government wants information about the quantity of alcohol consumed per year, in terms of the average amount consumed per adult. The population will consist of all the adults in this country. It would be impossibly expensive to survey the entire population, hence a random sample would be investigated. We must be careful to distinguish between the two means involved.

The **population mean**, μ, is the average amount, per adult, consumed by the whole population.

The **sample mean**, $\overline{X}$, is the average amount, per adult, consumed by the members of the sample.

The population mean, μ, is constant, even though it is unknown.

The sample mean, $\overline{X}$ litres, is a random variable. If the sample is carefully selected, it will be a fair approximation to the population mean. As the size of the sample increases, the sample mean will approach the population mean.

The topics of this chapter are connected with the distribution of samples. First we need to obtain results about adding and multiplying variables.

10.1 Sums and products of random variables

Sums

Suppose that you have placed two bets, one on a horse race and one on a greyhound race, and that you hope to win £5 on the horse and £3 on the dog. The total amount you hope to win is £8.

Suppose that the average weight of the soup in a particular size of can is 300 grams, and that the average weight of the can itself is 20 grams. Then the average weight of the full can is 320 grams.

In general, let X and Y be two random variables. They could be **discrete**, as defined in Chapter 5, or **continuous** as in Chapter 6. The expected value of their sum is the sum of their expected values.

$$E(X + Y) = E(X) + E(Y)$$

Suppose that a random variable is multiplied by a constant, a. Then the expected value is also multiplied by a.

$$E(aX) = aE(X)$$

Proof

We give the proof in the case that X is discrete.

$$E(aX) = \Sigma \, ai \, P(X = i)$$
$$= a \, \Sigma \, i \, P(X = i)$$
$$= aE(X)$$

Note

The proof for a continuous random variable is similar. The constant a is taken outside the integral sign instead of outside the summation sign.

We can combine these results, assuming a and b are constants.

$$E(aX + bY) = aE(X) + bE(Y)$$

In particular, if k is a constant, then adding k to X will add k to $E(X)$.

$$E(X + k) = E(X) + k$$

Products

Suppose X and Y are independent random variables. To find the expectation of their product we multiply their expectations.

$$E(XY) = E(X)E(Y)$$

The variance of the sum of independent variables is the sum of their variances.

$$Var(X + Y) = Var(X) + Var(Y)$$

The proof of this appears in the Mathematical appendix on page 333. This tidy property of variance shows that it is a mathematically convenient measure of dispersion.

If a variable, X, is multiplied by a constant, a, its variance is multiplied by a^2.

Proof

$$\begin{aligned}
\mathrm{Var}(aX) &= \mathrm{E}((aX)^2) - (\mathrm{E}(aX))^2 \\
&= \mathrm{E}(a^2X^2) - (a\mathrm{E}(X))^2 \\
&= a^2\mathrm{E}(X^2) - a^2(\mathrm{E}(X))^2 \\
&= a^2(\mathrm{E}(X^2) - (\mathrm{E}(X))^2) = a^2\mathrm{Var}(X)
\end{aligned}$$

Note

When X is multiplied by a, its variance is multiplied by a^2, not by a.

Put these results together. If X and Y are independent variables, and a and b are constant, then:

$$\mathrm{Var}(aX + bY) = a^2\mathrm{Var}(X) + b^2\mathrm{Var}(Y)$$

In particular, let $a = 1$ and $b = -1$. This will give us the variance of the difference of random variables.

$$\begin{aligned}
\mathrm{Var}(X - Y) &= 1^2\mathrm{Var}(X) + (-1)^2\mathrm{Var}(Y) \\
&= \mathrm{Var}(X) + \mathrm{Var}(Y)
\end{aligned}$$

So even when we subtract independent variables, we *add* their variances.

In particular, the variance of a constant is zero. So if we add a constant to a variable, the variance does not change.

$$\mathrm{Var}(X + k) = \mathrm{Var}(X)$$

EXAMPLE 10.1

Let X and Y be independent variables with means 2 and 3 respectively and variances 5 and 6 respectively. Find the mean and variance of $5X - 2Y$.

Solution

Apply the formula, with $a = 5$ and $b = -2$.

$$\mathrm{E}(5X - 2Y) = 5\mathrm{E}(X) - 2\mathrm{E}(Y) = 5 \times 2 - 2 \times 3 = 4$$

$$\mathrm{Var}(5X - 2Y) = 25\mathrm{Var}(X) + 4\mathrm{Var}(Y) = 25 \times 5 + 4 \times 6$$
$$= 149$$

$5X - 2Y$ has mean 4 and variance 149.

EXAMPLE 10.2

The marks for an examination have mean 60 and variance 100. They are to be scaled so that they are in accordance with those of previous years, in which the mean was 50 and the variance 81. Find the scaling, in the form $Y = aX + b$, where a and b are constant with a positive. What mark gets scaled to 68?

Solution
We have two equations.

$$E(Y) = aE(X) + b = 60a + b$$

$$\text{Var}(Y) = a^2\text{Var}(X) = 100a^2$$

From this we get: $50 = 60a + b$ $81 = 100a^2$

Hence $a = 0.9$ and $b = -4$.

The scaling is $0.9X - 4$.

If $Y = 68$, then $0.9X - 4 = 68$

This gives $X = 80$

The mark scaled to 68 is 80.

EXERCISE 10A

1 Variables X and Y have means 4 and 3 respectively. Find the means of the following.

a) $X + Y$ b) $X - Y$ c) $2X + 3Y$ d) $2X + 3$

e) $3Y - 7$ f) $2 - 2X$ g) $2X + 3Y + 4$ h) $X - 2Y + 7$

2 The mean volume of a cup of tea is 95 ml, and the mean volume of a cup of coffee is 115 ml. Find the mean total volume of three cups of tea and four of coffee.

3 The independent variables X and Y have means 5 and 4 and variances 2 and 3. Evaluate the following.

a) $\text{Var}(X + Y)$ b) $\text{Var}(X - Y)$ c) $\text{Var}(3X + 2Y)$ d) $\text{Var}(2X - 3Y)$

e) $\text{Var}(X + 3)$ f) $\text{Var}(2X - 7)$ g) $E(XY)$ h) $E(X^2)$

i) $E(Y^2)$ j) $E((X + 2)^2)$ k) $E((X + Y)^2)$ l) $E((2X + 3Y)^2)$

4 Vinaigrette is made with oil and vinegar. The amount, in grams, of oil has mean 120 and variance 42, and amount, in grams, of vinegar has mean 25 and variance 8. Assuming that the amounts are independent, find the mean and variance of the amount, in grams, of vinaigrette.

5 The amount, X ml, of hand cream in a particular size of jar has a mean of 60 and variance 5. The amount, Y ml, lost through evaporation after three weeks has mean 5 and variance 4. Assuming that X and Y are independent, find the mean and variance of the amount left over.

6 The times, t_1, t_2, t_3, t_4, in seconds, taken by four runners for their leg of a relay race have means 20, 21, 23, 25 respectively, and variances 1, 3, 2, 3 respectively. Assuming that their times are independent, find the mean and variance of the total time.

7 Let X and Y be independent variables with mean 10 and 12 respectively, and variances 6 and 7 respectively.

a) Find a and b such that $aX + b$ has mean 8 and variance 1.5.

b) Find integers a and b such that $aX + bY$ has mean 56 and variance 87.

8 The mean marks for A-level mathematics and sociology are 50 and 65 respectively, and their variances are 45 and 20 respectively. In order to disguise any difference between the results, the mathematic marks are to be scaled so that they have the same mean and variance as the sociology marks. Find the scaling, in the form $aX + b$, where a and b are constant and a is positive.

9 Let X have mean μ and variance σ^2. Show that $\dfrac{X - \mu}{\sigma}$ has mean 0 and variance 1.

10.2 Sample mean and variance

At the beginning of this chapter we stated the difference between a population mean and a sample mean. The sample mean is an **estimator** of the population mean. There are two properties we want the estimator to have:

- it should be fair,
- as the sample size increases the estimator converges to the true value.

Suppose the government is investigating the amount of alcohol consumed each year per adult. It will be interested in the mean amount consumed per adult, and its variance. It will estimate these figures from the amounts of alcohol consumed by a sample of people.

Suppose the sample mean is $\overline{X}$ litres. For the sampling operation to be useful, we require two things.

- The sample mean must be unbiased. That is, its expected value is equal to the population mean.
- The sample mean must not vary greatly between different samples, provided that the sample is reasonably large. That is, the variance of $\overline{X}$ becomes small as the size of the sample increases.

In general, suppose that θ is a property of the population (for example, θ might be the population mean, μ, or the population variance, σ^2). Suppose that U has been derived from a sample of size n (for example, U might be the sample mean $\overline{X}$ or the sample variance S^2).

- The estimator U is **unbiased** if $E(U) = \theta$.
- The estimator U is **consistent** if $Var(U)$ tends to zero as n tends to infinity.

So an unbiased estimator measures what it is supposed to measure. A consistent estimator tends to a fixed value as the sample size increases.

Clearly it is desirable that an estimator be unbiased. If we have two estimators, both of which are unbiased, then the one with smaller variance is more **efficient**. Clearly the more efficient an estimator is, the more it can be relied upon to give a correct estimate of the true value.

We can now apply the results of the previous section to the sample mean, which we shall show to be unbiased and consistent.

Let X be a random variable with mean μ and variance σ^2. Let X_1, X_2, ... , X_n be an independent sample from X. The sample mean $\overline{X}$ was defined in Chapter 1 as:

$$\overline{X} = \frac{1}{n}(X_1 + X_2 + ... + X_n)$$

This has mean and variance given by:

$$E(\overline{X}) = \mu \qquad Var(\overline{X}) = \frac{\sigma^2}{n}$$

Proof
Let $T = (X_1 + X_2 + ... + X_n)$. By the results of the previous section, T has mean and variance given by:

$$E(T) = n\mu \qquad Var(T) = n\sigma^2$$

The sample mean is $\overline{X} = \dfrac{T}{n}$. Again using the results above:

$$E(\overline{X}) = \frac{n\mu}{n} = \mu$$

$$Var(\overline{X}) = \frac{n\sigma^2}{n^2} = \frac{\sigma^2}{n}$$

Note
We see that $E(\overline{X}) = \mu$, showing that $\overline{X}$ is an unbiased estimator of μ. Also $Var(\overline{X})$ tends to 0 as n tends to infinity, showing that $\overline{X}$ is consistent.

The standard deviation of the sample mean is $\dfrac{\sigma}{\sqrt{n}}$, which is the **standard error of the sample mean**, often abbreviated to **standard error**.

EXAMPLE 10.3
A random variable, X, has standard deviation 2. How large an independent sample should be taken for the standard error of the sample mean to be less than $\frac{1}{2}$?

Solution
Here the variance of X is 4. If the sample has size n, then its variance is $\dfrac{4}{n}$. We require this to be less than $\frac{1}{2}^2$, i.e. $\frac{1}{4}$.

$$\frac{4}{n} < \frac{1}{4}$$

Hence $n > 16$

The sample size should be more than 16.

EXAMPLE 10.4

The mean weight of a certain flower is to be found. Two botanists, A and B, collected independent samples, of sizes 10 and 20 respectively. The sample collected by A had mean weight $\overline{X}$, and the sample collected by B had mean weight $\overline{Y}$.

Show that the following are both unbiased estimators of the mean weight. Which is more efficient?

(a) $\frac{1}{2}(\overline{X} + \overline{Y})$ (b) $\frac{1}{3}\overline{X} + \frac{2}{3}\overline{Y}$

Solution

Let the population mean and variance be μ and σ^2 respectively. Apply our results.

$$E(\tfrac{1}{2}(\overline{X} + \overline{Y})) = \tfrac{1}{2}E(\overline{X}) + \tfrac{1}{2}E(\overline{Y}) = \tfrac{1}{2}\mu + \tfrac{1}{2}\mu = \mu$$

$$E(\tfrac{1}{3}\overline{X} + \tfrac{2}{3}\overline{Y}) = \tfrac{1}{3}E(\overline{X}) + \tfrac{2}{3}E(\overline{Y}) = \tfrac{1}{3}\mu + \tfrac{2}{3}\mu = \mu$$

Both estimators are unbiased.

Now we find the variances of these estimators.

$$\mathrm{Var}(\tfrac{1}{2}(\overline{X} + \overline{Y})) = \tfrac{1}{4}\,\mathrm{Var}(\overline{X} + \overline{Y}) = \tfrac{1}{4}\,\mathrm{Var}(\overline{X}) + \tfrac{1}{4}\,\mathrm{Var}(\overline{Y})$$

$$= \tfrac{1}{4} \times \frac{\sigma^2}{10} + \tfrac{1}{4} \times \frac{\sigma^2}{20} = \frac{3\sigma^2}{80}$$

$$\mathrm{Var}(\tfrac{1}{3}\overline{X} + \tfrac{2}{3}\overline{Y}) = \tfrac{1}{9}\mathrm{Var}(\overline{X}) + \tfrac{4}{9}\mathrm{Var}(\overline{Y})$$

$$= \tfrac{1}{9} \times \frac{\sigma^2}{10} + \tfrac{4}{9} \times \frac{\sigma^2}{20} = \frac{\sigma^2}{30}$$

Notice that the variance of the second estimator is the smaller.
$\frac{1}{3}\overline{X} + \frac{2}{3}\overline{Y}$ **is more efficient.**

EXERCISE 10B

1 X is a distribution with mean 10 and variance 4. An independent sample of size 20 is taken. Find the expectation and variance of the sample mean $\overline{X}$.

   How large would a sample have to be for its standard error to be at most 0.1?

2 The variance of the heights of adult women in a population is 21 cm^2. An independent sample of size 30 is taken. What is the variance of the sample mean? How large a sample would have to be taken for its standard error to be at most 0.5 cm?

3 Three people are picked at random from a population. Their heights are X_1, X_2 and X_3. Show that each of the following is an unbiased estimator of the mean population height. Which is more efficient?

a) $\frac{1}{3}(X_1 + X_2 + X_3)$ b) $\frac{1}{9}(2X_1 + 3X_2 + 4X_3)$

4 The IQs of two samples of students are measured. The first sample had size 30 and sample mean $\overline{X}$, the second had size 20 and sample mean $\overline{Y}$. Assuming that they are independent random samples of the same student population, show that each of the following is an unbiased estimator of the mean student population IQ. Which is more efficient?

a) $\frac{1}{2}(\overline{X} + \overline{Y})$ **b)** $\frac{1}{3}\overline{X} + \frac{2}{3}\overline{Y}$

5 The mean IQ of a student population is to be found from the sample means $\overline{X}$ and $\overline{Y}$ of Question 4, using the estimator $a\overline{X} + b\overline{Y}$, where a and b are constant. Show that the estimator is unbiased if $a + b = 1$. Find the values of a and b which will give the most efficient estimator.

6 A post office has two scales A and B. If a parcel of weight k kg is placed on A or B, the weights registered will be X kg and Y kg respectively. Both scales are unbiased, in that $E(X) = E(Y) = k$. Scale A is more accurate, in that $Var(X) = 0.001$ and $Var(Y) = 0.003$.

A parcel is weighed on both the scales. Show that each of the following is an unbiased estimator of the true weight. Which is more efficient?

a) $\frac{1}{2}(X + Y)$ **b)** $\frac{2}{3}X + \frac{1}{3}Y$

7 The weight of a parcel is to be estimated using the scales of Question 6. The weight will be given as $aX + bY$, where a and b are constant. Find the values of a and b which make this estimator unbiased and most efficient.

8 It is thought that the weights of pedigree cats and mongrel cats have the same mean, μ kg, but that the variance for mongrel cats is half that for pedigree cats. The mean, μ, is to be estimated by weighing one mongrel cat and one pedigree cat, both selected at random.

Suppose the mongrel cat and the pedigree cat weigh X kg and Y kg respectively. Find constants a and b such that $aX + bY$ is an unbiased estimator of μ and is as efficient as possible.

Sample variance

Another fact about a population which we might want to know is its variance. The government might want to know how widely the population varies in terms of alcohol consumption. The variance will be estimated using the sample variance, as defined in Chapter 1 by:

$$S^2 = \frac{\Sigma(X_i - \overline{X})^2}{n} = \frac{1}{n}\Sigma X_i^2 - \overline{X}^2$$

In this definition the sample mean $\overline{X}$ may not be the true mean μ. We are estimating the mean from the data, and hence the sample variance is biased. Its expected value is not the population variance σ^2. In fact:

$$E(S^2) = \frac{n - 1}{n}\sigma^2$$

The proof of this appears in the Mathematical appendix, on page 333.

By multiplying S^2 by $\dfrac{n}{n-1}$, we can ensure that its expected value
is σ^2. This is the **unbiased sample variance**, $\hat{\sigma}^2$. Note that the symbol
wears a hat to distinguish it from the population variance.

$$\hat{\sigma}^2 = \frac{nS^2}{n-1} = \frac{\Sigma X^2 - n\overline{X}^2}{n-1}$$

On many scientific calculators there are two buttons, used to find
standard deviation, marked σ_n and σ_{n-1}. When squared, they will
give the sample variance and the unbiased sample variance respectively.

Note
If n is large, there is not much difference between S^2 and $\hat{\sigma}^2$.

EXAMPLE 10.5
Without the use of a calculator, find the unbiased sample variance
for the following set of data.

   10   8   4   7   6

Solution
The sum, Σx, of these numbers is 35, hence their mean is 7.

The sum of their squares, Σx^2, is 265. Apply the formula.

$$\hat{\sigma}^2 = \frac{\Sigma x^2 - n(\overline{X})^2}{n-1}$$

$$= \frac{265 - 5 \times 7^2}{4} = 5$$

The unbiased sample variance is 5.

EXERCISE 10C

1   Without using a calculator, find the unbiased sample variance for the following sets of numbers.
   Then check the result using a calculator which has a σ_{n-1} button.

   a) 12   17   13   10   9   21   **b)** 0.3   0.2   0.1   0.7   −0.3

   c) 107   172   165   142   182   142   136   175   188   190

2   The sample variance of a sample of size 10 was 8.1. Find the unbiased sample variance.

3   A sample of size 20 was found. The sum of the sample values was 203, and the sum of their
   squares was 2300. Find the unbiased sample variance.

4   Find the unbiased sample variance for each of the data sets summarised below.

   a) $n = 10, \Sigma x = 23, \Sigma x^2 = 5000$ **b)** $n = 20, \Sigma x = 141, \Sigma x^2 = 220\,000$

   c) $n = 12, \Sigma x = 0.7, \Sigma x^2 = 6$

5 The IQs of a sample of eight people were measured. Find the unbiased sample variance of these figures.

> 102   121   117   120   109   119   123   115

6 The weights, in grams, of ten eggs are given below. Find the unbiased sample variance of the weights.

> 23.1   25.1   26.4   22.1   22.7   19.8   27.4   25.0   26.4   24.3

7 Seven people estimated the distance to a nearby tree. The results, in metres, are given below. Find the unbiased sample variance of these estimates.

> 230   200   180   150   250   200   197

8 The lengths, in minutes, of six tracks on a cassette are given below. Find the unbiased sample variance of the lengths.

> 6.8   5.2   1.9   10.3   7.4   3.5

9 Use one of the data sets of Question 1 to verify that the σ_n and σ_{n-1} buttons on your calculator do give the appropriate values.

*10 A distribution has *known* mean μ and *unknown* variance σ^2. An independent sample of size n is taken. It is resolved to estimate σ^2 by $V = \dfrac{1}{n}\Sigma X_i^2 - \mu^2$. Show that V is unbiased, i.e. that $\mathrm{E}(V) = \sigma^2$.

10.3 Sums of normal variables

When we add independent variables, we add their means and their variances. If in addition the variables are normal, their sum is also normal.

Suppose X and Y are independent normal variables, with means μ and λ respectively, and variances σ^2 and v^2 respectively. Then $X + Y$ is normal with mean $\mu + \lambda$ and variance $\sigma^2 + v^2$.

> If $X \sim N(\mu, \sigma^2)$ and $Y \sim N(\lambda, v^2)$, then $X + Y \sim N(\mu+\lambda, \sigma^2+v^2)$

The proof of this result is beyond the scope of this book.

The result can be generalised if X and Y are multiplied by constants a and b. With the same assumptions about X and Y as above:

> $aX + bY \sim N(a\mu+b\lambda, a^2\sigma^2+b^2v^2)$
>
> In particular, $X - Y \sim N(\mu - \lambda, \sigma^2+v^2)$

The last result is very useful when we want to find the probability that one normal variable is greater than another. We find the probability that their difference is positive.

EXAMPLE 10.6

When Carl runs the 100 m, the time he takes, X seconds, is such that $X \sim N(12.3, 0.5)$. Desmond's time is Y seconds, where $Y \sim N(11.7, 0.7)$. If their times are independent of each other, find the probability that Carl will beat Desmond in a race.

Solution

By the results above, the difference between X and Y is also normal. Subtract the means and add the variances.

$$E(X - Y) = E(X) - E(Y)$$

$$\text{Var}(X - Y) = \text{Var}(X) + \text{Var}(Y)$$

Hence $X - Y \sim N(0.6, 1.2)$

Carl will beat Desmond if $X < Y$, i.e. if $X - Y < 0$.

$$P(X - Y < 0) = \Phi\left(\frac{0 - 0.6}{\sqrt{1.2}}\right) = \Phi(-0.548)$$

We can use tables to find that $\Phi(-0.548) = 0.292$.

The probability that Carl will beat Desmond is 0.292.

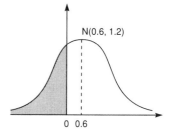

Fig. 10.1

EXERCISE 10D

1 Let X and Y be independent variables for which $X \sim N(4, 2)$ and $Y \sim N(3, 4)$. Write down the distribution of each of the following.

a) $X + Y$ **b)** $X - Y$ **c)** $2X + 3Y$ **d)** $3X - Y + 5$

2 Let X and Y be independent variables for which $X \sim N(5, 3)$ and $Y \sim N(4, 2)$. Evaluate the following.

a) $P(X + Y < 12)$ **b)** $P(2X + 3Y > 23)$ **c)** $P(X \geq Y)$ **d)** $P(2X < 3Y)$

3 A machine dispenses cups of white coffee by discharging amounts of coffee and milk, which are independent of each other, of weights, X grams and Y grams respectively, such that $X \sim N(60, 5)$ and $Y \sim N(10, 4)$. Find the probability that the total weight of liquid is more than 75 grams.

4 The time, X minutes, a commuter takes to get to work in the morning satisfies $X \sim N(35, 20)$. The time to get home in the evening is Y minutes, where $Y \sim N(45, 30)$. The times are independent of each other. Calculate the probability that:

a) the total commuting time will be more than 90 minutes,

b) the morning journey will take longer than the evening,

c) the evening journey will take more than 15 minutes longer than the morning.

5 The height, X inches, of adult women, is such that $X \sim N(63, 7)$. The height, Y inches, of adult men is such that $Y \sim N(69, 8)$. If an adult woman and an adult man are picked at random, find the probability that:

a) their total height is greater than 140 inches,   **b)** the man is taller than the woman,

c) the man is less than 2 inches taller than the woman.

Suppose a married couple is picked at random. Is the probability that the husband is taller than the wife the same as in (b)?

6 Pegs are manufactured so that their diameters are normally distributed with mean 1.1 cm and variance 0.003 cm². The holes into which they are to fit have diameters which are normally distributed with mean 1.12 cm and variance 0.005 cm². If a peg and a hole are selected at random, find the probability that:

a) the peg will fit into the hole,   **b)** the peg will fit in with a gap of less than 0.01 cm.

7 The lifetime in miles of a certain make of tyre is normally distributed with mean 60 000 and variance 10^8. If two tyres are picked at random, find the probability that:

a) their total lifetime will be more than 110 000 miles,

b) the difference in lifetime is less than 5000 miles.

8 At the beginning of a journey, the number of gallons of petrol in a car's tank is normally distributed with mean 6 and variance 2. The number of gallons of petrol needed for this particular journey is also normally distributed, with mean 5 and variance 2.5. Assuming independence of these quantities, find the probability that the tank will need refuelling.

9 The two acts of a play have lengths X minutes and Y minutes, which satisfy $X \sim N(50, 10)$ and $Y \sim N(60, 8)$. The length of the interval is Z minutes, where $Z \sim N(20, 12)$. Assuming that all the times are independent of each other, find the probability that the total time will be less than 140 minutes.

10 The time I take to walk to the station is X minutes, where $X \sim N(10, 3)$. The train will leave the station at Y minutes past 8 a.m. where $Y \sim N(6, 4)$. Assuming independence, if I leave for the station at 7.55 a.m. what is the probability I shall miss the train?

What is the latest I could set off to be 99 per cent sure of catching the train?

11 A doctor is due to see four patients, starting at 11 a.m. The number of minutes spent with each patient has a normal distribution, with mean 30 and variance 40. Each patient's time is independent of the others. The time between patients is negligible. What is the probability that the doctor will still be seeing a patient after 1.15 p.m?

What is the earliest time the doctor could set for his lunch break, and be 95 per cent sure that he will have seen all the patients by then?

12 A motorist is about to make two journeys: the numbers of gallons of petrol used are independent of each other, and are normally distributed with means 2 and 2.6 and variances 0.06 and 0.08. What is the least amount of petrol to be in the tank if the motorist is to be 99 per cent sure of not running out?

10.4 Distribution of a sample mean

Statistics is largely involved with making inferences from a sample. A very important case occurs when we take an independent sample from a normal distribution. We can combine the results from the previous two sections.

In Section 10.2 we showed that if $\overline{X}$ is the mean of an independent sample from a distribution with mean μ and variance σ^2, then $\overline{X}$ has expected value μ and variance $\dfrac{\sigma^2}{n}$.

In Section 10.3 we stated that the sum of two independent normal variables is also normal.

Hence if the sample is taken from a normal distribution, the sample mean will also be normal.

Suppose that X has a normal distribution with mean μ and variance σ^2, i.e. that $X \sim N(\mu, \sigma^2)$. Take an independent sample $X_1, X_2, ..., X_n$ from X. The sample mean $\overline{X}$ is also normal, with mean μ and variance $\dfrac{\sigma^2}{n}$.

$$\overline{X} \sim N\left(\mu, \frac{\sigma^2}{n}\right)$$

EXAMPLE 10.7
The amount, X cm^3, of liquid in cartons of orange juice satisfies $X \sim N(1003, 42)$. A random sample of 20 cartons is taken. Find the probability that the sample mean volume will be less than 1000 cm^3.

Solution
From the result above, the sample mean, $\overline{X}$ cm^3, is such that $\overline{X} \sim N(1003, 42/20)$. We find the probability that $\overline{X}$ is less than 1000.

$$P(\overline{X} < 1000) = \Phi\left(\frac{1000 - 1003}{\sqrt{2.1}}\right) = \Phi(-2.07)$$

From tables we find that $\Phi(-2.07) = 0.0192$.

The probability that the sample mean is less than 1000 cm^3 is 0.0192.

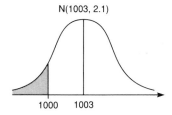

N(1003, 2.1)

1000   1003

Fig. 10.2

EXERCISE 10E

1   A sample of size 10 is taken from a normal distribution with mean 5 and variance 4. The sample mean is $\overline{X}$. Find the following probabilities.
   a) $P(\overline{X} < 6)$ b) $P(\overline{X} < 4.5)$ c) $P(4 < \overline{X} < 6)$ d) $P(|\overline{X} - 5| < 0.1)$

2   With $\overline{X}$ as defined in Question 1, find the values of k for which the following hold.
   a) $P(\overline{X} < k) = 0.95$ b) $P(\overline{X} > k) = 0.99$ c) $P(|\overline{X} - 5| < k) = 0.95$

3 Cartons of milk contain X ml of liquid, where $X \sim N(500, 20)$. An independent sample of 30 cartons is taken. Find the probability that the sample mean will be less than 499 ml.

4 Certain batteries have lifetimes X hours, where $X \sim N(9, 4)$. An independent sample of size 40 is taken. Find the probability that the sample mean lifetime is less than 8.9 hours.

5 The midday temperature in August at a resort is $X\,°F$, where $X \sim N(85, 20)$. Every year, the midday temperature on 1 August is recorded. The records for the last 20 years are checked and the mean is found. Find the probability that this mean is greater than 87°F.

6 A machine makes cakes whose mass should have mean 120 grams and standard deviation 5 grams. An independent sample of size 15 is taken. Find the probability that the sample mean is greater than 117 grams.

7 A machine dispenses tea in amounts X ml, where $X \sim N(60, 12)$. An independent sample of size 20 is taken. For what value of k can we be 95 per cent certain that the sample mean will exceed k ml?

8 The time, X minutes, a mechanic should take to mend a puncture is such that $X \sim N(25, 8)$. The mechanic is timed over 20 occasions, and the mean time is taken. Find the time, m minutes, for which we can be 99 per cent sure that the mean time will be less than m minutes.

9 A factory produces ball bearings with diameter X cm, where $X \sim N(1, 0.0002)$. An independent sample of size 30 is taken. For what value of k can the factory be 95 per cent sure that the sample mean will be within k cm of 1 cm?

10 The mark in an examination is normally distributed with mean 60 and variance 40. An independent sample of size 50 is taken. Find the value of m such that we are 99 per cent sure that the sample mean will lie within m of 60.

The central limit theorem

When the normal distribution was introduced in Chapter 9, we mentioned that it was the limiting distribution of many other distributions. The normal approximation to the binomial and Poisson distributions were examples. We are now in a position to state the general result.

The central limit theorem
Suppose X is any random variable with mean μ and variance σ^2. Take a random sample of size n from X. Let $\overline{X}$ be the sample mean. Then as n tends to infinity, the distribution of $\overline{X}$ tends to

$$N(\mu, \frac{\sigma^2}{n}).$$

The proof of the theorem is beyond the scope of this book.

EXAMPLE 10.8

The heights of adult males in a country have mean 175 cm and standard deviation 8 cm. Estimate the probability that the average height of 40 randomly selected men will be greater than 177 cm.

Solution

We are not told anything about the distribution of the heights. By the central limit theorem, however, the distribution of the sample average, $\overline{X}$, will be approximately normal.

$\overline{X}$ is approximately $\mathrm{N}\left(175, \dfrac{8^2}{40}\right)$

$$P(\overline{X} > 177) \simeq 1 - \Phi\left(\frac{177 - 175}{\sqrt{1.6}}\right) = 1 - \Phi(1.581)$$

We can use tables to find that $1 - \Phi(1.581) = 1 - 0.943 = 0.057$.

The probability that the average height is greater than 177 cm is 0.057.

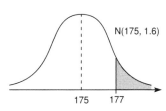

Fig. 10.3

EXERCISE 10F

1 When a fair die is rolled, its score has mean 3.5 and variance $2\frac{11}{12}$. The die is rolled 30 times. Find the probability that the average score is less than 3.6.

2 A fair coin is spun. A head gives a score of 1, and a tail a score of 0. Show that the score has mean 0.5 and variance 0.25. If the coin is spun 100 times, find the probability that the average score will be less than 0.49.

3 The time taken to complete a task of agility is X seconds, where X has mean 15 seconds and variance 65. Give a reason why the time cannot have a normal distribution.

A group of 80 randomly selected people undertake this task. Find the approximate probability that their average time exceeds 17 seconds.

4 A random variable, X, is uniformly distributed between -1 and 1. Find its mean and variance.

Estimate the probability that the mean of an independent sample of size 20 from X is greater than 0.1.

5 A random variable has a Poisson distribution with mean 3. An independent sample of size 10 is taken. Estimate the probability that the sample mean is greater than 4.

6 Three fair coins are spun. Find the mean and variance of the number of heads obtained.

This operation is repeated 40 times. Estimate the probability that the average number of heads is greater than 1.4.

7 A roulette wheel has the numbers 1 to 36 around its rim. Find the mean and variance of the number obtained in a single spin.

The wheel is spun 60 times. Estimate the probability that the average score is greater than 20.

LONGER EXERCISE

Verifying the central limit theorem

We have stated the central limit theorem, without attempting to give a proof. Here you can verify it for one particular distribution.

The random number button on your calculator or on a computer should produce a number which is uniformly distributed between 0 and 1. Show that the mean and variance of the numbers returned are 0.5 and $\frac{1}{12}$.

Suppose the random number button is pressed ten times. What are the mean and variance of the average of the numbers obtained?

Obtain the mean of ten random numbers. Repeat, many times. It would be sensible to share this work among many people, or to use a computer. (For this, see the Computer investigation on page 309.)

See how well your results fit a normal distribution with the required mean and variance.

EXAMINATION QUESTIONS

1 A secretary types letters onto sheets of paper 30 cm long and then folds the letters as shown.

The first fold is X cm from one edge of the paper and the second fold, Y cm from the other edge, is exactly in the middle of the remainder of the paper, so that $Y = \frac{1}{2}(30 - X)$.

Unfolded sheet

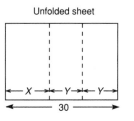

Folded sheet

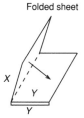

Envelope

Fig. 10.4

The distance X cm is normally distributed with mean 10.2 cm and standard deviation 1.2 cm.

(i)   Obtain the distribution of Y.

(ii) The letters have to fit into envelopes 11 cm wide. Find

    (A) $P(X > 11)$ (B) $P(Y > 11)$,

    (C) the proportion of folded letters which **will** fit into the envelope.

(iii) The 'overlap' is $X - Y$. Show that $X - Y = \frac{3}{2}(X - 10)$ and hence verify that $\text{Var}(X - Y)$ is **not** equal to $\text{Var}(X) + \text{Var}(Y)$.

(iv) Explain why the rule $\text{Var}(aX + bY) = a^2\text{Var}(X) + b^2\text{Var}(Y)$ does not apply in this case.

MEI 1994

2 Audrey is a regular customer of Toto's taxis. When she rings from home the time, X, a taxi takes to arrive is normally distributed with mean 19 minutes, standard deviation 3 minutes.

a) (i) What is the probability of her having to wait less than 15 minutes for a taxi?

    (ii) What waiting time will be exceeded with a probability of 0.1?

Audrey decides to try **Blue Star** taxis. The standard deviation of her waiting time, Y, is 7 minutes and the probability of Y exceeding 8 minutes is 0.97725.

b) Find the mean of Y, assuming a normal distribution.

c) What is the distribution of T where $T = Y - X$? (X and Y may be assumed independent.)
   If both firms were rung at the same time what is the probability that Toto would arrive first?

d) In order to catch a train Audrey needs a taxi within 10 minutes. Which firm would you advise her to ring? Explain your answer.

AEB 1993

3 A small bank has two cashiers dealing with customers wanting to withdraw or deposit cash. For each cashier, the time taken to deal with a customer is a random variable having a normal distribution with mean 150 s and standard deviation 45 s.

(i) Find the probability that the time taken for a randomly chosen customer to be dealt with by a cashier is more than 180 s.

(ii) One of the cashiers deals with two customers, one straight after the other. Assuming that the times for the customers are independent of each other, find the probability that the total time taken by the cashier is less than 200 s.

(iii) At a certain time, one cashier has a queue of 4 customers and the other cashier has a queue of 3 customers, and the cashiers begin to deal with the customers at the front of their queues. Assuming that the cashiers work independently, find the probability that the 4 customers in the first queue will all be dealt with before the 3 customers in the second queue are all dealt with.

C 1992

4 (In this question give three places of decimals in each answer.)

The mass of tea in Supacuppa teabags has a normal distribution with mean 4.1 g and standard deviation 0.12 g. The mass of tea in Bumpacuppa has a normal distribution with mean 5.2 g and standard deviation 0.15 g.

(i) Find the probability that a randomly chosen Supacuppa teabag contains more than 4.0 g of tea.

(ii) Find the probability that, of two randomly chosen Supacuppa teabags, one contains more than 4.0 g of tea and one contains less than 4.0 g of tea.

(iii) Find the probability that five randomly chosen Supacuppa teabags contain a total of more than 20.8 g of tea.

(iv) Find the probability that the total mass of tea in five randomly chosen Supacuppa teabags is more than the total mass of tea in four randomly chosen Bumpacuppa teabags.

C 1992

5 A sweet manufacturer produces two varieties of fruit sweet, Xtras and Yummies. The weights, X and Y in grams, of randomly selected Xtras and Yummies are such that

$$X \sim N(30,25) \text{ and } Y \sim N(32,16).$$

a) Find the probability that the weight of two randomly selected Yummies will differ by more than 5 g.

One sweet of each variety is selected at random.

b) Find the probability that the Yummy sweet weighs more than the Xtra.

A packet contains 6 Xtras and 4 Yummies.

c) Find the probability that the average weight of the sweets in the packet lies between 28 g and 33 g.

L 1992

6 The random variable X is distributed $N(\mu_1, \sigma_1^2)$ and the random variable Y is distributed $N(\mu_2, \sigma_2^2)$. X and Y are independent variables. State the form of the distribution of $(X + Y)$ and of $(X - Y)$ and give the mean and variance for each distribution.

A factory makes both rods and copper tubes. The internal diameter, X cm, of a copper tube is distributed $N(2.2, 0.0009)$.

a) Find, to 3 significant figures, the proportion of tubes with internal diameter less than 2.14 cm.

The diameter, Y cm, of a rod is distributed $N(2.15, 0.0004)$.

b) Find, to 3 decimal places, the proportion of rods with diameter greater than 2.1 cm and less than 2.2 cm.

c) A rod and a tube are chosen at random. Find, to 3 decimal places, the probability that the rod will not pass through the tube.

d) A rod and a tube are chosen at random. A second rod and a second tube are chosen at random and then a third rod and a third tube are chosen at random. Find, to 3 decimal places, the probability that each of two rods will pass through the tube which was selected at the same time and one will not.

L 1991

Summary and key points

10.1 The means and variances of combinations of variables obey the following rules.

$$E(X + Y) = E(X) + E(Y) \qquad E(aX) = aE(X)$$
$$E(aX + bY) = aE(X) + bE(Y) \qquad Var(aX) = a^2 Var(X)$$

In particular, $E(X + k) = E(X) + k$

If X and Y are independent, the following are also true.

$$E(XY) = E(X)E(Y) \qquad \mathrm{Var}(X + Y) = \mathrm{Var}(X) + \mathrm{Var}(Y)$$

$$\mathrm{Var}(aX + bY) = a^2\mathrm{Var}(X) + b^2\mathrm{Var}(Y)$$

In particular,

$$\mathrm{Var}(X - Y) = \mathrm{Var}(X) + \mathrm{Var}(Y)$$

and

$$\mathrm{Var}(X + k) = \mathrm{Var}(X).$$

Note that $\mathrm{Var}(X - Y)$ is not $\mathrm{Var}(X) - \mathrm{Var}(Y)$, that $\mathrm{Var}(aX)$ is not $a\mathrm{Var}(X)$ and that $\mathrm{Var}(X + k)$ is not $\mathrm{Var}(X) + k$.

10.2 Let $\overline{X}$ be an independent sample of size n from a distribution with mean μ and variance σ^2. Then $E(\overline{X}) = \mu$ and $\mathrm{Var}(\overline{X}) = \dfrac{\sigma^2}{n}$.

The sample variance $S^2 = \dfrac{1}{n}\Sigma X_i^2 - \overline{X}^2$ is biased. The unbiased sample variance is $\dfrac{nS^2}{n-1}$.

10.3 If X and Y are independent normal variables, then their sum is also normal. If $X \sim N(\mu_1, \sigma_1^2)$ and $Y \sim N(\mu_2, \sigma_2^2)$, then $aX + bY \sim N(a\mu_1 + b\mu_2, a^2\sigma_1^2 + b^2\sigma_2^2)$, where a and b are constant.

10.4 The mean of an independent sample of size n from $N(\mu, \sigma^2)$ has the distribution $N\left(\mu, \dfrac{\sigma^2}{n}\right)$.

Let X be any distribution with mean μ and variance σ^2. If we take an independent sample of size n, then as n tends to infinity the distribution of the sample mean tends to a normal distribution. This is the central limit theorem.

Tests 1

If we have collected a great mass of data, we shall want to draw some conclusions from it. In many cases, we shall want to find out whether the data provides evidence for or against some conjecture. Using the data, we perform a **test**.

In statistics, the results of any enquiry are seldom definite. We can rarely say we have proved something absolutely. At best we only prove something subject to a reservation in terms of probability. The most we can conclude is that, if the thing that we are trying to prove is not true, then there has been a coincidence.

Suppose for example that your local bus company claims that the average waiting time for its buses is 8 minutes. You may be sceptical, and test the claim by recording the waiting times over ten days. Suppose on average, you had to wait 10 minutes. Have you disproved the claim? It is possible that your long waiting times could have happened by chance, so you have not disproved the claim with certainty.

If the claim is correct, the probability that your average waiting time is as high as 10 minutes might be 0.02. The results you obtained provide a coincidence, of probability less than one in twenty.

However many times you wait for the bus, and however frequently the waiting time is greater than 8 minutes, you will never prove absolutely that the claim is false. If the bus keeps on being late, the assumption that the average waiting time is eight minutes forces you to admit that a greater and greater coincidence has occurred. Eventually the coincidence is so unlikely that you discard the claim.

11.1 Null and alternative hypotheses

When doing a statistical investigation, we are often examining the value of the parameter of a distribution. In particular, we might be investigating whether the mean, μ, of a distribution has a certain value.

The bus example we have just been discussing is of this form. If the company's claim is correct, the mean waiting time, μ, should be 8 minutes. If it is false, it is greater than 8 minutes.

In our investigation, we very often find there are two hypotheses to choose between.

The **null hypothesis**, H_0, is that the situation is as it should be, and that the parameter has a fixed value. That is, the mean, μ, is equal to a fixed value, μ_0.

For the bus example, the null hypothesis is that the claim is correct, and that the mean waiting time, μ, is 8 minutes.

The **alternative hypothesis**, H_1, is that the situation is not as it should be. That is, the mean μ is different from the fixed value, μ_0.

For the bus example, the alternative hypothesis is that the mean waiting time is greater than 8 minutes.

Note an important difference between these two hypotheses. The null hypothesis is precise. For the bus example, it says that the mean is *exactly* 8 minutes. The alternative hypothesis, however, is imprecise. It says merely that the mean is greater than 8 minutes, without specifying how much greater it is. Because the null hypothesis is precise, we can calculate probabilities from it. The alternative hypothesis is imprecise, so we cannot calculate probabilities from it. If we know merely that the mean waiting time is greater than 8 minutes, we cannot then calculate the probability that over ten days the average waiting time was 10 minutes or greater.

Having decided upon the null and alternative hypotheses, we then perform an experiment to obtain data. It might be by measurement, or by taking a survey. We then test the null hypothesis in the light of the data we have obtained.

Test statistic

A function which summarises the data is a **test statistic**. This often comes from the mean of the data. For the bus example, the test statistic will come from the average waiting time over the sample of ten days.

Suppose that the waiting time has a normal distribution, with standard deviation 3 minutes. If the null hypothesis that $\mu = 8$

minutes is true then, by results of Chapter 10, the distribution of the sample mean $\overline{X}$ is $N\left(8, \frac{3^2}{10}\right)$, i.e. N(8, 0.9). Reduce this normal distribution to the standard N(0, 1) distribution.

$$\frac{\overline{X} - 8}{\sqrt{0.9}} \sim N(0, 1)$$

This is our test statistic. The result of the test will depend on how large this test statistic is.

Critical region and critical value

The set of values of the test statistic for which we will reject the null hypothesis is the **critical region**. Often, this critical region consists of values greater than a certain value, which is the **critical value**.

Suppose the test statistic is the standard normal variable, $Z \sim N(0, 1)$. From tables, we can see that the value of z which cuts off the top 5 per cent of probability is 1.645. This is shown in Fig. 11.1. If z is greater than this critical value, i.e. falls in the critical shaded region, then we will reject the null hypothesis.

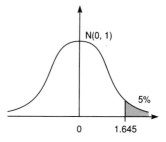

Fig. 11.1

The figure of 5 per cent of probability is arbitrarily chosen. It is the **level of significance** of the test. The level of significance gives the level of coincidence that we are prepared to put up with.

Result of a test

Let us suppose that the level of significance is 5 per cent. We perform our experiment, and see how different our results are from those predicted by the null hypothesis. We find whether our results give a value of the test statistic lying within the critical region. If it does lie in the critical region, we reject the null hypothesis and adopt the alternative hypothesis. If it doesn't lie in the critical region, then we retain the null hypothesis.

In the bus example, we found a sample mean, $\overline{X}$, equal to 10. This gives the value of the test statistic as 2.11. This lies inside the critical region, and hence we reject the null hypothesis. We reject the bus company's claim that the mean waiting time is 8 minutes.

Notes

1 If we retain the null hypothesis, that doesn't mean that we have proved it true. We have merely failed to reject it. We could never prove that the mean waiting time for a bus is *exactly* 8 minutes.

2 The method of the test and the significance level must be decided *before* looking at the data. We cannot look at the data and then decide what sort of test is appropriate.

EXAMPLE 11.1

The weights of the eggs produced at a poultry farm have a distribution which is normal with mean 40 grams and variance 20 grams². The farmer provides his hens with a food additive, and to find out whether it has been effective he tests the weight of 15 eggs from hens that have received the additive. The mean weight of these eggs is 41.5 grams. Is this significant at 5 per cent to show that the additive has been effective?

Solution

The eggs used to have a N(40, 20) distribution. Let the eggs produced by hens who have received the additive have a $N(\mu, \sigma^2)$ distribution. If the additive is ineffective, then nothing will have changed. If it is effective, then μ will be greater than 40.

$$H_0: \mu = 40 \qquad H_1: \mu > 40$$

Assuming H_0, the distribution of the sample mean $\overline{X}$ is N(40, $\frac{20}{15}$), i.e. N(40, $1\frac{1}{3}$). Find the corresponding value for the standard normal distribution, N(0,1).

$$\frac{41.5 - 40}{\sqrt{1\frac{1}{3}}} = 1.30$$

Notice that this is less than 1.645, the critical value for a 5 per cent significance test. At this level of significance we retain the null hypothesis.

At 5 per cent significance, we have not shown that the additive is effective.

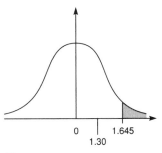

Fig. 11.2

EXERCISE 11A

1 It is thought that the distribution of X is N(10, 16). A sample of size 20 had sample mean $\overline{X}$ equal to 12. Is this significant at 5 per cent to show that the true mean of X is greater than 10?

2 It is thought that the distribution of X is N(5, 0.3). A sample of size 15 had sample mean $\overline{X}$ equal to 4.8. Is this significant at 5 per cent to show that the true mean of X is less than 5?

3 Over many trials, the distance, X metres, achieved by a javelin thrower satisfies $X \sim$ N(20, 26). After she receives extra training, her next ten throws reach an average of 22 m. Is this significant at 5 per cent to show that the training has improved her performance?

4 The weight of a certain sort of beetle is X grams, where $X \sim$ N(0.7, 0.03). It is suspected that after an exceptionally cold spell the weight of the beetles will have decreased, and 40 beetles are collected to test this hypothesis. If the sample mean weight is 0.65, are the suspicions justified at a significance level of 5 per cent?

5 The marks in a national examination are normally distributed with mean 50 and standard deviation 14. A college claims that its students are better than the average, and sets the examination for

40 of them. These 40 score an average of 53. Is this significant at 5 per cent to justify the college's claim?

6   The tourist board of a seaside resort claims that the midday temperature in August has mean 80°F and standard deviation 7°. This claim is tested by finding the midday temperature on ten August days. The mean temperature over these days was 76°F. Assuming that the temperature is distributed normally, and that the temperatures are independent of each other, is this significant at 5 per cent to discredit the tourist board's claim?

7   A university department regularly sets its students an examination at the end of their first term. The marks have been found to be normally distributed with mean 67 and variance 96. One year the department is forced to lower its entrance requirements, and at the end of the first year the 30 students achieved a mean mark of 62 in the test. Is this significant at 5 per cent to show that the standard of student attainment has fallen?

8   It is thought that the distribution of X is N(100, 240). A sample of size 25 had sample mean $\overline{X}$ equal to 106. Is this significant at 1 per cent to show that the true mean of X is greater than 100? (The critical value at 1 per cent is 2.326.)

9   It is thought that the distribution of X is N(0, 0.1). A sample of size 18 had sample mean $\overline{X}$ equal to -0.18. Is this significant at 1 per cent to show that the true mean of X is negative?

10   Intelligence quotient (IQ) has a N(100, 225) distribution. A random sample of 20 people are given a special fish diet, and their IQs are then tested. If they achieved an average score of 106, would this be significant at 1 per cent to show that the diet had increased their IQ?

11   The voltage of certain batteries should be normally distributed with mean 12 V and standard deviation 0.4 V. A sample of eight batteries from the day's production was tested, with the results, in volts, as given below. Find the sample mean voltage. Is this significant at 5 per cent to show that the day's production has a lower voltage than normal?

     11.5   11.7   12.1   11.9   12.1   11.6   11.7   11.8

12   The contents, X cm³, of certain juice cartons should satisfy $X \sim$ N(1005, 4). The volumes of a sample of ten cartons were measured, with the results, in cm³, as below. Find the sample mean volume. Is this significant at 5 per cent to show that the cartons contain less than they should?

     999 995 1002 1007 1005 1002 1006 998 994 998

11.2 Type I and Type II errors

We must always bear in mind that the results of a statistical test are not certain. Because we are dealing with probability, it is always possible that the conclusions are wrong. There are two ways that the results of a statistical test could be wrong.

Type I error

A **Type I error** is to reject the null hypothesis when it is true.

Type II error

A **Type II error** is to retain the null hypothesis when it is false.

Looking again at the bus example above, the errors are as follows.

Type I concluding that the mean waiting time is greater than 8 minutes when it isn't.

Type II failing to show that the mean waiting time is greater than 8 minutes when it is.

Probabilities of errors

The probability of a Type I error is the probability of rejecting the null hypothesis, even though it is true. This is the significance level of the test.

The probability of a Type II error is the probability of retaining the null hypothesis when it is false. In most cases, the alternative hypothesis is not precise, so we can only give the probability of a Type II error for a particular value of μ.

The probability of correctly rejecting the null hypothesis, i.e. of not making a Type II error, is the **power** of the test. Clearly we would like a test to be as powerful as possible, i.e. for the power to be as close to 1 as possible.

Penalties

With each type of error, there are penalties involved. These might be social or personal costs as well as straightforward financial ones. The test is arranged to take account of the penalties of making the two types of errors.

If a Type II error is costly compared to a Type I error, we shall make sure that it is easy to reject the null hypothesis. This can be done by setting a high significance level, say 10 per cent rather than 5 per cent.

If a Type I error is costly compared to a Type II error, we shall make sure that we only reject the null hypothesis when we are *very* confident that it is false. This can be done by setting a low significance level, say 1 per cent rather than 5 per cent.

There are four possible situations, which are shown in Fig. 11.3. In the top left and bottom right the correct decision is made. In the top right and bottom left an error is made.

	H_0 is True	H_0 is False
H_0 is Accepted	Correct decision	Type II error
H_0 is Rejected	Type I error	Correct decision

Fig. 11.3

EXAMPLE 11.2

A company makes fizzy soft drinks, of which the number of cans sold daily is normally distributed with mean 50 000 and standard deviation 4000. The advertising manager considers placing adverts in local radio stations. He does this for one week, and tests to see whether or not sales have increased.

State suitable null and alternative hypotheses. What would be Type I and Type II errors? What would be the penalties of these errors?

Solution

The manager is testing whether or not sales increase above 50 000. Let μ be the mean sales if the adverts do appear.

$$H_0 : \mu = 50\,000 \qquad H_1 : \mu > 50\,000$$

A Type I error is wrongly to reject the null hypothesis.

A Type I error is concluding that the adverts improve sales when they don't.

A Type II error is wrongly to retain the null hypothesis.

A Type II error is failing to recognise that the adverts improve sales when they do.

If a Type I error is made, then the firm will pay for useless advertisements. If a Type II error is made, then the firm will lose sales.

The penalty of a Type I error is the cost of the ineffective advert.

The penalty of a Type II error is the cost of lost sales.

EXAMPLE 11.3

The test of Example 11.2 will consist of taking the average daily sales over a period of five days. The test is at 5 per cent significance. Find the range of values of the average which will lead to the null hypothesis being rejected.

Suppose that if the adverts go ahead the mean daily sales will be 54 000. What is the probability of a Type II error?

Solution

Assuming the null hypothesis, the sample mean $\overline{X}$ is such that

$$\overline{X} \sim N\left(50\,000, \frac{4000^2}{5}\right).$$ The critical value at 5 per cent is 1.645.

Hence the null hypothesis will be rejected if the following is true.

$$\frac{\overline{X} - 50\,000}{\sqrt{\dfrac{4000^2}{5}}} > 1.645, \text{ i.e. } \overline{X} > 52\,900$$

The null hypothesis will be rejected if $\overline{X} > 52\,900$.

A Type II error is wrongly to retain the null hypothesis. This will happen if the sample mean is less than 52 900. If in fact the true mean is 54 000, the probability of this happening is

$$P(\overline{X} < 52\,900) = \frac{52\,900 - 54\,000}{\sqrt{\dfrac{4000^2}{5}}} = \Phi(-0.615) = 0.27$$

The probability of a Type II error is 0.27.

EXERCISE 11B

Each of Questions 1 to 6 involves a test. In each case identify the relevant Type I and Type II errors, and describe the penalties of these errors. No calculation is required.

1 A pig breeder is considering whether to feed his pigs an expensive food additive. He tests to see whether the additive does increase the weight of the pigs.

2 A machine produces washers which should have a certain diameter. The day's production of the machine is tested, to see whether the washers have too large a diameter.

3 If a car's engine is badly timed, its fuel consumption is higher than it should be. A motorist tests the fuel consumption of her car, to see whether or not the engine needs re-timing.

4 A slimmer is considering whether to base her diet on the expensive slimming food Kwikthin. She buys one week's supply and tests to see how effective it is.

5 The brake cables of a motor-cycle should have a certain breaking strength. The manufacturer of these cables tests a sample of the day's production to see whether they do have the correct strength.

6 A factory has applied for permission to release certain effluent into a river. The environment authority tests to see whether this effluent will decrease the weight of fish in the river.

Questions 7 to 12 refer to the situations in Questions 1 to 6 respectively.

7 The weights, in kg, of the pigs have a N(220, 160) distribution. The test is at 5 per cent significance. The farmer will be finding the mean weight, $\overline{X}$, of a sample of ten pigs that have been given the additive. Find the condition on $\overline{X}$ that will convince the farmer that the additive is effective. Find the probability of a Type II error if the additive increases the true mean weight to 228 kg.

8 The diameters, in cm, of the washers should have a N(1, 0.006) distribution. The test, on a sample of 20 washers, is at 5 per cent significance. Find the probability of a Type II error if the mean diameter has increased to 1.04 cm.

9 The fuel consumption, in m.p.g., should have a N(30, 5) distribution. The motorist applies a test at 5 per cent significance, on a sample of the number of miles driven on six gallons. Find the probability of a Type II error if the fuel consumption has fallen to 28 m.p.g.

10 Before going on the diet, the slimmer's weight, X kg, was such that $X \sim N(60, 2)$. After a week on the diet she weighs herself once. What values of this weight will convince her, at 5 per cent significance, that she has genuinely lost weight?

If in fact her mean weight is down to 58 kg, what is the probability of a Type II error?

11 The breaking strength, X newtons, should be such that $X \sim N(5000, 6000)$. The manufacturer finds the mean breaking strength of a sample of ten. The test is at 1 per cent significance. What values of the sample mean will convince the manufacturer that the true mean strength has fallen? Find the probability of a Type II error, if in fact the true mean is 4900 newtons.

12 The mass, X kg, of adult specimens of a certain species of fish satisfy $X \sim N(2, 0.3)$. The authority finds the mean weight, $\overline{X}$ kg, of a sample of 20 adult specimens. The test is at 5 per cent significance. Find the condition on $\overline{X}$ which will convince the authority that the mass has fallen. Find the probability of a Type II error if in fact the mass has fallen to 1.7 kg.

11.3 One-tailed and two-tailed tests

Manufacturers regularly test their products. A manufacturer of brake cables tests to see whether the breaking strength is high enough. A manufacturer of ball-bearings tests to see whether the diameters are correct.

For brake cables, there is only cause for worry if the strength is too low. For ball-bearings, there is cause for worry if the diameter is too low or too high, as in either case damage will be done to the machine in which they are used. We distinguish between two sorts of test, as follows.

In many tests, there is a null hypothesis which claims that a parameter has a certain value. It might claim that a certain mean μ is equal to 8. The alternative hypothesis is that the parameter is different from this value. It might be that the mean μ is different from 8, or that it is greater than 8.

Note the difference between these two alternative hypotheses.

H_0: $\mu \neq 8$ claims that the mean is different from 8, though without specifying whether it is greater or lesser.

H_0: $\mu > 8$ claims that the mean is greater than 8. We are not concerned with the possibility that the mean is less than 8.

The first case needs a **two-tailed** test. In the alternative hypothesis, we consider the possibility that the true value of the parameter could lie on either side of the claimed value.

The second case needs a **one-tailed** test. In the alternative hypothesis, we only consider the possibility that the true value of the parameter lies on one particular side of the claimed value.

As an example, if we suspect that buses are less frequent than the company claims, then we perform a one-tailed test, with an alternative hypothesis of the form $H_1 : \mu > 8$. If we suspect that the waiting time has changed, without knowing whether buses have become more or less frequent, then we perform a two-tailed test, with an alternative hypothesis of the form $H_1 : \mu \neq 8$.

We perform a one-tailed test in two situations.

- Before we do the test, we have reason to think that the true value lies on one particular side of the null hypothesis value.
- We are only interested if the true value lies on one particular side of the null hypothesis value.

Examples of situations where a one-tailed test is appropriate are:

- testing whether a batch of climbing ropes has too low a breaking strength
- testing whether or not extra tuition improves the grades obtained in Mathematics GCSE
- testing whether consumption of three glasses of wine results in a decrease in dexterity.

Examples of situations where a two-tailed test is appropriate are:

- testing whether the voltage delivered by a battery is not as claimed
- testing whether standards of numeracy have changed since the introduction of decimal currency.

Note
We must decide whether the test should be one or two tailed *before* doing the test. We cannot look at the data and then decide that the test should be one tailed.

Critical region

If our alternative hypothesis is that $\mu \neq 8$, then we shall be looking for abnormally low values of the test statistic as well as abnormally high values. For a 5 per cent significance test, the critical region will be in two parts: $2\frac{1}{2}$ per cent at the top and $2\frac{1}{2}$ per cent at the bottom. For a $N(0, 1)$ test statistic, the value of z which cuts off the top $2\frac{1}{2}$ per cent of probability is 1.96, as shown in Fig. 11.4. Hence this is our critical value.

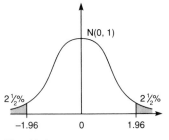

Fig. 11.4

EXAMPLE 11.4
An accident researcher is investigating whether there is a connection between the temperature inside a car and the skill of its driver. The connection will be tested by asking drivers to take a simulated test drive. It is known that, at normal room temperature, the

average score is 50. Several drivers performed the test-drive at ten degrees below room temperature, and their average score was found.

Should the test be one- or two-tailed? Set up suitable null and alternative hypotheses.

Solution
There is no reason to assume that driving standards will increase or decrease if the temperature falls. Cold might make the drivers more alert, but it might make them shiver.

A two-tailed test is appropriate.

Suppose the average score for the drivers in cold conditions is μ. The null hypothesis is that the cold has made no difference. The alternative hypothesis is that it has.

$$H_0 : \mu = 50 \qquad H_1 : \mu \neq 50.$$

EXAMPLE 11.5
Suppose that, in the situation of Example 11.4, ten drivers performed the test in the cold conditions, and achieved the scores as given below. Find the mean and unbiased sample variance of these scores. Assuming that the unbiased sample variance is correct, test at 5 per cent significance whether the cold has altered the score.

$$47 \quad 48 \quad 45 \quad 40 \quad 54 \quad 53 \quad 49 \quad 48 \quad 47 \quad 46$$

Solution
Using the methods of Chapter 10, we find that the sample mean $\overline{X}$ is 47.7, and the unbiased sample variance is 15.6.

The sample mean and unbiased sample variance are 47.7 and 15.6.

We use the null and alternative hypotheses above. Assuming the null hypothesis, and that the true variance is 15.6, the value of the test statistic is:

$$\frac{|47.7 - 50|}{\sqrt{\dfrac{15.6}{10}}} = 1.84$$

For a two-tailed test at 5 per cent, the critical value is 1.96. Our value is less than this, hence the results are not significant.

At 5 per cent significance, we have not shown that the cold alters the score.

Note
If we had done a one-tailed test, with an alternative hypothesis of the form $\mu < 50$, then our result would have been significant.

EXERCISE 11C

In Questions 1 to 7, determine whether a two-tailed or a one-tailed test is appropriate. Write down suitable null and alternative hypotheses. No calculation is required.

1 The average life of a car tyre is 15 000 miles. The government reduces expenditure on road main-tainance. A test is performed to see how this has affected the mean life, μ miles, of car tyres.

2 The mean waiting time for buses on the number 17 service is six minutes. The service is privatised. A test is performed to see how this has affected the mean waiting time, μ minutes.

3 A factory makes fishing lines which should have a breaking strength of 100 newtons. A cheaper production process is introduced. A test is performed to see whether this has affected the mean breaking strength, T N.

4 A farmer breeds pigs which at maturity have a mean weight of 320 lb. He changes the brand of pig feed they receive. He performs a test to see how this has affected their mean weight, μ lb.

5 The average time to read a certain passage is 30 minutes. A class receives a course in speed reading, and the results are tested by getting each member of the class to read the passage.

6 The mean weight of trout caught in a lake is 1.7 kg. A factory starts discharging effluent into the lake. A test is performed to see how this has affected the weight of the trout.

7 The manufacturers of a brand of cereal claim that the mean weight of the contents of the packets is 500 grams. The Trading Standards officer performs a test to see whether this claim is justified.

8 It is thought that the distribution of X is N(12, 18). A sample of size 50 had sample mean $\overline{X}$ equal to 11. Is this significant at 5 per cent to show that the true mean of X is different from 12?

9 It is thought that the distribution of X is N(1000, 200). A sample of size 30 had sample mean $\overline{X}$ equal to 1006. Is this significant at 5 per cent to show that the true mean of X is different from 10?

10 The weight, in kg, of mature specimens of a certain type of fish in a lake has a N(3, 0.8) distribution. After a factory has been discharging effluent into the lake, forty of the fish are caught and their mean weight is found to be 3.2 kg. Is this significant at 5 per cent to show that the effluent has affected the weight of the fish?

11 A motorist finds that the mean time in minutes he takes along a certain route is N(20, 10). Traffic lights are introduced on the route, and over the next 20 working days the average journey time was 22 minutes. Is this significant at 5 per cent to show that the lights have altered the journey time?

12 The time in hours that Emily sleeps has a normal distribution with mean 8 and variance 1.6. She wonders whether this will change after her A-levels. For the first ten nights after the exams, she sleeps an average of 7.7 hours. Is this significant at 5 per cent to show that her sleeping time has been affected?

13 Alan finds that the time in seconds he takes to run 100 m has a N(12, 0.5) distribution. After a change of diet he runs 100 m 20 times, and achieves an average of 11.6 seconds. Test at 1 per cent significance whether the change in diet has affected his time. (The critical value of z for a two-tailed test at 1 per cent is 2.576.)

14 The daily takings in a store, in £1000s, have a N(20, 38) distribution. A new manager is appointed, and the daily takings for the next eight days are as given below. Find the mean for these days. Is there evidence, significant at 5 per cent, to show that the mean of the daily takings has altered?

Takings (in £1000s)   18   19   20   16   13   27   12   22

15 The marks for a national examination have a normal distribution with mean 63 and variance 250. A school picks ten students at random to enter the exam, and their marks are as below. Find the mean of these marks. At 5 per cent, are they significantly different from the national average?

71   81   60   77   68   59   70   83   80   72

16 A manufacturer of hour-glasses claims that the sand should run through in a time which is normal with mean 4 minutes. Nine were tested, with the times in minutes as given below. Find the sample mean and the unbiased sample variance. Assuming that this variance is correct, test at 5 per cent significance whether the claim is justified.

4.3   4.7   3.8   4.1   4.5   4.2   4.4   4.4   4.3

11.4 Confidence intervals

Suppose we don't have any prior knowledge of what a particular mean is. Then we find the mean from a sample. We won't be certain that the sample mean is the true mean. All that we can say is that, with certain probability, the sample mean is reasonably close to the true mean.

The range of values which, with probability 95 per cent, contains the true mean, is a 95 per cent **confidence interval** for the mean.

Suppose the height, X cm, of certain plants has a N(μ, 4) distribution. Suppose we take a random sample of 16 plants, and find that the sample mean height, $\overline{X}$ cm, is equal to 10 cm. Then as $\overline{X} \sim$ N($\mu, \frac{4}{16}$):

$$P\left(\frac{|\mu - 10|}{\sqrt{\frac{4}{16}}} < 1.96\right) = 0.95$$

$$P(|\mu - 10| < 1.96\sqrt{\tfrac{1}{4}}) = 0.95$$

$$P(-1.96 \times \tfrac{1}{2} < \mu - 10 < 1.96 \times \tfrac{1}{2}) = 0.95$$

$$P(10 - 1.96 \times \tfrac{1}{2} < \mu < 10 + 1.96 \times \tfrac{1}{2}) = 0.95$$

The 95 per cent confidence interval is therefore $9.02 < \mu < 10.98$. We are 95 per cent confident that this interval contains the true value of μ.

In general, suppose the distribution of the population is $N(\mu, \sigma^2)$, where σ is known but μ is unknown. Take a sample of size n, and find the sample mean $\overline{X}$. The distribution of the sample mean is:

$$\overline{X} \sim N\left(\mu, \frac{\sigma^2}{n}\right)$$

The critical value for a 5 per cent significance test is 1.96. Hence, with probability 0.95, $\overline{X}$ lies within $1.96\sqrt{\dfrac{\sigma^2}{n}}$ of μ.

$$P\left(|\mu - \overline{X}| < 1.96\sqrt{\frac{\sigma^2}{n}}\right) = 0.95$$

$$P\left(-1.96\sqrt{\frac{\sigma^2}{n}} < \mu - \overline{X} < 1.96\sqrt{\frac{\sigma^2}{n}}\right) = 0.95$$

$$P\left(\overline{X} - 1.96\sqrt{\frac{\sigma^2}{n}} < \mu < \overline{X} + 1.96\sqrt{\frac{\sigma^2}{n}}\right) = 0.95$$

The confidence interval for μ is therefore:

$$\overline{X} - 1.96\sqrt{\frac{\sigma^2}{n}} < \mu < \overline{X} + 1.96\sqrt{\frac{\sigma^2}{n}}$$

Notes

1 If we repeatedly took samples of size n, and calculated a confidence interval based on the sample mean, we would expect the interval to capture the true mean in 95 per cent of cases. A computer investigation relevant to this is on page 309.

2 The confidence interval contains all those values of μ which would not be rejected by a two-tailed test at 5 per cent significance. Hence if a particular value μ_0 lies outside the confidence interval, then the null hypothesis that $\mu = \mu_0$ would be rejected in a 5 per cent two-tailed test.

3 Because the interval is symmetric about $\overline{X}$, it is sometimes described as a **symmetric** confidence interval.

Use of the central limit theorem

Our critical values are found from the normal distribution. The central limit theorem allows us to assume that the mean of a reasonably sized sample has a normal distribution. Hence we can apply the normal critical values to sample means from distributions which are not necessarily normal.

EXAMPLE 11.6
The time to solve a particular agility test has a normal distribution with variance 24 s². A group of 20 people took the test, and their

average time was 30 s. Find a 95 per cent confidence interval for the mean time.

Solution

Here $\sigma^2 = 24$, $n = 20$ and $\overline{X} = 30$. The confidence interval for the mean μ is:

$$30 - 1.96 \sqrt{\frac{24}{20}} < \mu < 30 + 1.96 \sqrt{\frac{24}{20}}$$

$$27.85 < \mu < 32.15$$

A 95 per cent confidence interval for the mean is between 27.85 and 32.15 seconds.

EXAMPLE 11.7

An explorer finds a new species of beetle. He captures and weighs 40 of them. The sum of their masses is 83 grams, and the sum of the squares of their masses is 250 grams^2. Find a 99 per cent confidence interval for the mean mass of the beetles.

Without any further calculation, comment on a claim that the true mean mass is 1.4 grams.

Solution

We are not given the variance of the weights. So we shall use the unbiased sample variance.

$$\hat{\sigma}^2 = \frac{n}{n-1} \left(\frac{\sum X_i^2}{n} - \left(\frac{\sum X_i}{n} \right)^2 \right)$$

$$= \frac{40}{39} \left(\frac{250}{40} - \left(\frac{80}{40} \right)^2 \right) = 1.994$$

We do not know that the distribution is normal. As we are taking the mean from a sample of size 40, the central limit theorem justifies the assumption that the distribution of the sample mean, $\overline{X}$, is approximately normal. The critical value for a test at 1 per cent significance is 2.576, hence the confidence interval for the mean μ is:

$$\overline{X} - 2.576 \sqrt{\frac{\hat{\sigma}^2}{n}} < \mu < \overline{X} + 2.576 \sqrt{\frac{\hat{\sigma}^2}{n}}$$

Here $\overline{X} = \frac{83}{40} = 2.075$, and $\hat{\sigma}^2 = 1.994$.

$$2.075 - 2.576 \sqrt{\frac{1.994}{40}} < \mu < 2.075 + 2.576 \sqrt{\frac{1.994}{40}}$$

$$1.50 < \mu < 2.65$$

A 99 per cent confidence interval for the mean mass is between 1.50 grams and 2.65 grams.

Note that the value of 1.4 grams lies outside this confidence interval.

At 1 per cent significance, we reject the claim that the mean weight is 1.4 grams.

EXERCISE 11D

1 In the following, a sample from a normal distribution has been taken. The sample size, n, the population variance, σ^2, and the sample mean, $\overline{X}$, are given. In each case find a 95 per cent confidence interval for the population mean μ.

   a) $n = 10, \sigma^2 = 12, \overline{X} = 4.3$ **b)** $n = 20, \sigma^2 = 251, \overline{X} = 1015$

   c) $n = 15, \sigma^2 = 0.001, \overline{X} = 0.04$ **d)** $n = 45, \sigma^2 = 78, \overline{X} = 53$

2 Find 99 per cent confidence intervals for each of the cases of Question 1.

3 For a national examination, the marks obtained have a normal distribution with variance 130. A sample of 20 pupils from a school obtained a mean mark of 61. Find a 95 per cent confidence interval for the mean mark for the school as a whole.

4 The rainfall in July in a certain town is normal with variance 21 cm². For ten years the July rainfall was measured, and the mean was 32 cm. Find a 95 per cent confidence interval for the mean July rainfall.

   Without any further calculation, comment on a claim that the true mean rainfall is 29 cm.

5 A machine produces washers with diameters whose distribution is normal. The mean can be adjusted, but the standard deviation is fixed at 0.01 cm. A sample of 40 washers had mean diameter 1.043 cm. Find a 99 per cent confidence interval for the mean diameter of the washers produced by the machine.

   Without any further calculation, comment on a claim that the true mean diameter has been set at 1.02 cm.

6 The mature mass of a certain breed of dog has a normal distribution with standard deviation 0.5 kg. Ten of these dogs had masses, in kg, as given below. Find the mean of these masses, and hence find a 95 per cent confidence interval for the mean mass of the breed.

   3.2   4.4   3.8   3.6   3.1   3.7   4.3   4.0   4.6   3.7

7 The marks obtained nationally in an examination have a normal distribution with variance 190. The marks obtained by a sample of ten students from a particular school are listed below. Find the sample mean mark, and hence find a 95 per cent confidence interval for the mean mark of the students from the school.

   64   61   58   70   49   56   66   60   52   74

8 The times, x seconds, taken by 100 people to complete a test of reaction speed are summarised by $\Sigma x = 657$ and $\Sigma x^2 = 4716$. Calculate the sample mean and the unbiased sample variance. Assuming that this variance is correct, find a 95 per cent confidence interval for the time people take to complete the test.

9 In an investigation into the fuel economy of a certain make of car, 50 cars were driven on one gallon of petrol and the distance, x miles, that each of them travelled was recorded. The results are summarised by $\Sigma x = 1576$ and $\Sigma x^2 = 50\,300$. Find the sample mean and the unbiased sample variance.

Assuming that this variance is correct, find a 95 per cent confidence interval for the mean fuel economy in miles per gallon. Without any further calculation, comment on a claim of the manufacturer that the mean is greater than 32 m.p.g.

LONGER EXERCISE

Trial by jury

A court trial is a test of the innocence or guilt of the accused. Under English law the accused is innocent until proven guilty. There are many similarities between a statistical test and a court trial.

What is the null hypothesis in a trial? What is the alternative hypothesis?

What are Type I and Type II errors in the verdict of the court? It is said that it is better that ten guilty men walk free rather than that one innocent man be convicted. How does this relate to Type I and Type II errors? How does this affect the level of significance?

A woman runs a catering firm. She sells sandwiches which, she claims, contain a minimum of 30 grams of chicken. A Trading Standards inspector tests 50 of her sandwiches, and finds that their chicken content, x grams, is summarised by $\Sigma x = 1400$ and $\Sigma x^2 = 39\,700$. The woman is prosecuted under the Trades Description Act.

How, in statistical jargon, would you summarise the evidence,

    a) as the prosecuting counsel,   **b)** as the defence counsel?

What should the court decide?

EXAMINATION QUESTIONS

1 An athletics coach has the use of a gymnasium which he sets out for circuit training. The time taken by a new athlete to complete the circuit on each of a large number of occasions is noted. The mean value of this time and the standard deviation are calculated to be 100 seconds and 3 seconds, respectively. The distribution of times may be assumed to be normal. Three months later, after the athlete has been training daily, his times, in seconds, to complete the circuit on 10 occasions are

    96.8   101.2   98.2   99.6   98.0   95.6   98.0   100.0   95.2   97.4

Verify that these values show, at the 5% level of significance, that the athlete's performance in circuit training has improved.

Calculations based on a large number of further trials show that at this stage the mean value of the time taken by the athlete is 98 seconds and the standard deviation is 3 seconds. What would be the maximum total time for 10 circuits at some later stage which would provide evidence, at the 5% level of significance, of further improvement?

C AS 1993

2 Give an example, from your projects if you wish, of the steps used in carrying out a test of significance.

Climbing rope produced by a manufacturer is known to be such that one-metre lengths have breaking strengths that are normally distributed with mean 170.2 kg and standard deviation 10.5 kg. Find, to 3 decimal places, the probability that

a) a one-metre length of rope chosen at random from those produced by the manufacturer will have a breaking strength of 175 to the nearest kg,

b) a random sample of 50 one-metre lengths will have a mean breaking strength of more than 172.4 kg.

A new component material is added to the ropes being produced. The manufacturer believes that this will increase the mean breaking strength without changing the standard deviation. A random sample of 50 one-metre lengths of the new rope is found to have a mean breaking strength of 172.4 kg. Perform a significance test at the 5% level to decide whether this result provides sufficient evidence to confirm the manufacturer's belief that the mean breaking strength is increased. State clearly the null and alternative hypotheses which you are using.

L 1988

3 Define Type I and Type II errors.

At a large school, there was an investigation of the distances from the school to the children's homes.

The distance from school, X kilometres, measured to the nearest kilometre, was recorded for each of a random sample of 60 children and the results summarised as follows.

$$\Sigma x = 464 \qquad \Sigma x^2 = 5769$$

a) Calculate unbiased estimates of the mean and the variance of the population from which this sample was drawn.

It is claimed that children from the school live on average less than 10 kilometres away from the school.

b) Stating any assumptions you make, use your results from (a) to test this claim. State clearly your hypotheses and use a 5% level of significance.

L 1994

4 The random variable X is normally distributed with mean μ and standard deviation 11. The null hypothesis $\mu = 52$ is to be tested against the alternative hypothesis $\mu > 52$ using a 5 per cent significance level. The mean $\overline{X}$ of a random sample of 150 observations of X is to be used as the test statistic.

(i) Find the range of values of the test statistic which lie in the critical region.

(ii) When $\mu = 54$ calculate, to two decimal places, the probability of a type-2 error and the power of the test.

N 1991

5 A Primary school teacher measured the height of the 44 boys in year five in his school. He found the mean height to be 142.0 cm. Records for girls of the same age group in the whole local authority showed that the distribution of heights of the girls is Normal and has a mean of 144.6 cm and a standard deviation of 9.61 cm.

a) The teacher wondered whether there was sufficient evidence to support his view that on average, boys are shorter than girls at this age. Set up suitable hypotheses and conduct a test at the 5% level.

b) What conclusions do you draw from the result of your test? What assumptions have you had to make in order to carry out the test?

O 1992

6 Explain what you understand by the term 'Central Limit Theorem', illustrating your answer with reference to any experiment you may have conducted.

In 1988 a meteorologist recorded the length of time (hours) the sun shone at her work station for each of the 31 days during December. She then calculated the mean daily figure for that month. Her data can be summarised as

$$\Sigma x_i = 44.48 \qquad \Sigma x_i^2 = 83.5008$$

where $i = 1$ to 31 and x_i represents the daily sunshine in hours.

a) Write down a point estimate of the mean daily hours of sunshine. Calculate an unbiased estimate for the variance of the daily sunshine. Hence find the 'standard error' of the mean.

b) Calculate a 95% confidence interval for the expected hours of sunshine for a day in December. In December 1989, the sun shone for a total of 62.62 hours. Is this sufficient evidence to suggest that there was a change in the average daily sunshine? Justify your response.

O 1990

7 A machine is known to dispense liquid into cartons such that the volume dispensed is normally distributed with a standard deviation of 3.4 ml. It is claimed by the manufacturer of the machine that the mean volume dispensed is 100 ml.

In a series of trials on the machine the following values were recorded.

104.4   101.7   103.6   99.2   102.2   107.6   96.2   105.8   104.7   98.6

a) Find a 95% symmetrical confidence interval for the mean volume of liquid dispensed by the machine.

b) Use your interval to comment on the claim of the manufacturer.
Comment on the likely reaction of customers receiving cartons from the machine.

c) Estimate how many samples should be taken if the probability that the sample mean is within 1.5 ml of the true value is 0.95.

L 1995

Summary and key points

11.1 A hypothesis test obtains a conclusion from data about a distribution.

The null hypothesis is that a parameter of the distribution has a fixed value.

The alternative hypothesis is that the parameter takes a different value.

When doing a test, we assume the null hypothesis. We find the probability of obtaining results as extreme as those of the data. If this probability is less than the level of significance, then the null hypothesis is rejected. Otherwise the null hypothesis is retained.

A test statistic is a function of the experimental data. Often there is a critical region, where the null hypothesis will be rejected if the test statistic lies in this region.

Note that we can never prove the null hypothesis. We can only fail to reject it.

11.2 A Type I error is wrongly to reject the null hypothesis. A Type II error is wrongly to retain the null hypothesis. There are penalties attached to both these errors.

11.3 Suppose we are testing whether a parameter, θ, takes a fixed value θ_0. In a two-tailed test the alternative hypothesis is that $\theta \neq \theta_0$. A one-tailed test is either that $\theta < \theta_0$ or that $\theta > \theta_0$.

A two-tailed test is performed, unless there is prior reason to think that the deviation could only go one way, or if we are only concerned if the deviation goes one way.

11.4 A 95 per cent confidence interval for a mean, μ, is an interval which contains the true value of μ with probability 0.95. If $\overline{X}$ is the mean of a sample of size n from a $N(\mu, \sigma^2)$ distribution, the interval is:

$$\overline{X} - 1.96 \sqrt{\frac{\sigma^2}{n}} < \mu < \overline{X} + 1.96 \sqrt{\frac{\sigma^2}{n}}$$

Tests 2

In Chapter 11 Tests 1, we introduced many of the basic concepts of tests. These included the null and alternative hypotheses, one- and two-tailed tests, level of significance and so on. Here we show how these principles can be applied in other cases and to other distributions.

12.1 Difference of means

In Chapter 11 we discussed examples of tests of whether the mean of a population had a certain value. We often need to test whether the means of two populations are the same, regardless of what they are. In this case we shall be testing whether their difference is zero.

We might want to test whether left-handed and right-handed people have the same level of agility. We could set an exercise involving agility for random samples of both left-handed and right-handed people. We would test whether the average score of the left-handed people was significantly different from that of the right-handed people.

Suppose we find that the mean sample scores for left-handers and right-handers were 107 and 98 respectively. Have we shown that left-handers are better? How significant is the difference of 9? In order to find this out, we need to know the distribution of $\overline{X} - \overline{Y}$, the difference between the mean sample scores.

In general, suppose our populations are $X \sim N(\mu_1, \sigma_1^2)$ and $Y \sim N(\mu_2, \sigma_2^2)$. The null hypothesis is that the means are the same, and the alternative hypothesis that they are different (if we are doing a two-tailed test).

$$H_0\!: \mu_1 = \mu_2 \qquad H_1\!: \mu_1 \neq \mu_2$$

Collect independent samples $X_1, X_2, ..., X_n$, and $Y_1, Y_2, ..., Y_m$. The sample means are $\overline{X}$ and $\overline{Y}$ respectively. By results from Chapter 10:

$$\overline{X} \sim N\!\left(\mu_1, \frac{\sigma_1^2}{n}\right) \text{ and } \overline{Y} \sim N\!\left(\mu_2, \frac{\sigma_2^2}{m}\right)$$

$$\overline{X} - \overline{Y} \sim N\left(\mu_1 - \mu_2, \frac{\sigma_1^2}{n} + \frac{\sigma_2^2}{m}\right)$$

Assuming the null hypothesis, $\mu_1 = \mu_2$. Hence:

$$\overline{X} - \overline{Y} \sim N\left(0, \frac{\sigma_1^2}{n} + \frac{\sigma_2^2}{m}\right)$$

The test statistic will therefore be:

$$\frac{|\overline{X} - \overline{Y}|}{\sqrt{\frac{\sigma_1^2}{n} + \frac{\sigma_2^2}{m}}}$$

If this is greater than 1.96 (the cut-off point for a two-tailed test with 5 per cent significance) then at 5 per cent significance we shall have proved that the means are different.

If both X and Y have the same known variance σ^2 then the test statistic is:

$$\frac{|\overline{X} - \overline{Y}|}{\sqrt{\frac{\sigma^2}{n} + \frac{\sigma^2}{m}}}$$

EXAMPLE 12.1

The mark in a national examination has variance 10. A sample of 20 boys from a school took the exam and obtained a mean mark of 40. A sample of 25 girls from the same school had mean mark 38. Is this significant at 5 per cent to show that there is a difference in the abilities of boys and girls?

Solution

Let X represent the mark for boys, and Y the mark for girls. Let these have means μ and μ' respectively. We assume that they have a common variance of 10.

$$H_0: \mu = \mu' \qquad H_1: \mu \neq \mu'$$

Assuming H_0, the difference between the sample means has distribution

$$\overline{X} - \overline{Y} \sim N\left(0, \frac{10}{20} + \frac{10}{25}\right) \text{ i.e. } N(0, 0.9)$$

The value of the test statistic is therefore:

$$\frac{40 - 38}{\sqrt{0.9}} = 2.11$$

This is greater than 1.96. The null hypothesis is rejected.

At 5 per cent significance, we have shown that there is a difference in ability.

EXAMPLE 12.2
Considering again the situation of Example 12.1, obtain a 95 per
cent confidence interval for the difference $\mu - \mu'$ between the
mean marks for boys and girls.

Solution
As above, the variance of the difference between sample means is
0.9. Hence the confidence interval is

$$2 - 1.96\sqrt{0.9} < \mu - \mu' < 2 + 1.96\sqrt{0.9}$$

The confidence interval is $0.14 < \mu - \mu' < 3.86$.

Note
This confidence interval does not include 0. This is consistent with
the result of Example 12.1, that the difference between sample
means is significantly different from zero.

EXERCISE 12A

1 In the following, the random variables, X and Y, both come from normal distributions with variance as given. Samples are taken from both X and Y. The sample means are given. In each case
test whether the results are significant at 5 per cent to show whether there is a difference between
X and Y.

a) $\sigma^2 = 20$, sample sizes both 15, $\overline{X} = 24.1$, $\overline{Y} = 26.9$

b) $\sigma^2 = 10$, sample sizes 20 and 25, $\overline{X} = 13.1$, $\overline{Y} = 14.5$

c) $\sigma^2 = 30$, sample sizes 25 and 30, $\overline{X} = 56.8$, $\overline{Y} = 60.2$

d) $\sigma^2 = 0.025$, sample sizes 10 and 15, $\overline{X} = 0.25$, $\overline{Y} = 0.37$

2 Repeat Question 1, this time testing whether the data shows that the mean of Y is significantly
greater than the mean of X.

3 The variance of the number of miles that a certain make of car will drive on a gallon of petrol is
5.8. A new petrol additive is to be tested. Ten cars were driven on a gallon of petrol without the
additive, and covered a mean distance of 30.3 miles. Another ten cars driven on a gallon of petrol
with the additive covered a mean distance of 31.5. Is this significant at 5 per cent to show that the
additive has improved the fuel economy of the cars?

4 The time taken to complete an exercise which involves speed of reaction, has standard deviation
0.9 seconds. A group of 20 people were deprived of sleep for 24 hours and then given the exercise.
Their mean time was 2.6 seconds. A control group of 20 people who had slept normally achieved
a mean time of 2.1 seconds. Is this significant at 1 per cent to show that sleep deprivation has
increased the reaction time?

5 The daily takings, in £1000s, in a Sainsways store have variance 24. A Safebury store opens nearby. In the 20 days before the opening the daily takings in Sainsways had mean £26 000, and in the 20 days after the opening the daily takings had mean £23 000. Is this significant at 5 per cent to show that the opening of the new rival store has resulted in a loss of takings?

6 The standard deviation of the lifetime of certain bulbs is 250 hours. A new manufacturing process is introduced. The mean lifetime of a sample of 25 bulbs made by the old process was 1120 hours. The mean lifetime of a sample of 30 bulbs made by the new process was 1036. Are these results significant at 5 per cent to show that the new process results in a different lifetime?

7 The rainfall in April in a certain town has variance 9 cm². Over the ten years of the 1970s, the average monthly rainfall was 28 cm. Over the 1980s, the average was 25 cm. Is this significant at 5 per cent to show that the 1980s were drier than the 1970s?

8 Two machines pack bags of flour. The means of the masses packed can be adjusted, but the standard deviations are fixed, at 20 grams for Machine A and 5 grams for Machine B.

   A sample of 15 bags from Machine A had mean mass 505 grams, and a sample of 20 bags from Machine B had mean mass 513 grams. Is this significant at 5 per cent to show that the machines have been set differently?

   Obtain a 95 per cent confidence interval for the difference between the means.

9 In two resorts A and B, the standard deviations of the number of hours of sunshine per day are 3.2 and 1.2 respectively. Over 30 days, the mean number of hours of sunshine per day in resort A was 8.3. Over 20 days, the mean number of hours of sunshine per day in resort B was 9.7. Is this significant at 5 per cent to show that one resort is sunnier than the other?

   Obtain a 95 per cent confidence interval for the difference between the means.

10 The weight of fruit produced by apple trees in an orchard has a normal distribution with standard deviation 25 lb. A new sort of insecticide is tried with a group of ten trees, while the old sort is applied to another group of ten trees. Their yields are shown in the table below. Find the sample means, and test at 5 per cent significance whether the new insecticide is more effective than the old.

Old yield (lb)	135	152	142	137	143	150	162	183	160	130
New yield (lb)	157	139	169	177	180	183	159	169	179	180

11 An independent school which has both boarding and day pupils wishes to test whether IQs differ for the two sorts of pupil. It tested 12 boarders and 14 day boys, with results as below. The IQs are normally distributed with variance 225. Test at 5 per cent significance whether there is a difference.

Boarders	108	115	98	125	117	105	104	110	114	106	106	105		
Day boys	107	121	128	106	116	109	101	114	117	118	109	104	116	117

12.2 Binomial tests

So far we have been testing the value of the mean of a population. Often we need to test the probability of a certain event, or the proportion of a population which has a certain property.

Suppose that you encounter a gambler, who insists on using his own die. After a few games you suspect that the die is biased towards the number 5. When the gambler is out of the room you roll the die ten times, and 5 comes up on four of those times. Have you proved that the die is biased? It is possible that 5 could have come up frequently by chance, so you have not proved *certainly* that the die is biased.

For a normal die the probability that it will land 5 uppermost is $\frac{1}{6}$. Is the probability for this particular die different from $\frac{1}{6}$? Our null hypothesis would be that the probability is $\frac{1}{6}$. The alternative hypothesis is that it is greater than $\frac{1}{6}$.

In general, suppose a particular experiment has probability p of success. To test whether p has a particular value p_0, perform the experiment independently n times. The number of successes will have the binomial distribution $B(n, p)$. The null and alternative hypotheses will be:

$$H_0: p = p_0 \qquad H_1: p \neq p_0 \qquad (\text{or } p < p_0 \text{ or } p > p_0)$$

Critical region and critical value

As with our previous tests, the set of values of the test statistic for which we shall reject the null hypothesis is the critical region. Often this **critical region** consists of values greater than a certain value, in which case this is the **critical value**.

Consider the die example. If the null hypothesis that $p = \frac{1}{6}$ is true, then the distribution of the number of 5s is $B(10, \frac{1}{6})$. A bar chart of this distribution is shown in Fig. 12.1. The shaded bars on the right contain up to 5 per cent of the probability. The critical region therefore consists of 5, 6 up to 10. Hence if, in ten rolls, the number 5 comes up five times or more, then we shall reject H_0 and infer that the die is biased.

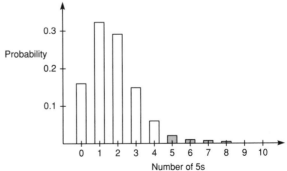

Fig. 12.1

EXAMPLE 12.3

There are 36 holes in a roulette wheel, of which 18 are red and 18 black. The manager of the casino suspects that the croupier is letting red come up less often than black. Write down suitable null and alternative hypotheses for a test to see whether or not this is the case.

The wheel is spun 20 times, and the ball lands in a red hole five times. What can be inferred at a 5 per cent level of significance?

Solution

Let p be the probability that the ball will land in a red hole. The null hypothesis is that the wheel is as it should be, so that the ball is equally likely to land in red or black holes. The manager suspects that red holes are less likely than black.

$$H_0: p = \tfrac{1}{2} \qquad H_1: p < \tfrac{1}{2}$$

Assume H_0. Let X be the number of times the ball lands in a red hole. This is our test statistic, and it has a binomial distribution, $B(20, \tfrac{1}{2})$.

Look at the table of cumulative binomial probability for $n = 20$ and $p = \tfrac{1}{2}$. The critical region consists of those values of X at which the cumulative probability is less than 0.05. We see from the table below that the critical region contains 0, 1, 2, 3, 4 and 5.

$n = 20$

$p = 0.05$	0.1	0.15	1/6	0.2	0.25	0.3	1/3	0.35	0.4	0.45	0.5
$i =$											
0 0.3585	0.1216	0.0388	0.0261	0.0115	0.0032	0.0008	0.0003	0.0002	0.0000	0.0000	0.0000
1 0.7358	0.3917	0.1756	0.1304	0.0692	0.0243	0.0076	0.0033	0.0021	0.0005	0.0001	0.0000
2 0.9245	0.6769	0.4049	0.3287	0.2061	0.0913	0.0355	0.0176	0.0121	0.0036	0.0009	0.0002
3 0.9841	0.8670	0.6477	0.5665	0.4114	0.2252	0.1071	0.0604	0.0444	0.0160	0.0049	0.0013
4 0.9974	0.9568	0.8298	0.7687	0.6296	0.4148	0.2375	0.1515	0.1182	0.0510	0.0189	0.0059
5 0.9997	0.9887	0.9327	0.8982	0.8042	0.6172	0.4164	0.2972	0.2454	0.1256	0.0553	0.0207
6 1.0000	0.9976	0.9781	0.9629	0.9133	0.7858	0.6080	0.4793	0.4166	0.2500	0.1299	0.0577
7 1.0000	0.9996	0.9941	0.9887	0.9679	0.8982	0.7723	0.6615	0.6010	0.4159	0.2520	0.1316
8 1.0000	0.9999	0.9987	0.9972	0.9900	0.9591	0.8867	0.8095	0.7624	0.5956	0.4143	0.2517
9 1.0000	1.0000	0.9998	0.9994	0.9974	0.9861	0.9520	0.9081	0.8782	0.7553	0.5914	0.4119
10 1.0000	1.0000	1.0000	0.9999	0.9994	0.9961	0.9829	0.9624	0.9468	0.8725	0.7507	0.5881

The experimental value found was $X = 5$. This is in the critical region. Hence at this significance level we reject H_0, and we accept H_1.

At a 5 per cent level, we have shown that the wheel is biased against red numbers.

EXERCISE 12B

1 Suppose the roulette wheel of Example 12.3 is spun 30 times, and comes up red 11 times. What can be inferred at a 5 per cent level of significance?

Suppose the wheel is spun 40 times, and gives 14 reds. What can be inferred at a 5 per cent level of significance?

2 The numbers generated by a random number program should have a uniform distribution between 0 and 1. A programmer writes a new program to generate random numbers, but suspects that the numbers generated will be biased towards low values, in that more than half will be less than $\frac{1}{2}$. Write down suitable null and alternative hypotheses for a test.

Of the first 30 numbers, 20 were less than $\frac{1}{2}$. What can be inferred at a significance level of 5 per cent?

3 A coin is suspected of being biased towards heads. Write down suitable null and alternative hypotheses for a test.

The coin will be tested by spinning it 20 times, and counting the number of heads obtained. What is the critical region for this test, at 5 per cent level of significance?

The coin was spun 20 times, and heads occurred 14 times. What can be inferred?

4 A firm which makes instant coffee claims that people cannot tell the difference between its brand and real coffee made from beans. A sample of 20 people are given cups of both the instant and the real coffee, and asked to state which is which. If 15 got it right, what can be inferred at a 5 per cent level of significance?

5 The median weight of a certain sort of beetle is 0.2 grams. It is suspected that after an exceptionally cold spell the weight of the beetles will decrease. After such a cold spell, 40 beetles are collected to test this hypothesis. If 24 beetles are under 0.2 grams, are the suspicions justified at a significance level of 5 per cent?

6 The upper quartile of the scores in a national examination is 140 (i.e. a quarter of the population scored more than 140). A college claims that its students are better than the average, and sets the examination to 40 of them. Write down suitable null and alternative hypotheses for a test of the college's claim.

Find the critical region for a test at 5 per cent. What can be inferred if 18 out of the 40 scored more than 140?

7 Brian claims to be able to mind-read. In particular, he claims to be able to tell the suit of a card being looked at by someone else. State suitable null and alternative hypotheses for a test of his claim.

Another person will look at 40 cards, and Brian will state the suit of each. What is the critical region for a test at 1 per cent significance level?

In fact, he got 19 right out of 40. What can be inferred at a significance level of 5 per cent?

8 A roulette wheel has holes numbered 1 to 36. A gambler suspects that the croupier is biasing the wheel towards numbers 1 to 12 inclusive. In a sequence of 30 spins there were 15 numbers from 1 to 12. What can be inferred at a significance level of 5 per cent?

Normal approximation

In Example 12.3 and in Exercise 12B, the number of trials, n, and the probability, p, were such that we were able to use the cumulative binomial tables. If the number of trials or the probability we are testing does not appear in the tables, then we may have to use the normal approximation to the binomial distribution. This will be permissible if np and $n(1 - p)$ are large enough.

A standard case of this occurs when opinion polls are taken. Suppose that the true proportion of the electorate which supports the Purple Party is π. An opinion poll of 1000 people is taken, and the number, X, of people who say they support the party is found. We want to known whether there is evidence, significant at 5 per cent, to show that a majority of the electorate supports the Purple Party.

The distribution of X is B(1000, π). The null hypothesis is that $\pi = \frac{1}{2}$. The alternative hypothesis is that $\pi > \frac{1}{2}$. So assuming the null hypothesis

$$X \sim B(1000, 0.5)$$

The sample is large enough for the normal approximation to be used.

$$X \text{ is approximately N(500, 250)}$$

We now proceed as in Chapter 11 to see whether the value of X is significantly greater than 500.

EXAMPLE 12.4
A sample of 2000 people are asked whether or not they support the return of capital punishment. A total of 1050 reply that they do. Is this significant at 5 per cent to show that a majority of the population supports capital punishment?

Solution
Suppose that, in the population as a whole, the proportion of people who support capital punishment is π. We are concerned whether or not π is greater than $\frac{1}{2}$.

$$H_0: \pi = \frac{1}{2} \qquad H_1: \pi > \frac{1}{2}$$

Let X be the number of people in a sample of 2000 who support capital punishment. Then assuming the null hypothesis:

$$X \sim B(2000, \frac{1}{2})$$

This distribution is approximately N(1000, 500). Using the continuity correction, we consider the probability that X is greater than 1049.5. The value of the test statistic is:

$$\frac{1049.5 - 1000}{\sqrt{500}} = 2.21$$

The value of 2.21 is greater than 1.645, the cut-off point for a one-tailed test at 5 per cent significance.

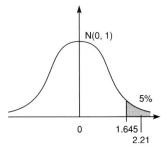

Fig. 12.2

At 5 per cent significance, we have shown that a majority of the population supports capital punishment.

A similar method can be used for tests involving a Poisson distribution.

EXAMPLE 12.5

The number, X, of accidents per month which occur along a particular stretch of road is such that $X \sim \text{Po}(3.7)$. A speed limit is introduced, and in the following 12 months there were 32 accidents. Is this significant at 5 per cent to show that there has been a reduction in the number of accidents?

Solution

The number, Y, of accidents in 12 months has a $\text{Po}(\lambda)$ distribution. If the incidence of accidents is unchanged, then $\lambda = 12 \times 3.7$, i.e. $\lambda = 44.4$.

$$H_0{:}\lambda = 44.4 \qquad H_1{:}\ \lambda < 44.4$$

Assume H_0. The distribution of Y is $\text{Po}(44.4)$, which is approximately $N(44.4, 44.4)$. The value of the test statistic is (using a continuity correction):

$$\frac{|32.5 - 44.4|}{\sqrt{44.4}} = 1.80$$

This is greater than 1.645, the cut-off value for a one-tailed test at 5 per cent significance.

At 5 per cent significance, we can infer that the number of accidents has been reduced.

EXERCISE 12C

1 In the following, an experiment is repeated independently n times. The number of successes is X. Is the result significant at 5 per cent to show that the probability of success is not the p_0 given?

   a) $n = 100$, $X = 57$, $p_0 = \frac{1}{2}$ **b)** $n = 1000$, $X = 826$, $p_0 = 0.8$

   c) $n = 800$, $X = 176$, $p_0 = \frac{1}{4}$ **d)** $n = 2000$, $X = 1321$, $p_0 = \frac{2}{3}$

2 A coin is spun 200 times, and shows heads 123 times. Is this significant at 5 per cent to show that the coin is biased?

3 A die is rolled 600 times, and gives a six 119 times. Is this significant at 5 per cent to show that the die is biased towards six?

4 Support for the Reactionary Party is running at 25 per cent of the electorate. The party changes its leader, and an opinion poll of 1000 people reveals a 27 per cent support for the party. Is this significant at 5 per cent to show that the change of leader has altered the support for the party?

5 A tennis player normally gets 40 per cent of her first serves in. After coaching, she serves 60 times and gets 31 of her first serves in. Is this significant at 5 per cent to show that coaching has improved her play?

6 In a general knowledge game, the contestants are asked a sequence of 50 questions, each of which has four possible answers. A contestant answers 21 questions correctly. Is this significant at 5 per cent to show that he has not been answering at random?

7 The buses that call at a bus stop are either the blue service or the green service. There are twice as many blue buses as green buses. The green service is privatised, and a passenger keeps records on how often a green bus comes before a blue bus. She finds that this happened on 24 days out of 55. Is this significant at 5 per cent to show that the service has been altered?

8 Desirée finds that the lower quartile of the time she takes to run the 100 m is 13.3 seconds (i.e. when she runs 100 m, her time is under 13.3 seconds on a quarter of the occasions). After a change of diet she runs 100 m 25 times, and beats 13.3 seconds on nine of them. Is this significant at 5 per cent to show that the change has altered her running time?

9 A large school has equal numbers of boys and girls. A group of 35 is selected to go on a theatre trip. If 23 girls are selected, is there evidence, significant at 5 per cent, to show that there has been some sexual discrimination?

10 To determine whether a coin is biased towards heads, it is spun 100 times. The test is at 5 per cent significance. What is the least number of heads scored that will lead to the conclusion that the coin is biased?

If the true probability of heads is 0.6, what is the probability of a Type II error?

11 A political party commissions an opinion poll of 1000 people to see whether its support is less than 40 per cent. The test is at 5 per cent significance. What is the greatest number of supporters in the sample that will lead to the conclusion that support is less than 40 per cent?

If support is running at 35 per cent, what is the probability of a Type II error?

12 The number, X, of misprints in a magazine is such that $X \sim \text{Po}(40)$. The publishers employ a new typesetter, and find that the number of misprints in the next issue is 52. Is this significant at 5 per cent to show that the incidence of misprints has altered?

13 The number of cases seen by a surgery, per week, of people scalded by cooking oil has a Poisson distribution with mean 1.8. A campaign for greater safety in the home is undertaken and, in the following 20 months, 24 cases are seen. At 5 per cent level, has there been a significant reduction in the incidence of these accidents?

14 The number, X, of customers in an antique shop per day is such that $X \sim \text{Po}(56)$. On an exceptionally hot day there were 42 customers. Is this significant at 5 per cent to show that the weather has affected the number of customers?

12.3 Tests on proportion

In Section 12.2 we tested whether a proportion or a probability had a certain value. We can also do this by considering the distribution of the sample proportion.

Suppose the true proportion with a certain property is π. Take a random sample of size n, and let the proportion of the sample with the property be p. If n is reasonable large, the distribution of p is approximately $N\left(\pi, \dfrac{\pi(1 - \pi)}{n}\right)$.

Proof

The number X with the property has the $B(n, \pi)$ distribution, which is approximately $N(n\pi, n\pi(1 - \pi))$. The sample proportion is given by $p = \dfrac{X}{n}$. Using results from Chapter 10, this is approximately:

$$N\left(\frac{n\pi}{n}, \frac{n\pi(1 - \pi)}{n^2}\right) \quad \text{i.e.} \quad N\left(\pi, \frac{\pi(1 - \pi)}{n}\right)$$

EXAMPLE 12.6

A garden centre claims that at least $\frac{3}{4}$ of the crocus bulbs it sells will flower. A gardener buys 60 bulbs, and finds that only $\frac{2}{3}$ of them flower. Is this significant at 5 per cent to discredit the garden centre's claim?

Solution

Let π be the true proportion of crocuses which flower. A one-tailed test is appropriate.

$$H_0: \pi = \tfrac{3}{4} \qquad H_1: \pi < \tfrac{3}{4}$$

Assuming H_0, the proportion, p, out of 60 bulbs that flower has, approximately, a $N(\frac{3}{4}, 0.003\,125)$ distribution. The value of the test statistic is therefore:

$$\frac{|\frac{2}{3} - \frac{3}{4}|}{\sqrt{0.003\,125}} = 1.49$$

This is less than 1.645. The null hypothesis is retained.

At 5 per cent significance, we have not discredited the claim.

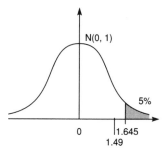

Fig. 12.3

EXERCISE 12D

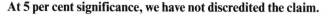

1 In each part of this question, it is claimed that a proportion is equal to π. A sample of size n is found, and the sample proportion p is found. In each case find whether or not there is evidence to discredit the claim, significant at 5 per cent.

a) $\pi = \frac{1}{2}, n = 90, p = 0.55$ **b)** $\pi = \frac{1}{3}, n = 1000, p = 0.3$

c) $\pi = 0.2, n = 200, p = 0.25$ **d)** $\pi = 0.6, n = 150, p = 0.5$

2 For a certain psychiatric condition, it is known that 30 per cent of sufferers will recover without any treatment. A therapy is devised, and out of 120 sufferers receiving the therapy one third recovered. Is this significant at 5 per cent to show that the treatment is effective?

3 A washing powder company claims that at least 40 per cent of households use its product. A sample of 500 households was investigated, and it was found that 35 per cent of them used the product. Is this significant at 5 per cent to discredit the company's claim?

4 A manufacturer of milk cartons claims that at most 10 per cent leak. In a sample of 80 cartons, the proportion that leaked was 15 per cent. Is this significant at 5 per cent to discredit the claim?

5 A college claims to recruit men and women equally. It was found that one year it recruited 520 men students and 435 women students. Is this significant at 5 per cent to discredit the college's claim?

*6 The *Monte Carlo* method for finding the area of a region involves picking points at random and seeing how many of them fall within the region.

To estimate π, a circle was drawn within a square as shown in Fig. 12.4. Out of 300 points chosen within the square, 219 landed within the circle. Is this significant at 5 per cent to show that the points were not chosen randomly?

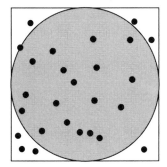

Fig. 12.4

Difference in proportion

If we want to test whether or not a proportion has a certain value, we can do it either by a binomial test, as in Section 12.2, or by a test on proportion as in this section. To test whether or not two proportions are the same, we have to consider the distribution of the difference between the sample proportions.

Suppose we want to test the difference in proportion between two groups. For example, we might want to find whether men and women differ in terms of their support for a political party. We might, for example, poll 1000 men and 1500 women, and find that 400 men and 450 women support the Purple Party. Then the sample proportions are

$$p_1 = \frac{400}{1000} = 0.4 \qquad \text{and } p_2 = \frac{450}{1500} = 0.3$$

Is the difference of 0.1 significant, or might it have come about by chance? To answer this we need to know the distribution of the difference $p_1 - p_2$.

In general, suppose the true population proportions are π_1 and π_2 respectively. The null and alternative hypotheses are (for a two-tailed test)

$$H_0: \pi_1 = \pi_2 \quad H_1: \pi_1 \neq \pi_2$$

Suppose the two samples have size n and m. Let the numbers having the property in the two groups be X_1 and X_2 respectively. Let the sample proportions be p_1 and p_2 respectively.

If the samples are large enough, then the distributions of the sample proportions are approximately:

$$p_1 \sim N\left(\pi_1, \frac{\pi_1(1 - \pi_1)}{n}\right) \quad p_2 \sim N\left(\pi_2, \frac{\pi_2(1 - \pi_2)}{m}\right)$$

Under the null hypothesis, $\pi_1 = \pi_2 = \pi$ say. Hence the difference of the sample proportions will have approximate distribution:

$$p_1 - p_2 \sim N\left(0, \pi(1 - \pi)\left(\frac{1}{n} + \frac{1}{m}\right)\right)$$

We don't know the true value of π. Hence we estimate π by the proportion obtained by combining both groups, i.e. by $\dfrac{X_1 + X_2}{n + m}$.

For the example above, we shall estimate π by:

$$\pi \simeq \frac{400 + 450}{1000 + 1500} = 0.34$$

EXAMPLE 12.7
A new medicine is developed to alleviate the symptoms of Lurgy. 200 sufferers were split into two equal groups: one was given the medicine, the other given a placebo (an inactive substance which seems the same as the real medicine). None of the patients knew which group they were in. After a week, the numbers of patients reporting an improvement were 50 for the patients given the real medicine, and 35 for the patients given the placebo. Is there evidence, significant at 5 per cent, to show that the medicine is effective?

Solution
Suppose the medicine or the placebo were administered to all the sufferers from the disease. Let the proportions of people who would report an improvement be π_1 for those given the medicine, and π_2 for those given the placebo. The null and alternative hypotheses are:

$$H_0: \pi_1 = \pi_2 \qquad H_1: \pi_1 > \pi_2$$

(A one-tailed test is appropriate.)

Assuming the null hypothesis, that $\pi_1 = \pi_2 = \pi$ say, the difference in sample proportions has the approximate distribution:

$$p_1 - p_2 \sim N(0, \pi(1 - \pi)(\tfrac{1}{100} + \tfrac{1}{100}))$$

We estimate π by the overall proportion of patients who reported an improvement, i.e. by:

$$\pi \simeq \tfrac{85}{200} = 0.425$$

The sample proportions are $p_1 = 0.5$ and $p_2 = 0.35$. The value of the test statistic is:

$$\frac{0.5 - 0.35}{\sqrt{(0.425(1 - 0.425)(\tfrac{1}{100} + \tfrac{1}{100}))}} = 2.15$$

This is greater than 1.645. Hence the null hypothesis is rejected.

At 5 per cent significance, we have shown that the medicine is effective.

EXERCISE 12E

1 In each part of this question two samples of sizes n and m were taken from two populations. The proportions with a certain property in the samples were p and q. Test at a 5 per cent significance level whether or not there is a difference between the proportions in the populations.

   a) $n = 100, m = 200, p = 0.45, q = 0.5$ **b)** $n = 100, m = 100, p = 0.26, q = 0.44$

   c) $n = 200, m = 300, p = 0.56, q = 0.58$

2 To test the effectiveness of sowing seeds under glass, 50 seeds were sown in a greenhouse, and 50 were sown outside in the open air. The proportions germinating under glass and outside were 0.6 and 0.5 respectively. Is this significant at 5 per cent to show that sowing under glass improves the rate of germination?

3 In a school there are 300 boys and 280 girls. Of these, 110 boys and 75 girls are short-sighted. Is this significant at 5 per cent to show that one sex is more likely to be short-sighted than the other?

4 Two stockbrokers each recommended 50 shares to their clients. Of the first stockbroker's recommendations, 30 are classified as having done well. The corresponding number for the second stockbroker is 35. Is this significant at 5 per cent to show that one stockbroker is better than the other?

5 To test the reliability of two different makes of car, samples of size 100 were taken of each. For make A, 33 had broken down at least once in the first year. For make B, 25 had broken down. Is this significant at 5 per cent to show that one make is more reliable than the other?

6 A cereal company started a series of advertisements, which were shown on English television but not on Scottish. Market research was done on 160 English households and 100 Scottish households. The proportions buying the company's product were 0.25 and 0.18 respectively. Assuming that before the advertising campaign the proportions in England and Scotland were the same, is there evidence, significant at 5 per cent, to show that the campaign has been effective?

7 An opinion poll was taken, of 600 women and 400 men. Of these, 260 women and 140 men supported the Crimson Party. Test at 5 per cent significance whether men and women differ in terms of support for the Crimson Party.

Confidence intervals for proportion

On the basis of a sample, we can find a confidence interval for a proportion. This is particularly useful in opinion polls. On the basis of a survey, we can find a range of values within which we expect the true value of a party's support to lie. Suppose the confidence interval is 49 per cent to 52 per cent. Then 50 per cent lies within the interval, and we aren't sure whether the party is supported by a majority of the electorate.

Suppose the proportion of the population with a certain property is π. We take a sample of size n. Suppose that the sample proportion is p. If the sample is reasonably large then p has the distribution:

$$p \sim N\left(\pi, \frac{\pi(1 - \pi)}{n}\right)$$

In order to find the confidence interval we need to know the variance. This depends on π, which of course we don't know. But we won't be too far out if we use p instead of π to estimate the variance.

Let $s^2 = \dfrac{p(1 - p)}{n}$. Then a 95 per cent confidence interval for π is:

$$p - 1.96s < \pi < p + 1.96s$$

We have given results for a 95 per cent confidence interval. To obtain a 99 per cent confidence interval, replace 1.96 by 2.576.

EXAMPLE 12.8
An opinion poll sample of 1000 voters found that 40 per cent of them supported the Purple Party. Find a 95 per cent confidence interval for the support in the whole electorate.

How large a sample would give a confidence interval of width less than 2 per cent?

Solution
The sample proportion is 0.4. Assuming that this is reasonably close to the true proportion, the variance of the sample proportion is approximately:

$$s^2 = \frac{0.4(1 - 0.4)}{1000} = 0.000\,24$$

The confidence interval for the true proportion π is:

$$0.4 - 1.96\sqrt{0.000\,24} \leq \pi \leq 0.4 + 1.96\sqrt{0.000\,24}$$

$$0.37 \leq \pi \leq 0.43$$

A 95 per cent confidence interval for the Purple Party support is between 37 per cent and 43 per cent.

Suppose the sample is increased to n. Assuming that the proportion of Purple Party supporters is still about 40 per cent, the confidence interval will be $1.96\sqrt{\dfrac{0.4(1 - 0.4)}{n}}$ on either side of 0.4.

Hence the width of the confidence interval will be:

$$2 \times 1.96\sqrt{\dfrac{0.4(1 - 0.4)}{n}}$$

If this is less than 2 per cent, we need:

$$2 \times 1.96\sqrt{\dfrac{0.4(1 - 0.4)}{n}} < 0.02$$

$$\left(\dfrac{2 \times 1.96\sqrt{0.24}}{0.02}\right)^2 < n$$

The sample size must be at least 9220.

EXERCISE 12F

1 In each part of this question, a sample of n items from a population is found to contain m with a certain property. In each case find a 95 per cent confidence interval for the proportion π within the population as a whole, with the property.

   a) $n = 500, m = 200$ **b)** $n = 1000, m = 300$ **c)** $n = 200, m = 150$ **d)** $n = 2000, m = 1400$

2 Find 99 per cent confidence intervals for the population proportion for each of the cases in Question 1.

3 Out of a random sample of 500 people, 60 were left-handed. Find a 95 per cent confidence interval for the proportion of left-handers in the population as a whole.

4 A bent coin was spun 200 times, and came up heads 120 times. Find a 95 per cent confidence interval for the probability that this coin will come up heads.

5 A die was rolled 300 times, and gave a six 70 times. Find a 95 per cent confidence interval for the probability that this die will give a six.

6 A survey of 400 households was conducted, and it was found that 320 of them possessed a video recorder. Find a 95 per cent confidence interval for the proportion of households in the country possessing a video recorder.

7 Two opinion polls were taken, of 1000 and 2000 people. Of these, 450 and 980 respectively supported the Reactionary Party. Find 95 per cent confidence intervals for the percentage support for the Reactionary Party in the country

   a) using the result of the first poll,   **b)** using the result of the second poll,

   c) using the combined results of both polls.

8 Out of a sample of 200 silicon chips produced by a machine, 65 were defective. Find a 95 per cent confidence interval for the proportion of defective chips produced by the machine.

   How large a sample would have to be taken for the confidence interval to be less than 0.02 wide? How large would it have to be for a 99 per cent confidence interval to be less than 0.02 wide?

9 Out of 200 seeds sown, 70 germinated. Find a 95 per cent confidence interval for the probability that a similar seed will germinate.

   How many seeds would have to be tested for the width of the confidence interval to be under 0.01?

10 An education authority surveyed recent leavers from its schools, and found that out of a sample of 200, 60 per cent had found jobs. Find a 95 per cent confidence interval for the percentage of school leavers as a whole who had found jobs.

   How large should the sample be for the width of the confidence interval to be less than 4 per cent?

LONGER EXERCISE

Power curves

The power of a test gives the probability of correctly rejecting the null hypothesis, i.e. of not making a Type II error. The power depends on the true value of the parameter being tested. A graph showing the power for different values is a **power curve**. It shows how effective the test is.

Suppose we are testing whether a coin is biased against heads. We shall spin it many times. If it comes up heads fewer than a critical number of times we shall conclude that it is biased. Even if the coin is biased, the number of heads might exceed the critical value. In this case a Type II error will be made. The likelihood of a Type II error decreases as the probability of heads decreases.

The power curve might be as shown in Fig. 12.5. Explain the shape of the curve.

Suppose the test is at 5 per cent significance, and that the coin is tossed 20 times. Find the critical value of the number of heads. Find the power of the test at different values, and sketch the power curve.

What would happen to the curve as the number of tosses increases? What shape would we like a power curve to have?

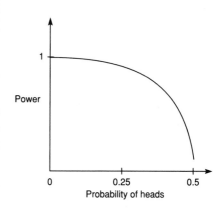

Fig. 12.5

EXAMINATION QUESTIONS

1 A golf professional P measured the length, x yards, of each of 112 drives which he made using balls of brand A. The following results were calculated:

$$\Sigma x = 26\,992 \qquad \Sigma x^2 = 6\,521\,056.$$

Calculate unbiased estimates for the mean μ_A and the variance of the lengths of drives made by P using balls of brand A. Use your results to calculate an approximate 95 per cent confidence interval for μ_A, and state two assumptions you have made.

The manufacturer of golf balls of brand B claim that the mean length of drives made by professional golfers will be increased by more than 10 yards when balls of brand B are used instead of balls of brand A. To test this claim, P measured the lengths of 97 drives which he made using balls of brand B and calculated unbiased estimates of 256 and 228 for the mean and the variance of the lengths (in yards) of drives made by P using balls of brand B. Stating suitable null and alternative hypotheses, determine whether there is sufficient evidence at the 1 per cent significance level to support the manufacturer's claim.

N 1990

2 Before I sat an examination, my teacher told me that I had a 60% chance of obtaining a grade A, but I thought I had a better chance than that.

In preparation for the examination, we did 7 tests each of the same standard as the examination. Assuming my teacher is right, find the probability that I would get grade A on

(i) all 7 tests   (ii) exactly 6 tests out of 7   (iii) exactly 5 tests out of 7.

In fact I got a grade A on 6 tests out of 7. State suitable null and alternative hypotheses and carry out a statistical test to determine whether or not there is evidence that my teacher is underestimating my chances of a grade A.

MEI 1992

3 Charlotte-Anne claims to have extra-sensory powers. To test the claim she is asked to predict the suit (clubs, spades, hearts or diamonds) of a series of 20 cards chosen at random, with replacement, from a well-shuffled pack.

Assuming that Charlotte-Anne does not, in fact, have extra-sensory powers, but merely guesses at random, find the probability that:

(i)   she gets exactly 5 of the 20 predictions correct.

(ii) she gets 9 or more predictions correct.

Now suppose that a hypothesis test is to be carried out to examine Charlotte-Anne's claim.

(iii) Write down suitable null and alternative hypotheses.

(iv) Determine how many correct predictions out of 20 Charlotte-Anne would need to justify her claim at the 1% level of significance.

In a hypothesis test on a separate occasion, Charlotte-Anne is given a series of n cards and she correctly predicts the suit of each of them.

(v) Find the least value of n which would justify her claim at the 5% level of significance.

MEI 1994

4 a) Within the context of hypothesis testing, state, briefly, the meaning of the terms '5% level of significance' and 'critical region'.

b) (i) A company, Alpha Ltd, is considering the relocation of its business offices to one of two possible areas and is interested in the difference in house prices for the two areas. Random samples of prices for detached houses with certain specifications in the two areas are summarised below:

Area	Sample size	Mean price	Standard deviation
1	50 (n_1)	£100 000	£25 000
2	100 (n_2)	£90 000	£20 000

Find a 90% confidence interval for the difference in mean prices for detached houses with certain specifications in these areas. State, precisely, the conclusion one would reach on the basis of this confidence interval.

Another company, Beta Ltd, is also interested in the relocation of its business offices to one of the two areas. To save costs it decides to take a total sample of 100 so that $100 = n_1 + n_2$. Assuming the standard deviations given in part (i):

(ii) write down an expression for the variance of the test statistic in terms of n_1;

(iii) calculate the values of n_1 and n_2 which should be taken to ensure that the test statistic has minimum variance.

NI 1992

5 Employees of a firm carrying out motorway maintenance are issued with brightly coloured waterproof jackets. These come in five different sizes numbered 1 to 5. The last 40 jackets issued were of the following sizes

2 3 3 1 3 3 2 4 3 2 5 4 1 2 3 3 2 4 5 3 2 4 4 1 5 3 3 2 3 3 1 3 4 3 3 2 5 1 4 4

a) (i) Find the proportion in the sample requiring size 3. Assuming the 40 employees can be regarded as a random sample of all employees calculate an approximate 95% confidence interval for the proportion, p, of all employees requiring size 3.

(ii) Give two reasons why the confidence interval calculated in (i) is approximate rather than exact.

b) Your estimate of p is $\hat{p}$.

(i) What percentage is associated with the approximate confidence interval $\hat{p} \pm 0.1$?

(ii) How large a sample would be needed to obtain an approximate 95% confidence interval of the form $\hat{p} \pm 0.1$?

A 1993

6 Over a long period of time it has been found that in Enrico's restaurant the ratio of non-vegetarian to vegetarian meals ordered is 3 to 1.

During one particular day at Enrico's restaurant, a random sample of 20 people contained 2 who ordered a vegetarian meal.

a) Carry out a significance test to determine whether or not the proportion of vegetarian meals ordered that day is lower than is usual. State clearly your hypotheses and use a 10% significance level.

In Manuel's restaurant, of a random sample of 100 people ordering meals, 31 ordered vegetarian meals.

b) Set up null and alternative hypotheses and, using a suitable approximation, test whether or not the proportion of people eating vegetarian meals at Manuel's is different from that at Enrico's restaurant. Use a 5% level of significance.

L 1992

7   A certain production process is said to be out of control when the proportion p of its output which is defective exceeds 5%. A test is required to decide between the hypotheses:

$H_0: p = 0.05$ and $H_1: p > 0.05$

The test suggested is to take a random sample of 20 items from the output and reject H_0 if more than 2 items are defective. Calculate

(i)   the significance level of this test,

(ii)   the power of the test when 10% of the output is defective.

Without carrying out any further calculations, state briefly why the answers to (i) and (ii) should cause some concern.

Suggest a modification which could be made to the test in order that both the significance level and the power might be improved.

N 1990

8   Large numbers of articles of a certain type are manufactured in two sections of a factory.

(i)   A random sample of 150 articles manufactured in one section was selected and their lengths measured. The sum of these lengths was 486 cm and the sum of the squares was 1978 cm². Calculate unbiased estimates for the mean μ_1 and the variance of the lengths of articles manufactured in this section.

(ii)   A random sample of 100 articles manufactured in the other section was selected and their lengths measured. From these results symmetric 95 per cent confidence limits for μ_2, the mean length of articles manufactured in this section, were calculated using a normal approximation to the sampling distribution of the sample mean. The limits were found to be 2.71 cm and 3.39 cm. Deduce the unbiased estimates for the mean and the variance of the lengths of the articles manufactured in this section which were used in the calculation of the confidence limits.

(iii)   Calculate an approximate 95 per cent symmetric confidence interval for $(\mu_1 - \mu_2)$.

(iv)   Without further calculation, state, with a reason, whether the observed difference between the sample means is significant at the 5 per cent level.

N 1992

Summary and key points

12.1 To test whether two means are the same, test whether the difference between the sample means is significantly different from zero.

12.2 Suppose we are testing whether the probability of success in a trial is p_0. Repeat the trial independently n times, and let X be the number of successes. $X \sim B(n, p_0)$.

We may be able to use the binomial cumulative tables to find whether the value of X is significantly high or low. If not, we may be able to use the approximation $X \sim N(np_0, np_0(1 - p_0))$.

12.3 To test whether a proportion is equal to π, take a sample of size n and find the proportion p in the sample with the given property. The test statistic is:

$$\frac{|p - \pi|}{\sqrt{\dfrac{\pi(1 - \pi)}{n}}}$$

To test whether two proportions differ, find the difference between the sample proportions. Test whether this is significantly different from zero. The variance used in the test can be found by pooling the results from the samples.

A 95 per cent confidence interval for a proportion π, where p is the proportion obtained from a sample of size n, is:

$$p - 1.96 \sqrt{\frac{p(1 - p)}{n}} \leq \pi \leq p + 1.96 \sqrt{\frac{p(1 - p)}{n}}$$

The probability that the confidence interval contains the mean or the proportion is 0.95. It is *misleading* to speak of the proportion having probability 0.95 of lying in the interval.

Consolidation section C

Chapter 9

1 Let $Z \sim N(0, 1)$. Find $P(Z \le 1.36)$. Find k such that $P(Z > k) = 0.346$.

2 Let $X \sim N(4, 9)$. Find $P(X < 6.123)$. Find k such that $P(X \ge k) = 0.648$.

3 A battery lasts T hours, where $T \sim N(16, 10)$. Find the probability the battery will last more than 20 hours.

4 A machine in a food factory produces cakes whose weights are normally distributed with standard deviation 20 grams. The mean weight depends on the setting of the machine. What should the mean be to ensure that 90 per cent of the cakes weigh over 500 grams?

5 In a particular resort in August, 20 per cent of days had over 12 hours of sunlight. The proportion of days with less than six hours is 30 per cent. Assuming that the number of hours of sunlight has a normal distribution, find its mean and variance.

6 A roulette wheel has holes numbered 1 to 36. A gambler bets that one of the numbers from 1 to 12 (inclusive) will come up. What is the probability that she will win fewer than 30 times if she makes this bet 100 times?

7 The number of letters received per working day has a Poisson distribution with mean 1.2. What is the probability that more than 40 letters are received in 30 working days?

Chapter 10

8 Let X and Y be random variables with expected values 5 and 8 respectively. Find the following.

    a) $E(X + 5)$ **b)** $E(3X + 2Y)$ **c)** $E(4X - 2Y)$

9 Suppose that the variables X and Y of Question 8 are independent and have variances 6 and 10 respectively. Find the following.

    a) $Var(7X)$ **b)** $Var(3Y + 2)$ **c)** $Var(3X + 2Y)$ **d)** $Var(7X - 2Y)$

    e) $E(3XY)$ **f)** $E(X^2)$ **g)** $E((X + Y)^2)$

10 The marks for an exam have mean 55 and variance 125. How could they be scaled so that they have mean 65 and variance 80?

11 A random variable has mean 10 and variance 20.

a) An independent sample of size 40 is taken from X. What are the mean and variance of the sample mean?

b) How large should a sample be to ensure that the variance of its mean is at most 0.1?

12 Without the use of a calculator, find the mean and unbiased sample variance of the following numbers.

4   2   6   3   5   3   5   3   9   3

13 Let X and Y be independent normal variables with means 10 and 12 respectively, and variances 5 and 8 respectively. Find the following.

a) $P(X + Y < 25)$ **b)** $P(2X + 4Y \geq 80)$ **c)** $P(5X > 4Y)$

14 In Tokyo in August, the noon temperature is $T°$F, where $T \sim N(90, 25)$. The temperature in New York is $Y°$F, where $Y \sim N(85, 60)$. Assuming that the temperatures are independent of each other, find the probabilities that, at noon on a day in August:

a) in both towns the temperature is over 95°F,   **b)** New York is hotter than Tokyo.

15 The voltage of certain batteries has a normal distribution with mean 12 V and standard deviation 0.6 V. Find the probability that the mean voltage of a sample of 50 of these batteries will be less than 11.9 V.

16 The annual salary of a certain class of employees has mean £25 000 and standard deviation £4000. If the salaries of 35 employees are found, use the central limit theorem to estimate the probability that the sample mean will be less than £25 500.

Chapter 11

17 A sample of size 20 from a normal distribution with variance 80 was found to have sample mean 35. Test at 5 per cent significance whether the population mean is greater than 32.

18 The current along a circuit should have a normal distribution with mean 5 amps and standard deviation 0.2 amps. The currect is tested on 15 independent occasions, and the results, in amps, are as shown below. Do these results show, at a 5 per cent significance level, that the mean current is not as it should be?

5.3   5.2   5.0   4.9   5.2   5 1   5.3   5.3   5.2   4.8   5.0   5.1   5.3   5.4   5.0

19 A machine cuts out dough to be made into rolls. The weight of the portion cut out should have mean 50 grams and standard deviation 5 grams. Every session a sample of 20 portions is examined to test whether the machine is operating properly. If the test is at 5 per cent significance, find the range of sample mean weights which will lead to the conclusion that the machine is not operating properly.

If the machine is now producing portions with mean weight 53 grams, find the probability of a Type II error.

20 The fuel economy of a new car is to be tested. Ten motoring journalists take it on a test drive, and their average fuel economy was 32.6 m.p.g. If the standard deviation of fuel economy for similar cars is 2.7 m.p.g., obtain a 95 per cent confidence interval for the mean fuel economy of this car.

21 Essays for a certain Open University course should be about 1500 words in length. A tutor counts the words in 16 essays submitted for an assignment, with the following results. Find the sample mean and unbiased sample variance of these figures.

    1623   1723   1539   1476   1590   1500   1672   1724

    1846   1840   1420   1559   1634   1739   1420   1907

Assuming that the variance found is the correct one, find a 95 per cent confidence interval for the mean length of essays submitted for this assignment. Is there significant evidence that students write essays which are too long?

Chapter 12

22 The weights of cakes produced by machine in a food factory should have standard deviation 20 grams. A sample of 20 cakes from machine A had sample mean 295 grams. A sample of 30 cakes from machine B had sample mean 301 grams. Does this show, at 5 per cent significance, that the machines are set differently?

23 An octahedral (eight-faced) die has the numbers 1 to 8 written on its faces. It is rolled 200 times, and gives 8 on 34 occasions. Is this significant at 5 per cent to show that the die is biased towards 8?

24 There are worries that standards of numeracy have fallen. An examination, which was passed by 50 out of 80 schoolchildren in 1960, is given to a similar group of present-day children. If 45 out of 100 of the present-day children passed the examination, is this significant at 5 per cent to show that standards have fallen?

25 In an opinion poll of 1500 people, 48 per cent of them were in favour of Britain withdrawing from the European Union. Find a 95 per cent confidence interval for the proportion in the population as a whole in favour of withdrawal.

A Eurosceptic organisation claims that over half the electorate supports withdrawal from the European Union. Without doing any further calculation, comment on the claim in the light of the results above.

MIXED QUESTIONS

1 In Chapter 12 we found that a test on a proportion could be done either using the binomial distribution or using the sample proportion. What is the difference between these tests? Is one better than the other?

2 If a confidence interval is found from a sample of size n, then the width of the interval is inversely proportional to $\sqrt{n}$.

A 95 per cent confidence interval from a sample of size 100 has width 0.2.

a) What sample size would give an interval of width 0.1?

b) What sample size would give a 99 per cent confidence interval of width 0.1?

3   A sample of size 50 was used to find a 95 per cent confidence interval of the form $2.1 < \mu < 2.9$. Find the sample mean and the variance of the distribution from which the data came.

Another confidence interval, using the same data, was $2 < \mu < 3$. Find the percentage associated with this interval.

4   Let Y be a variable which takes the value 1 with probability p, and 0 with probability q, where $q = 1 - p$. Show that $E(Y) = p$ and $\text{Var}(Y) = pq$.

If $X \sim B(n, p)$, show that X can be regarded as the sum of n independent observations of Y. Hence find $E(X)$ and $\text{Var}(X)$.

5   A roulette wheel has holes numbered 1 to 36. A gambler suspects that it is biased towards the numbers divisible by 9. Let p be the probability that the ball will land in a hole whose number is divisible by 9.

The wheel is spun, and the ball lands in the number 9 hole. What conclusions can be drawn?

The wheel is spun a second time, and the ball lands in the number 27 hole. What conclusions can be drawn?

6   An astrologer claims that she is able to tell a person's birth sign (of which there are 12). A sceptic thinks she is guessing, and decides to test her by asking her to state the birth sign of various people. Let p be the probability that she gets someone's birth sign correct.

What conclusions can be drawn if:

a) she states the birth sign of one person, and gets it right,

b) she states the birth signs of two people, and gets them both right?

7   The numbers generated by a random number program should have a uniform distribution between 0 and 1. A programmer writes a new program to generate random numbers, but suspects that the numbers generated will be biased towards low values. The first number it comes up with is 0.06. Does this show that the distribution is not uniform?

8   How many ways can three people be arranged in an order?

Three people have entered a race. Jane reckons that she can predict the order in which they will finish. Joe denies this, and says that she is picking an order at random.

In fact, she predicts the order correctly. What conclusions can be drawn?

9   How many different pairs of people can be selected from seven people?

A school's tennis team has contained seven regular players, among whom are the headmaster's two sons. At the end of the season the headmaster awards two prizes to members of the team. If he gives both the prizes to his sons, does this prove that he has been biased?

10 The number of fish in a lake is to be estimated. Fifty are caught, tagged, and returned to the lake. A week later 100 fish are caught, and ten of these have already been tagged. Find a 95 per cent confidence interval for the total number of fish in the lake. What assumptions are you making?

11 Suppose $Z \sim N(0, 1)$. Let $X = |Z|$. What is the median of X? What is its mean? Sketch the graph of the p.d.f. of X.

DISCUSSION QUESTIONS

1 *Statistician*: 'This sample shows, at a significance level of 5 per cent, that the true mean is not 10.'

Sceptic: 'Oh yes? How many samples did you try before you got this one?'

2 A roulette wheel has holes numbered 1 to 36. It is spun, and the ball lands in the hole numbered 17. If the wheel is unbiased, the probability of this happening is $\frac{1}{36}$, which is less than 0.05. Do we have evidence, significant at 5 per cent, to show that the wheel is biased?

3 The unbiased sample variance $\hat{\sigma}^2$ is an unbiased estimator of σ^2. Is $\hat{\sigma}$ an unbiased estimator of σ?

4 Let X be a variable with variance σ^2. Let $Y = 2X$. From results in Chapter 10, $\mathrm{Var}(Y) = 2^2\mathrm{Var}(X) = 4\sigma^2$. But if we let $Y = X + X$, then $\mathrm{Var}(Y) = \mathrm{Var}(X) + \mathrm{Var}(X) = 2\sigma^2$. Why is there a difference?

LONGER EXERCISE

Normal probability paper

This special sort of paper (a reduced example is shown in Fig. C1) enables you to investigate the normal distribution.

Along the horizontal axis mark $-2, -1.5, -1, -0.5, 0, 0.5, 1, 1.5$ and 2. The numbers along the vertical axis are thousandths. For example, 500 corresponds to $\frac{500}{1000}$, i.e. $\frac{1}{2}$. For values of z on the horizontal axis find $\Phi(z)$, and enter points on the graph paper. For example, $\Phi(0) = \frac{1}{2}$, so enter $(0, 500)$ on the graph. What can you say about the points?

On a new sheet mark 10, 20, 30, 40, 50, 60, 70, 80 and 90. Plot points at $(20, 6)$, $(30, 76)$, $(40, 360)$, $(50, 770)$, $(60, 960)$ and $(70, 998)$. What can you say about these points? What distribution do they come from? What is the mean and standard deviation of the distribution?

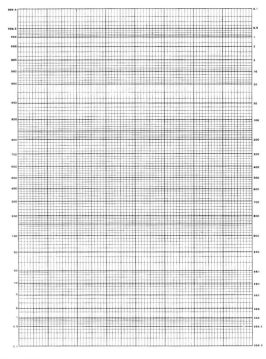

Fig. C1

What shape of curve would result from a non-normal distribution? What if it were skewed, or were more peaked than the normal distribution? Investigate.

EXAMINATION QUESTIONS

1 State the conditions under which a Poisson distribution is a suitable model to use in statistical work.

In a particular district it has been found, over a long period, that the number, X, of cases of measles reported per month has a Poisson distribution with parameter 1.5. Find, to 3 decimal places, the probability that in this district

a) in any given month, exactly 2 cases of measles will be reported,

b) in a period of 6 months, fewer than 10 cases of measles will be reported.

Imagine that you are a statistician working on reported illnesses in that district. During the month of February this year you find that 4 cases of measles are reported. Perform a statistical test to decide at the 5% level whether or not this number of reported cases gives rise for concern that an unusually large outbreak of measles may be occurring in the district. State clearly the null and alternative hypotheses which you are using.

Your results and conclusions are to be presented to a local Health Committee whose members probably have no statistical training. Write a paragraph suitable for this purpose.

L 1990

2 State the conditions under which the binomial distribution B(n, p) can be approximated by

a) a Poisson distribution   **b)** a normal distribution.

State the parameters of the appropriate distribution.

Over a long period it is found that in music examinations 25% of the candidates fail, while 9% of the candidates obtain a distinction.

c) Calculate, to 3 decimal places, the probability that in a random group of 8 candidates, exactly 2 will fail the examination.

Estimate, giving your answer to 3 decimal places, the probability that

d) in a random group of 100 candidates, at most 20 will fail the examination,

e) in a random group of 40 candidates, more than 2 will obtain a distinction.

L 1991

3 a) A continuous random variable X is such that $\ln X$ is normally distributed with mean value $\ln 100$ and standard deviation $\ln 2$. Calculate the probability that

(i) $\ln X > \ln 200$,   (ii) $50 < X < 150$.

b) Among garments offered to a charity shop as stock items, only 70% are suitable. Use a normal approximation to calculate the probability that, out of a random sample of 525 garments offered, at least 350 are suitable.

C AS 1992

4 Bars of soap are produced to have an alkali content which is normally distributed with mean 4 units and standard deviation 1 unit. A control process is applied to reject any bars of soap whose alkali content is less than 2.5 units or greater than 5 units. Calculate:

(i) the percentage of bars of soap rejected by the control process,

(ii) the percentage which would be rejected if the control process altered the mean of the alkali content so as to minimise the percentage of bars of soap rejected. The standard deviation may be assumed to remain at 1 unit.

NI 1992

5 **a)** At the beginning of this decade, a report was published which indicated that 35% of 17- and 18-year olds were cigarette smokers. A group of sixth-formers were discussing the report. Briefly outline the conditions that need to be met for a Binomial distribution to be an appropriate model.

b) Making use of the appropriate tables, demonstrate clearly that there is greater than a 93% chance that a random observation from the Binomial distribution with n equal to 16 and p equal to 0.35 (with the usual notation) lies between 3 and 9 inclusive.

c) What conditions need to be met for it to be reasonable to approximate a Binomial distribution by a Normal distribution? State the parameters of the Normal in terms of those of the Binomial. What is meant by the expression *continuity correction*?

d) Consider the Binomial where n is 160 and p is 0.35. Find an approximate value for the probability that a random observation from this distribution lies between 40 and 70 inclusive.

O 1991

6 A city centre car park first becomes full at T minutes past 9.00 a.m., where T is Normally distributed with mean 30 and standard deviation 10.

Find the probability that, on a randomly chosen day,

(i) the car park is full at 9.15 a.m.,

(ii) there is still space in the car park at 9.35 a.m.

I leave home at the same time each day but traffic conditions mean that I arrive at the car park at U minutes past 9.00 a.m., where U is Normally distributed with mean 10 and standard deviation 5. Assume that T and U are independent.

(iii) Write down the mean, variance, and distribution of $T - U$.

(iv) Find the probability that when I arrive the car park is already full.

(v) How much earlier would I have to leave home in order to have a 99% chance of finding space on the car park assuming traffic conditions remain the same?

MEI 1994

7 **a)** The masses of apples of type A are normally distributed with mean 128.5 grams and standard deviation 16 grams. Calculate the probability that:

(i) a randomly chosen apple of type A will have mass less than the minimum acceptable mass of 110 grams,

(ii) the mean mass of a random sample of 100 apples of type A will differ from the population mean by less than 2 grams.

b) The masses, x grams, of a random sample of 100 apples were recorded and the following results calculated.

$$\Sigma x = 12\,650 \qquad \Sigma x^2 = 1\,622\,500.$$

(i) Calculate unbiased estimates for the mean μ and variance of the masses of apples from which this sample was taken.

(ii) It is claimed that the apples were of type A. Investigate this claim by firstly commenting on the variance and secondly by testing the null hypothesis $\mu = 128.5$ against a suitable alternative hypotheses at the 5 per cent level of significance.

N 1993

8 A market researcher performs a survey in order to determine the popularity of SUDZ washing powder in the Manchester area. He visits every house on a large housing estate in Manchester and asks the question: 'Do you use SUDZ washing powder?' Of 235 people questioned, 75 answered, 'Yes'. Treating this sample as being random, calculate a symmetric approximate 95% confidence interval for the proportion of households in the Manchester area which use SUDZ.

Comment on the assumption of randomness and also on the question posed.

N 1991

9 A food manufacturer delivers tins of baked beans packed in cardboard boxes, each box containing 24 tins. The mass, F, of a full tin of baked beans is a normally distributed random variable having mean 510 g and standard deviation 2.5 g. The mass, B, of an empty cardboard box is a normally distributed random variable having mean 150 g and standard deviation 1.5 g. Find, to three decimal places,

(i) the probability that the mass of a randomly chosen full tin will lie between 505 g and 515 g,

(ii) the probability that the total mass of a randomly chosen box of tins will exceed 12.4 kg.

Furthermore, it is known that the mass, E, of an empty tin used by the manufacturer is a normally distributed variable having mean 55 g and standard deviation 0.5 g. Stating clearly an assumption concerning independence, find the probability that the mass, C, of the contents of a randomly chosen tin of baked beans will exceed 450 g.

N 1992

10 The mass of flour in bags produced by a particular supplier is normally distributed with mean μ grammes and standard deviation 7.5 grammes, where the actual value of μ may be set accurately by the supplier. Any bag containing less than 500 grammes of flour is said to be underweight. The trading standards inspector takes a sample of n bags of flour at random from the bags packed by the supplier. The supplier will be prosecuted if the mean mass of flour in the n bags is less than 500 grammes.

(i) Given that $\mu = 505$ and $n = 10$, find the probability that the supplier will be prosecuted.

(ii) The supplier wishes to ensure that, when $n = 10$, the probability of not being prosecuted is not greater than 0.001. Calculate, to one decimal place, the least value at which μ should be set.

(iii) The inspector wishes to ensure that, if the supplier's mean setting procedure produces 80% of bags underweight, the chance that he will escape prosecution is less than one in a thousand. Determine the least value of n that the inspector can use in taking his sample.

N 1990

11 A, B, C, D are four members of a 4×100 m freestyle swimming relay team. In a race each member of the team swims a 100 m leg. The times taken by A, B, C, D to swim their 100 m legs are independent and normally distributed with means 52.5 s, 52.0 s, 53.5 s, 51.5 s and standard deviations 0.3 s, 0.6 s, 1.2 s, 0.6 s, respectively.

Calculate the probabilities that in a particular race:

(i)   A will swim his leg in less than 52.2 s,

(ii) the team will complete the race in less than 3 min 31.3 s,

(iii) B will swim his leg in a shorter time than D.

N 1991

12 When a biased cubical die is rolled, the probability that a six will be obtained is an unknown constant p. The die is rolled 40 times and the number, X, of sixes obtained is recorded. The number, Y, of sixes obtained when the die is rolled a further 60 times is also recorded. Show that

$$T_1 = \frac{3X + 2Y}{240} \text{ and } T_2 = \frac{X + Y}{100}$$

are both unbiased estimators for p. Find, in terms of p, the standard errors of T_1 and T_2, and state, with a reason, which of these two estimators you consider the better.

N 1991

t- and χ^2 distributions

Chapter outline

13.1 The *t*-distribution   **13.2** Goodness of fit

13.3 Contingency tables

The tests we have used so far have involved the binomial distribution, the Poisson distribution and the normal distribution. There are many other distributions which are used in tests, in this chapter we shall discuss two of them, the *t*-distribution and the χ^2 distribution.

13.1 The *t*-distribution

In previous chapters we tested means of normal variables. In every case, either the variance was given or it was taken from the sample variance.

Suppose a biologist discovers a new species of beetle, and wants to give a confidence interval for the mean mass of adult specimens. The masses of a sample of eight might be (in grams):

   1.24   1.35   1.31   1.42   1.19   1.38   1.44   1.40.

We do not know the true variance of the masses of these beetles. The confidence interval will have to be based on the unbiased sample variance. It may be that these eight specimens are unusually close together in mass, or unusually far apart. The calculations that the biologist does should take account of this.

The sample variance may not be the true variance. When using it to find the test statistic, an extra degree of uncertainty is introduced. The distribution which takes account of this is the *t*-**distribution**.

Suppose X has a normal distribution with mean μ. Suppose a sample of size n is taken, with sample mean $\overline{X}$ and unbiased sample variance $\hat{\sigma}^2$. The test statistic is:

$$\frac{|\overline{X} - \mu|}{\sqrt{\dfrac{\hat{\sigma}^2}{n}}}$$

Degrees of freedom

This expression was obtained from n items of data. If we are selecting data to fit a distribution with given variance, we can choose the first $n - 1$ freely, but the nth term is chosen so that we ensure that the sample variance is correct. We say that there are $n - 1$ **degrees of freedom.**

The test statistic has a t-distribution with $n - 1$ degrees of freedom. The Greek letter ν is often used for the number of degrees of freedom. We then say that the distribution has a t_ν distribution.

Graphs of the p.d.f. of this distribution are shown in Fig. 13.1, for different values of ν.

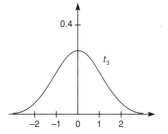 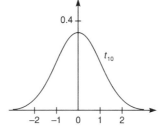 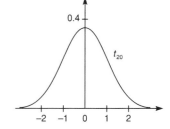

Fig. 13.1

Notes

1 The graphs are symmetric about the origin. Hence the mean of the distribution is 0.
2 As ν increases, the graph tends to that of the N(0, 1) distribution. This makes sense – as the sample size increases, we become more confident that the sample variance is close to the real variance.
3 The t-distribution is not normal. However, when using it, we assume that the population from which the data come is normal.
4 We divide by $(n - 1)$ to obtain the unbiased sample variance. However, for the test statistic we divide by n.

Full tables of the t-distribution are not necessary. Instead we have tables showing the cut-off points for various levels of probability. They are used in exactly the same way as the cut-off points for the normal distribution.

Suppose we are doing a t test with eight degrees of freedom. If the test is one tailed at 5 per cent significance level, then look at where row 8 meets the column 5, finding 1.860. Hence if the test statistic is greater than 1.860, we shall reject the null hypothesis.

Significance for 1-tail test (2-tail in brackets)

$v=$	10% (20%)	5% (10%)	2.5% (5%)	1% (2%)	0.5% (1%)
1	3.078	6.314	12.706	31.821	63.657
2	1.886	2.920	4.303	6.965	9.925
3	1.638	2.353	3.182	4.541	5.841
4	1.533	2.132	2.776	3.747	4.604
5	1.476	2.015	2.571	3.365	4.032
6	1.440	1.943	2.447	3.143	3.707
7	1.415	1.895	2.365	2.998	3.499
8	1.397	(1.860)	2.306	2.896	3.355
9	1.383	1.833	2.262	2.821	3.250
10	1.372	1.812	2.228	2.764	3.169
11	1.363	1.796	2.201	2.718	3.106

For a two-tailed test at 5 per cent significance, look at where row 8 meets column 2.5, finding 2.306.

Note that as the number of degrees of freedom increases, the t cut-off values approach those for the normal distribution.

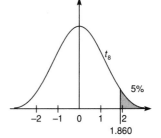

Fig. 13.2

EXAMPLE 13.1
The tourist board of a seaside resort claims that its average maximum daily temperature in August is over 80°F. A holiday-maker has visited the resort on the bank holiday every August for the past ten years, and has measured the maximum temperature as shown below.

Is there evidence, significant at 5 per cent, that the tourist board is exaggerating the temperature? Assume that the distribution of the maximum temperature is normal.

Maximum daily temperature in °F	78	80	74	81	77	79	70	71	72	78

Solution
Let the true mean of the maximum daily temperature in August be μ. The null and alternative hypotheses are:

$$H_0: \mu = 80 \qquad H_1: \mu < 80$$

(A one-tailed test is appropriate.)

The mean and unbiased sample variance of the figures above are:

$$\overline{X} = 76 \qquad \hat{\sigma}^2 = 15\tfrac{5}{9}$$

The test statistic is: $\dfrac{|\overline{X} - \mu|}{\sqrt{\dfrac{\hat{\sigma}^2}{n}}}$

This has value: $\dfrac{|76 - 80|}{\sqrt{\dfrac{15\frac{5}{9}}{10}}} = 3.207$

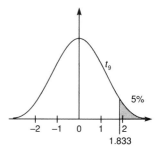

Assuming H_0, the test statistic has a *t*-distribution with nine degrees of freedom. The cut-off point for 5 per cent probability is 1.833, as shown in Fig. 13.3. The value of 3.207 exceeds this.

At 5 per cent significance, we have shown that the average maximum daily temperature is less than 80°F.

Fig. 13.3

When data consist of pairs of values, we can test the pairs by considering their differences.

EXAMPLE 13.2

Ten people were asked to undertake a test involving reaction time, in the morning and in the afternoon. The results are given below, in seconds. Test at 5 per cent whether there is any significant difference in the reaction times. Assume that the times are distributed normally.

Person	A	B	C	D	E	F	G	H	I	J
Morning time	3.1	4.9	2.5	2.3	3.5	2.8	3.5	4.9	5.1	2.4
Afternoon time	3.2	5.2	2.4	2.1	3.2	3.7	4.7	5.2	5.5	2.9

Solution

The data come in matched pairs. Hence we can do a paired sample test. Write out an extra row for the differences between the times.

	0.1	0.3	−0.1	−0.2	−0.3	0.9	1.2	0.3	0.4	0.5

Let μ be the expected difference between the times. The null hypothesis is that there is no difference, and the alternative hypothesis is that there is. A two-tailed test is appropriate.

$H_0: \mu = 0$ $H_1: \mu \neq 0$

The differences have mean 0.31 and unbiased sample variance 0.225. The value of the test statistic is

$$\dfrac{|0.31 - 0|}{\sqrt{\dfrac{0.225}{10}}} = 2.06$$

Assuming H_0, this has a *t*-distribution with nine degrees of freedom. The 5 per cent critical value for a two-tailed test is 2.262. This is greater than the value found. The null hypothesis is retained.

We have not shown that there is a significant difference between reaction times.

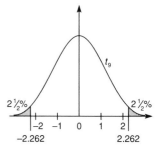

Fig. 13.4

EXERCISE 13A

1 The time a motorist takes for a journey usually has mean 28 minutes. New traffic signals are introduced on the route, and the next ten journey times are listed below. Test at a 5 per cent significance level whether the time for the journey has been altered.

    29   31   27   26   32   29   33   27   29   30

2 The average score nationally in an exam is 56 per cent. A group of eight students selected at random from a college obtained the scores given below. Test at 5 per cent whether or not the average for the college is better than the national average.

    63   58   55   60   59   65   71   69

3 Certain bottles of wine are sold as containing an average of 750 ml of liquid. A sample of nine bottles were found to contain the following volumes (in ml). Is this significant at 1 per cent to show that the bottles are containing less than they should?

    745   748   751   746   740   742   749   753   744

4 Certain electrical components should have an average resistance of 20 ohms. A sample of 11 components from a day's production were tested, and their resistances in ohms are listed below. Test at 5 per cent significance whether the components do have the correct resistance.

    19   18   21   20   22   18   19   18   20   19   17

5 A new car is advertised as having an average fuel economy of 32 miles per gallon. Ten motoring journalists each took the car on a test drive, and measured the fuel economy as given below. Test at 1 per cent significance whether the economy of the car is less than claimed.

    31   30   29   33   29   28   31   32   31   29

6 Ten people were asked to weigh themselves on Saturday morning and on Monday morning. The results, in kg, are given below. Test at 5 per cent whether there is any significant difference in their weights.

Saturday	70	81	68	61	59	71	56	81	71	77
Monday	71	83	66	61	60	71	57	82	72	77

7 A farmer tested whether or not a new food additive will increase the yield of his cows. The yields, in litres, of eight cows before and after being given the additive are listed below. Test at 5 per cent whether or not the additive has increased the yield.

Cow	A	B	C	D	E	F	G	H
Before	22	19	18	24	20	21	19	22
After	24	21	18	25	22	19	22	24

8 To test whether or not the climate has changed, the temperature at midday at a certain spot on certain dates throughout the 1980s was compared with that in the 1960s. The results are listed below. Is the difference significant?

Date	1 Jan	1 Mar	1 May	1 July	1 Sep	1 Nov
1980s	43	51	63	68	73	58
1960s	30	55	52	66	65	60

Confidence intervals

In Section 12.4 of the previous chapter, we found confidence intervals for the means of normal variables. In every case we were given the variance or assumed that the sample variance was correct.

If the variance is estimated from the sample, an extra degree of uncertainty is introduced. Instead of using the normal cut-off values, we use those from the appropriate *t*-distribution. For example, if the mean is based on a sample of size 9, then the appropriate *t*-distribution has eight degrees of freedom. The cut-off point for a two-tailed test at 5 per cent is 2.306, hence the 95 per cent confidence interval is

$$\overline{X} - 2.306 \sqrt{\frac{\hat{\sigma}^2}{9}} < \mu < + 2.306 \sqrt{\frac{\hat{\sigma}^2}{9}}$$

EXAMPLE 13.3
An electronics factory sets its workers an agility test. The test is taken by 12 employees, and their results are shown below. Assuming that the distribution of the times is normal, find a 95 per cent confidence interval for the mean time.

Time in seconds	15.8	12.4	15.3	16.9	10.4	11.7
	12.0	13.5	17.4	14.2	14.8	13.9

Solution
Let the mean time be μ. The sample mean and unbiased sample mean of the figures above are:

$$\overline{X} = 14.025 \qquad \hat{\sigma}^2 = 4.604$$

There are 11 degrees of freedom. The 2.5 per cent cut-off value for t_{11} is 2.201. The 95 per cent confidence interval is:

$$14.025 - 2.201 \sqrt{\frac{4.604}{12}} < \mu < 14.025 + 2.201 \sqrt{\frac{4.604}{12}}$$

$$12.66 < \mu < 15.39$$

The 95 per cent confidence interval for the mean time is between 12.7 and 15.4.

EXERCISE 13B

1 The data sets below come from normal distributions. In each case find a 95 per cent confidence interval for the mean of the distribution.

a) 102   112   98   102   117   109   111   110   100

b) 3.85   3.80   3.83   3.79   3.82   3.84   3.85

c) 0.012   0.009   0.016   0.010   0.008   0.011   0.013   0.010   0.009   0.008

2 A biologist discovers a new species of mouse. The masses (in grams) of ten specimens are listed below. Obtain a 95 per cent confidence interval for the mean mass of these mice.

83   73   70   84   65   69   81   71   70   85

3 Eight students are randomly selected from a college and their IQs are found. The results are listed below. Obtain a 95 per cent confidence interval for the mean IQ of the college's students.

115   123   109   112   129   117   110   117

4 The lifetime of a tyre is measured by how many miles it travels before the tread reaches the legal minimum. Ten examples of a certain make of tyre were tested. Their lifetimes, in thousands of miles, are listed below. Obtain a 99 per cent confidence interval for the mean lifetime of these tyres.

63   57   60   74   68   55   47   55   61   75

5 A motorist drives over a route on seven occasions. The times taken, in minutes, are listed below. Find a 99 per cent confidence interval for the mean time to drive over this route.

48   42   55   50   48   46   59

6 The heights, in cm, of ten plants before and after being given a fertiliser are given below. Find a 95 per cent confidence interval for the increase in the height.

Before	13.1	14.6	15.1	12.6	13.8	16.9	17.2	18.5	15.3	16.0
After	13.4	14.7	15.1	12.9	14.0	17.3	17.5	18.6	15.4	16.3

7 The prices of cans of eight brands of beer in two off-licences are listed in the table below. Find a 95 per cent confidence interval for the difference in prices.

Off-licence A	89	80	95	80	75	77	82	90
Off-licence B	89	79	90	79	70	75	79	89

13.2 Goodness of fit

In many of the examples so far we have assumed that a variable has a particular distribution. We have assumed, for example, that X is normally distributed, or that X follows a Poisson distribution. In this section we show how to find out whether these assumptions are justified, i.e. whether a particular distribution is a good fit for data. The test we perform is a **goodness of fit** test.

Suppose that we have a three-sided spinner, and want to find out whether it is fair. We might spin it 30 times, and find that it gave the following results.

Number	1	2	3
Frequency	8	9	13

These are **observed** frequencies. The null hypothesis is that the die is fair, and so each number has equal likelihood of coming up. The **expected** frequencies are listed below.

Number	1	2	3
Frequency	10	10	10

We want to measure the difference between the observed and expected frequencies. The function we use is:

$$\frac{(10-8)^2}{10} + \frac{(10-9)^2}{10} + \frac{(10-13)^2}{10}$$

The size of this expression will tell us whether or not the null hypothesis is to be retained.

In general, suppose that the data are organised into a frequency table. The frequencies are observed frequencies, called f_o. We fit a distribution to the data. For each of the observed frequencies, there will be frequencies predicted by the distribution. These are expected frequencies, written f_e.

If the theoretical distribution is a good fit for the data, then f_e will be close to f_o. The test statistic is:

$$\frac{\Sigma(f_o - f_e)^2}{f_e}$$

Clearly the $(f_o - f_e)^2$ terms measure the positive differences between the observed and expected frequencies. We divide by f_e in order to compensate for the number of data.

Degrees of freedom

Suppose there are n frequencies given, and that m facts have been used in fitting the theoretical distribution. Then there are $n - m$ **degrees of freedom** and $n - m = v$. When we fit the distribution, there are n boxes into which to put numbers, but there are m restrictions, and so we have only $n - m$ free choices to make.

The distribution of the test statistic above is χ^2 with v degrees of freedom. We write $\chi^2(v)$. This is pronounced 'chi-squared'.

The p.d.f.s for various χ^2 distributions are shown in Fig. 13.5. Notice that the variable is always positive.

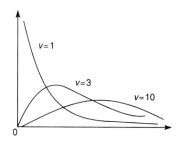

Fig. 13.5

We do not need complete tables for the χ^2 distributions. Instead we have values of the cut-off points for certain probabilities. For example, the cut-off point for 5 per cent of probability for $\chi^2(8)$ is 15.51, as shown in Fig. 13.6.

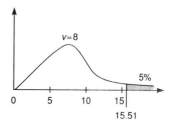

EXAMPLE 13.4

A computer program is written to produce random digits. The first 200 digits generated give the following frequency table. Is the program biased?

Fig. 13.6

Digit	0	1	2	3	4	5	6	7	8	9
Frequency (observed)	15	19	20	13	21	26	28	18	25	15

Solution

The figures above are the observed frequencies f_o. The null hypothesis is that program is unbiased, and hence that the theoretical distribution which fits the frequencies is uniform. Each of the ten digits has probability $\frac{1}{10}$ of being produced, and hence the expected frequencies are each 20.

Digit	0	1	2	3	4	5	6	7	8	9
Frequency (expected)	20	20	20	20	20	20	20	20	20	20

There are ten groups. But when fitting the theoretical distribution, we had to ensure that the sum of the frequencies was the same for expected as for observed. Hence the number of degrees of freedom is $10 - 1$, i.e. 9.

The test statistic is: $\sum \dfrac{(f_e - f_o)^2}{f_e}$

This has value: $\dfrac{(20 - 15)^2}{20} + \dfrac{(20 - 19)^2}{20} + \dots + \dfrac{(20 - 15)^2}{20} = 11.5$

Look at the $\nu = 9$ row in the tables. The cut-off point for 5 per cent probability is 16.92, which is greater than 11.5.

At 5 per cent significance, we have not shown that the program is biased.

In Example 13.4 there was only one restriction found when fitting the theoretical distribution. In the next example there are three.

In Example 13.4 all the expected frequencies were 20, which is reasonably large. If an expected frequency is small, then when we divide by it there will be a disproportionate effect on the test statistic. By convention, therefore, if an expected frequency is less than 5, it is amalgamated with the next frequency. This will be demonstrated in the next example.

	significance level	
$\nu =$	5%	1%
1	3.84	6.64
2	5.99	9.21
3	7.82	11.34
4	9.49	13.28
5	11.07	15.09
6	12.59	16.81
7	14.07	18.48
8	15.51	20.09
9	16.92	21.67
10	18.31	23.21
11	19.68	24.73
12	21.03	26.22
13	22.36	27.69
14	23.68	29.14
15	25	30.58

EXAMPLE 13.5

The following frequency table summarises the heights of 100 army recruits. Is it reasonable to suppose that the distribution of the heights is normal?

Height (in inches)	< 62	62–64	64–66	66–68	68–70	70–72	72–74	> 74
Frequency	2	5	9	17	23	21	17	6

Solution

If we model the data by a normal distribution $N(\mu, \sigma^2)$, then the mean and variance of the expected data should be the same as for the observed data. The mean and variance of the data above are given by:

$$\mu = 69.3 \qquad \hat{\sigma}^2 = 10.94$$

For a $N(69.3, 10.94)$ distribution, the probability that a value will lie in the region below 62 is:

$$\Phi\left(\frac{62 - 69.3}{\sqrt{10.94}}\right) = \Phi(-2.268) = 0.0137$$

Multiply this by 100 to find the expected frequency in this range to be 1.36. The other expected frequencies are found similarly.

Height (in inches)	< 62	62–64	64–66	66–68	68–70	70–72	72–74	> 74
Frequency (expected)	1.37	4.09	10.47	18.79	23.67	20.90	12.95	7.77

The first figure is less than 5. Amalgamate the < 62 range with the 62–64 range. This is done for the observed frequencies as well as the expected frequencies. The table of observed and expected frequencies is now like this.

Height (in inches)	< 64	64–66	66–68	68–70	70–72	72–74	> 74
Frequency f_o	7	9	17	23	21	17	6
Frequency f_e	5.46	10.47	18.79	23.67	20.90	12.95	7.77

There are now seven boxes. When fitting the theoretical distribution $N(69.3, 10.94)$, we had to ensure that:

1 the totals of the frequencies were the same
2 the means were the same
3 the variances were the same.

Hence there were three restrictions in fitting the theoretical distribution. The number of degrees of freedom is $7 - 3$, i.e. 4.

The value of the test statistic is:

$$\frac{(5.46 - 7)^2}{5.46} + \dots + \frac{(7.77 - 6)^2}{7.77} = 2.5$$

Look in the tables to find that the 5 per cent cut-off point for $\chi^2(4)$ is 9.49. This is greater than the value we have found. A normal distribution is a good fit.

At 5 per cent significance, we have shown that the data could have a normal distribution.

EXERCISE 13C

1   A die was rolled 120 times. The frequency of each number scored is given on the right. Perform a χ^2 test at a significance level of 5 per cent to see whether the die is fair.

Number	1	2	3	4	5	6
Frequency	15	24	19	12	26	24

2   A child made a tetrahedral (four-sided) shape out of cardboard. The numbers 1, 2, 3 and 4 were written on the sides. The shape was rolled 40 times, and the number on the face on which it landed was recorded. The results are summarised on the right. Is there evidence, significant at 5 per cent, to show that the shape is biased?

Number	1	2	3	4
Frequency	8	15	3	14

3   In a national examination, the proportions of candidates failing, passing and obtaining distinction are 40 per cent, 50 per cent and 10 per cent respectively. Of the 200 candidates from a particular college, 60 failed, 135 passed and five obtained distinction. Is this significant at 1 per cent to show that the college differs from the national average?

4   The population of a borough is classified as White, Black and Asian. The proportions of each of the groups are 60 per cent, 15 per cent and 25 per cent respectively. The 60 members of a local club contain 29 White, 15 Black and 16 Asian. At 5 per cent significance, is this ethnic make-up different from that of the borough?

5   A darts player throws three darts at the board, aiming for the triple 20. This is repeated 50 times. The number of darts he gets in the triple 20 are summarised on the right.

Number	0	1	2	3
Frequency	10	15	17	8

Find the probability, p, that a given dart hits the treble 20. If the data came from a $B(3, p)$ distribution, what would the corresponding frequencies be? Could these data have come from this distribution? Test at 5 per cent significance.

6   Eggs come in cartons of six. 100 boxes were examined, and the cracked eggs were counted. The results are summarised on the right.

Number cracked	0	1	2	≥ 3
Frequency	53	34	13	0

Find the probability, p, that a given egg is cracked. Find the probabilities for a $B(6, p)$ distribution. Test at 5 per cent significance whether the data above could have come from a $B(6, p)$ distribution.

7   Over 100 one-minute periods, the number of telephone calls received at a switchboard were as summarised on the right. Find the mean number, λ, of calls per minute.

Number of calls	0	1	2	3	4	5	≥ 6
Frequency	12	23	28	13	8	6	10

Find the probabilities for a Po(λ) distribution. Test at 5 per cent significance whether the data could have come from a Poisson distribution.

8   The errors in 40 typed documents were counted. The results are summarised on the right.

Number	0	1	2	3	≥ 4
Frequency	15	16	8	1	0

Is the Poisson distribution a suitable model for these data?

9   The midday temperatures at a certain spot over 100 August days are summarised in the table below.

Temperature	<70	70–80	80–90	90–100	>100
Frequency	12	24	26	20	18

Estimate the mean, μ, and the variance, $\hat{\sigma}^2$, of these values. Find the corresponding frequencies for the N(μ, $\hat{\sigma}^2$) distribution. Test at 5 per cent significance whether the data could have come from a normal distribution.

10   The times taken by 120 runners for a race are summarised in the table below. Test at a 5 per cent significance level whether the data could be fitted by a normal distribution.

Time	120–125	125–130	130–135	135–140	140–145	145–150
Frequency	7	26	38	21	18	10

13.3 Contingency tables

In sociology, the medical sciences and so on, it is very common to ask whether two classifications are associated. We might want to know the associations between:

- social class and health
- religion and political views
- diet and incidence of disease.

To establish whether or not there is an association we perform a test on a **contingency table**.

Suppose we interview a sample of people, and classify them by social class (A, B, C, D, E) and health. The result can be displayed in a table as shown.

		\multicolumn{4}{c}{Social class}
		D/E	**C**	**A/B**	**Totals**
	Good	29	47	22	98
Health	**Medium**	18	64	13	95
	Bad	30	20	7	57
	Totals	77	131	42	250

These are the observed frequencies, f_o. The null hypothesis is that there is no association between social class and health. Hence a person in good health is just as likely to belong to one class as to another.

There are 98 people in good health out of 250, and 77 D/E people out of 250. Hence if the qualities are independent of each other, the probability that a person picked at random is in good health and D/E is:

$$P(\text{good health and D/E}) = P(\text{good health}) \times P(\text{D/E})$$

$$= \frac{98}{250} \times \frac{77}{250}$$

Hence, if the null hypothesis is true, the number of people we would expect to find in the top left entry is:

$$\frac{98}{250} \times \frac{77}{250} \times 250 = \frac{98 \times 77}{250} = 30.184$$

The same applies to the other entries. In each case we multiply the row and column totals, and divide by the grand total. This will provide a table of the expected frequencies, f_e. We then perform a χ^2 test on the difference between f_o and f_e.

Degrees of freedom

Suppose there are n rows and m columns. Then there are nm entries. When constructing the f_e table, we ensure that the row and column totals are the same as for the f_o table. Hence there are $(n-1)(m-1)$ degrees of freedom. In the example above, there are 2×2, i.e. 4, degrees of freedom.

Yates' correction

The χ^2 distribution is continuous, and we are using it to analyse discrete data. When we have a 2×2 table, we apply a continuity correction called **Yates' correction**, which consists of subtracting $\frac{1}{2}$ from each difference between f_o and f_e.

Small values

If any of the values of f_e is small, by convention less than 5, we amalgamate the row or column in which that entry occurs.

EXAMPLE 13.6

A sociologist wishes to establish whether or not there is an association between extraversion and selfishness. She classifies 100 people by these categories as below. Is there evidence, significant at 5 per cent, to show that there is an association?

	Selfish	Unselfish	Total
Extraverted	23	28	51
Introverted	34	15	49
Total	57	43	100

Solution

The null hypothesis is that there is no association between these qualities. The alternative hypothesis is that there is. The table gives the observed frequencies. Assuming the null hypothesis, the expected frequencies are found by multipying the appropriate column and row totals and dividing by the grand total. For example, the expected frequency in the top left corner is $57 \times 51 \div 100$, i.e. 29.07.

	Selfish	Unselfish	Total
Extraverted	29.07	21.93	51
Introverted	27.93	21.07	49
Total	57	43	100

This is a 2 by 2 table. The number of degrees of freedom is $(2-1)(2-1)$, i.e. 1. Apply Yates' correction by subtracting $\frac{1}{2}$ from the differences between the f_o and the f_e. We obtain:

$$\frac{(|29.07 - 23| - \frac{1}{2})^2}{29.07} + \ldots + \frac{(|21.07 - 15| - \frac{1}{2})^2}{21.07} = 5.065$$

Assuming the null hypothesis, the test statistic has a $\chi^2(1)$ distribution. The cut-off point for 5 per cent for this distribution is 3.84, less than the value we found. The null hypothesis is rejected.

At 5 per cent significance, we have shown that there is an association between extraversion and selfishness.

EXAMPLE 13.7

The 118 students of a particular subject who passed their university finals were classified by sex and by class of degree. The results are summarised below. Test at 5 per cent significance whether there is an association between sex and class of degree.

		\multicolumn{4}{c}{**Class of degree**}			
		First	**Upper second**	**Lower second**	**Third**
Sex	**Male**	4	8	9	8
	Female	12	26	31	20

SOLUTION

The null hypothesis is that there is no association between sex and class of degree. The alternative hypothesis is that there is an association. There are 29 male students, and 16 with first class degrees. Hence the expected frequency in the top left hand entry is:

$$29 \times 16 \div 118 = 3.93$$

This is less than 5. The first column must be amalgamated with another. Clearly it makes sense to amalgamate it with the upper second column. We obtain a revised table.

		\multicolumn{3}{c}{**Class of degree**}		
		First and upper second	**Lower second**	**Third**
Sex	**Male**	12	9	8
	Female	38	31	20

These are the observed frequencies. The expected frequency table is shown below.

		\multicolumn{3}{c}{**Class of degree**}		
		First and upper second	**Lower second**	**Third**
Sex	**Male**	12.3	9.8	6.9
	Female	37.7	30.2	21.1

The number of degrees of freedom is now $(2-1) \times (3-1)$, i.e. 2. The value of χ^2 is 0.343. This is less than the critical value.

At 5 per cent significance, we have not shown an association between sex and class of degree.

EXERCISE 13D

1 In November, some of the pupils of a boarding school are given inoculations against 'flu. In March, the numbers of pupils who have caught 'flu are recorded. The results are summarised below.

	Had inoculation	**Escaped inoculation**
Caught 'flu	156	38
Escaped 'flu	126	80

Is this significant at 5 per cent to show that there is an association between having the inoculation and catching the disease?

2 The candidates for an examination can fail, pass or gain a distinction. The results for the students of a college, classified by sex, are summarised on the right.

Does this provide evidence of an association between exam result and sex? Use a 5 per cent significance level.

		Result		
		Fail	Pass	Distinction
Sex	**Male**	23	28	13
	Female	17	39	10

3 To investigate the advantages of playing at home the performance of a football team was analysed and the results are summarised on the right. Test at the 5 per cent significance level whether there is an association between the result and the venue.

		Result		
		Win	Draw	Lose
Venue	**Home**	37	10	16
	Away	26	12	35

4 A sociologist investigates the association between social class and views on capital punishment. The results are summarised on the right. Is there significant evidence of an association between them?

		Social class		
		A/B	C	D/E
	Pro	8	25	38
Views	**Neutral**	12	13	15
	Anti	28	24	12

5 Do the citizens of different countries have different blood groups? The data on the right were collected. Are they significant at 1 per cent to show that there is an association between blood group and country?

		Country	
		Country X	Country Y
	A	23	35
Blood group	B	14	10
	O	56	31

6 Do bad reviews affect the sales of novels? An association of crime novelists collects data concerning reviews of crime books and their sales. The results are summarised in the contingency table on the right. Show that there is a significant association between reviews and sales.

		Review		
		Good	Neutral	Foul
Sales	**Good**	23	12	8
	Average	31	12	18
	Bad	12	28	39

The Tufnell Park Mystery received a foul review, and its sales were very poor. Its author, on reading the statistical result above, decided to sue the reviewer for causing the loss in sales. Was he justified?

7 A small factory has two workers responsible for final assembly. The numbers of defective items they assemble are recorded in the contingency table on the right. Comment.

		Quality	
		Non-defective	**Defective**
Worker	Worker A	88	12
	Worker B	72	28

8 In each of two supermarkets, 50 cartons of eggs were examined to see how many cracked eggs they contained. The results are summarised on the right. At 5 per cent, do these data show that there is a significant difference between the supermarkets?

		Number of broken eggs			
		0	1	2	⩾ 3
Supermarket	A	30	17	3	0
	B	16	21	9	4

9 A sociologist wants to see whether there is an association between social class and longevity. The table below gives details for 123 people, in terms of their class and whether they were over 75 at date of death. Is the data significant at 5 per cent to show an association?

		Class			
		Upper	**Upper-middle**	**Lower-middle**	**Lower**
Age at death	**Over 75**	8	26	22	13
	Under 75	3	14	14	23

10 A group of people are classified by whether they are meat-eaters, vegetarians who will eat dairy products, honey etc, or vegans (who don't eat any animal products at all). They are asked if they have never smoked regularly, used to smoke regularly but have given up, or are still smokers. The results are summarised below. Test at 5 per cent significance whether there is an association.

		Diet		
		Meat-eating	**Vegetarian**	**Vegan**
Smoking status	**Never smoked**	31	26	7
	Given up smoking	58	35	5
	Still smoking	32	16	1

11 At the beginning of this section, on page 264, there was a example concerning social class and health. Test at 5 per cent significance whether there is an association between these categories.

LONGER EXERCISE

χ^2 **and normal**

Where does the χ^2 distribution function come from? A χ^2 distribution with n degrees of freedom is the sum of the squares of n standard normal variables. That is:

$$\chi^2(n) = Z_1^2 + Z_2^2 + \ldots + Z_n^2 \qquad \text{where the } Z_i \text{ are N(0, 1) and are independent.}$$

In Questions 1 to 3, use properties of the normal distribution and the normal tables.

1   What is the mean of $\chi^2(1)$?

2   What is the median of $\chi^2(1)$? Check the 5 per cent and 1 per cent cut-off points for $\chi^2(1)$.

3   What are the *lower* 5 per cent and 1 per cent cut-off points for $\chi^2(1)$?

The χ^2 distribution has many other uses besides those given in this chapter. In particular, if a random sample of size n is taken from a normal distribution with variance σ^2, the distribution of the sample variance is found using the following.

$$\frac{nS^2}{\sigma^2} \text{ has a } \chi^2(n-1) \text{ distribution.}$$

4   Take some of the data sets given in Exercise 13A. Find the left-hand ends of 95 per cent confidence intervals for the variance of the data from which they came. What would you need for the right-hand ends?

EXAMINATION QUESTIONS

1   The toner cartridges in my laser printer are stated by the manufacturer to need replacing after 10 000 sheets, on average, have been printed. I suspect they do not last so long. I have therefore checked the counter in the printer to see how many sheets were printed with each of the last six cartridges. The figures are:

   9741, 9320, 9072, 9893, 9960, 9776

(i)   Find the mean and variance of the data.

(ii)   Carry out an appropriate test of significance at the 5% level to determine whether my suspicions are justified or not. You should state the null and alternative hypotheses under test, and state also the important assumptions necessary for your test to be valid.

(iii)   Supposing the manufacturer's statement is correct, and making the same assumptions as in (ii), find the probability that 6 cartridges out of 6 would need replacing after less than 10 000 sheets each. What conclusions follow from this method of analysis?

MEI 1993

2   A fruit farmer's apples are graded on a scale from A to D before sale. Lengthy past experience shows that the percentages of apples in the four grades are as follows.

Grade	A	B	C	D
Percentage	29%	38%	27%	6%

The farmer introduces a new treatment and applies it to a small number of trees to see if it affects the distribution of grades. The apples produced by these trees are graded as follows.

Grade	A	B	C	D
Number of apples	79	94	58	19

(i) Write down suitable null and alternative hypotheses for a chi-squared test.

(ii) Calculate the expected number of apples in each grade under the null hypothesis.

(iii) Carry out the chi-squared test at the 5% level of significance. State the conclusions of the test clearly.

MEI 1994

3 a) Some years ago a Polytechnic decided to require all entrants to a science course to study a non-science subject for one year. In the first year of the scheme entrants were given the choice of studying French or Russian. The number of students of each sex choosing each language is shown in the following table:

	French	Russian
Male	39	16
Female	21	14

Use a χ^2 test (including Yates' correction) at the 5% significance level to test whether choice of language is independent of sex.

b) The choice of non-science subjects has now been widened and the current figures are as follows.

	French	Poetry	Russian	Sculpture
Male	2	8	15	10
Female	10	17	21	37

Use a χ^2 test at the 5% significance level to test whether choice of subject is independent of sex. In applying the test you should combine French with another subject. Explain why this is necessary and the reasons for your choice of subject.

c) Point out two features of the data (other than the increase in the number of options and in the total number of students) which have changed markedly over the years.

AEB 1992

4 During hockey practice, each member of a squad of 60 players attempted to hit a ball between two posts. Each player had 8 attempts and the numbers of successes were as follows.

3 4 8 1 0 3 3 4 4 2 6 7 3 2 2 5 5 5 8 1 3 5 6 1 3 4 4 4 1 0
5 3 6 0 6 7 4 3 5 7 0 1 2 6 1 8 0 0 3 0 4 4 1 3 5 0 8 1 8 8

a) Form the data into an ungrouped frequency distribution.

b) Use the χ^2 distribution at the 5% significance level to test whether the binomial distribution is an adequate model for the data.

c) State, giving a reason, whether the data support the view that the probability of success is the same for each player.

AEB 1994

5 The numbers of incidences of different categories of crime over a certain period are recorded in the table below.

Category of crime	A	B	C	D	E	F	G	H
Number of incidences	23	19	14	20	21	28	26	37

a) Write down the mean number of incidences per category, and illustrate the data in an appropriate graphical form.

b) One theory concerning these categories of crime is that their incidences are equal. Write down hypotheses which might be used in statistically testing the data against this theory.

c) Conduct a chi-squared goodness-of-fit test to determine a response to the theory and make your conclusions clear at the 5% level.

O 1992

6 The number of breakdowns per day on a certain stretch of a motorway was monitored for 75 days, and the results were summarised in the table below.

Number of breakdowns	0	1	2	> 2
Frequency	45	18	12	0

It is suggested that the number of breakdowns per day can be modelled by a Poisson distribution. Using a 5% level of significance test whether or not the Poisson distribution is a suitable model.

L 1994

7 The following table is the result of analysing a random sample of the invoices submitted by branches of a large chain of bookshops.

	Novel	Textbook	General interest
Hardback	24	10	22
Paperback	66	10	18

Using an appropriate χ^2 statistic assess, at the 5% level of significance, whether or not there is any association between the type of book sold and its cover.

State clearly your null and alternative hypotheses.

L 1994

8 In the mathematics department of a college, candidates in an examination are graded A, B, C, D or E. Records from previous years show that examiners have awarded a grade A to 15% of candidates, B to 20%, C to 35%, D to 25% and E to 5%. A new syllabus is examined by a new board of examiners who award the grades to 200 candidates as follows:

　　A, 33;　B, 37;　C, 81;　D, 36;　E, 13

a) Stating clearly your hypotheses and using a 5% level of significance investigate whether or not the new board of examiners awards grades in the same proportions as the previous one.

In addition to being classified by examination grades, these 200 students are classified as male or female and the results summarised in a contingency table. Assuming all expected values are 5 or more, the statistic $\sum_{i=1}^{10} \dfrac{(O_i - E_i)^2}{E_i}$ was 14.27.

b) Stating your hypotheses and using a 1% significance level, investigate whether or not sex and grade are associated.

L 1993

Summary and key points

13.1 Suppose a sample of size n is taken from a normal distribution with unknown mean, μ, and unknown variance. Let $\overline{X}$ be the sample mean, and $\hat{\sigma}^2$ be the unbiased sample variance. Then the following has a t-distribution with $n - 1$ degrees of freedom.

$$\frac{|\overline{X} - \mu|}{\sqrt{\dfrac{\hat{\sigma}^2}{n}}}$$

Critical values of this distribution can be found from tables. These critical values can also be used to find confidence intervals.

The population distribution must be normal. Divide $\hat{\sigma}^2$ by n, not by $(n - 1)$.

13.2 Suppose data are given by frequencies f_o. To test whether the data could have come from a particular theoretical distribution, find the corresponding theoretical frequencies f_e. The test statistic is:

$$\sum \frac{(f_e - f_o)^2}{f_e}$$

If the data come from the distribution, then the statistic has a χ^2 distribution. The number of degrees of freedom is found by subtracting the number of requirements to fit the distribution from the number of frequency classes.

If any f_e is less than 5, amalgamate its class with a neighbouring one. This restriction applies to the f_e, not to the f_o.

13.3 A frequency table showing data classified under two headings is a contingency table. For each entry f_o, the corresponding f_e is found by multiplying the row and column totals and dividing by the grand total. The test statistic is then found as above.

If the table has n rows and m columns, there are

$$(n - 1)(m - 1) \text{ degrees of freedom.}$$

For a 2 by 2 contingency table, Yates' correction subtracts $\frac{1}{2}$ from the absolute differences between each f_e and f_o.

Correlation and regression

Very often statistical investigation involves the connections between two quantities. Here are some examples.

Medicine

Doctors might be concerned whether there is an association between a certain food and a certain disease.

Sociology

Sociologists might investigate the relationship between such social factors as the crime rate and unemployment.

Chemistry

Scientists could investigate the connection between the temperature of chemicals and the rate at which they react with each other.

If two quantities are connected, they are said to be **correlated**. Figure 14.1 shows scatter diagrams for quantities showing positive correlation, negative correlation and no correlation.

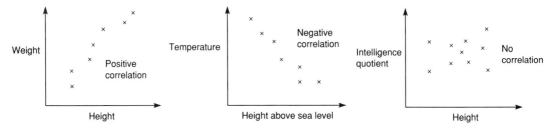

Fig. 14.1

If two quantities are correlated, then we can draw a line of best fit on the scatter diagram. Figure 14.2 shows such a line. The equation of the line can be calculated, as an equation of linear regression.

It is important to realise that correlation between two quantities does not imply that one *causes* the other. In the nineteenth century it was pointed out that there was a strong negative correlation between wearing top hats and cholera. This does not mean that the wearing of a top hat will prevent anyone from catching cholera. The two factors were connected because they were both related to a third factor, that of wealth. The wearers of top hats were rich, and the people who lived in the conditions that breed cholera were poor.

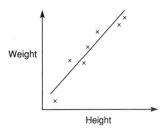

Fig. 14.2

14.1 Correlation coefficient

Suppose there are two random variables, X and Y, which might be connected in some way. A measure of their connection is the **product moment correlation coefficient**, or **correlation coefficient** for short.

If X and Y have means μ and λ respectively, and variances σ^2 and v^2 respectively, the coefficient ρ is defined as:

$$\rho = \frac{E((X - \mu)(Y - \lambda))}{\sigma v}$$

The coefficient can be shown to be equal to:

$$\rho = \frac{E(XY) - \mu\lambda}{\sigma v}$$

Justification
Consider the expression $E((X - \mu)(Y - \lambda))$ in the first version. This is the **covariance** of X and Y, written as $\text{Cov}(X, Y)$.

If X and Y increase and decrease in the same direction, then X will be greater than μ when Y is greater than λ, and X will be less than μ when Y is less than λ. In both cases $(X - \mu)(Y - \lambda)$ will be positive. Hence $\text{Cov}(X, Y)$ will be positive.

If X and Y increase and decrease in opposite directions, then X will be greater than μ when Y is less than λ, and X will be less than μ when Y is greater than λ. Hence $\text{Cov}(X, Y)$ will be negative.

The covariance will depend on the magnitudes of X and Y. Hence the standard deviations of X and Y are put in as scaling factors.

Properties of ρ

The value of ρ lies between -1 and 1. If $\rho > 0$, the correlation is positive. If $\rho < 0$, the correlation is negative.

If $\rho = 1$, then there is a linear relationship between X and Y with positive gradient, e.g. $Y = 3X - 5$.

If $\rho = -1$, then there is a linear relationship between X and Y with negative gradient, e.g. $Y = -3X + 7$.

If $\rho = 0$, the variables X and Y are uncorrelated.

Note

If X and Y are unconnected, then $\rho = 0$. The converse does not hold. If $\rho = 0$ it does not follow that X and Y are unconnected. See Question 7 of Exercise 14A for an example of this.

Sample correlation coefficient

The correlation coefficient ρ applies to the populations of X and Y. These may be infinite. We may have to rely on a sample from X and Y.

Collect a sample of pairs of values, (x_1, y_1), (x_2, y_2), ..., (x_n, y_n). Their means are $\bar{x}$ and $\bar{y}$, and their variances S_X^2 and S_Y^2. The **sample correlation coefficient** between X and Y is defined as:

$$r = \frac{\dfrac{1}{n}\Sigma(x_i - \bar{x})(y_i - \bar{y})}{S_X S_Y} = \frac{\dfrac{1}{n}\Sigma x_i y_i - \bar{x}\,\bar{y}}{S_X S_Y}$$

Note that the sample variance of X can be written as:

$$S_X^2 = \frac{1}{n}\Sigma x_i^2 - \left(\frac{1}{n}\Sigma x_i\right)^2$$

S_Y^2 can be written similarly. Hence in order to find r, we use the following six numbers concerning the sample values:

$$n \quad \Sigma x_i \quad \Sigma x_i^2 \quad \Sigma y_i \quad \Sigma y_i^2 \quad \Sigma x_i y_i$$

Many scientific calculators have the facility to work out r. You may find that the six numbers above are stored in the memories of the calculator.

Figure 14.3 shows scatter diagrams to illustrate the cases $r > 0$, $r < 0$ and $r = 0$.

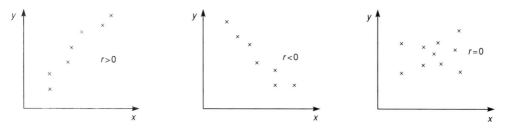

Fig. 14.3

EXAMPLE 14.1

Eight constituencies were investigated. In each case, the percentage, X, of people voting Conservative and the percentage, Y, of residences which were owner occupied were found. The results are below. Find the correlation coefficient between the two percentages.

Voting Conservative (%)	X	55	25	32	19	42	49	61	24
Owner-occupied (%)	Y	71	31	30	12	42	57	78	33

Solution

The six numbers used to find r are as follows.

$$n = 8 \quad \Sigma x_i = 307 \quad \Sigma x_i^2 = 13\,497 \quad \Sigma y_i = 354$$
$$\Sigma y_i^2 = 19\,232 \quad \Sigma x_i y_i = 15\,975$$

From this we find the following.

$$S_X^2 = \tfrac{1}{8} \times 13\,497 - (\tfrac{1}{8} \times 307)^2 = 214.5$$

$$S_Y^2 = \tfrac{1}{8} \times 19\,232 - (\tfrac{1}{8} \times 354)^2 = 445.9$$

$$\frac{1}{n}\Sigma x_i y_i - \bar{x}\,\bar{y} = \tfrac{1}{8} \times 15\,975 - (\tfrac{1}{8} \times 307)(\tfrac{1}{8} \times 354) = 298.8$$

Now use the definition of r.

$$r = \frac{\dfrac{1}{n}\Sigma x_i y_i - \bar{x}\,\bar{y}}{S_X S_Y}$$

$$= \frac{298.8}{\sqrt{214.5}\sqrt{445.9}} = 0.966$$

The sample correlation coefficient is 0.966.

Note

This correlation coefficient is very near 1, indicating a close connection between the two quantities.

EXERCISE 14A

1 For each of the following, find the sample correlation coefficient between X and Y. State the nature of the correlation between them.

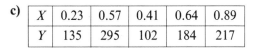

a)

X	1	2	3	4	5	6
Y	43	27	68	82	91	88

b)

X	23	53	91	53	64	33	42
Y	82	62	26	59	42	71	68

c)

X	0.23	0.57	0.41	0.64	0.89
Y	135	295	102	184	217

2 Pairs of sample values (x_i, y_i) are taken, and are summarised below. In each case find the sample correlation coefficient.

a) $n = 5$ $\Sigma x_i = 20$ $\Sigma x_i^2 = 90$ $\Sigma y_i = 502$ $\Sigma y_i^2 = 61\,086$ $\Sigma x_i y_i = 2269$

b) $n = 8$ $\Sigma x_i = 152$ $\Sigma x_i^2 = 3148$ $\Sigma y_i = 614$ $\Sigma y_i^2 = 51\,402$ $\Sigma x_i y_i = 11\,653$

c) $n = 10$ $\Sigma x_i = 18.14$ $\Sigma x_i^2 = 53.7868$ $\Sigma y_i = -15.24$ $\Sigma y_i^2 = 43.398$ $\Sigma x_i y_i = -25.1845$

3 The following figures give the incomes and ages of seven employees of a firm. Find the correlation coefficient between them.

Age	24	31	61	32	45	27	22
Income (£1000s)	18	27	52	20	22	31	17

4 In nine towns the rate of adult male unemployment and the average age at death were found. The figures are given below. Find the correlation coefficient between them.

Unemployment rate (%)	10	5	25	17	3	30	12	7	15
Age at death	72	78	66	67	77	64	70	71	69

5 Seeds of a certain plant were sown and kept under different temperatures. The table below gives the temperature and the percentage germination rate. Find the correlation coefficient between them.

Temperature (°C)	5	10	15	20	25	30	35
Germination rate (%)	10	23	51	68	60	53	21

6 The response time to a stimulus was measured for ten people of varying ages. The results are summarised below. Find the correlation coefficient between time and age.

Time (seconds)	0.9	0.8	1.3	1.1	1.2	1.5	1.4	1.7	1.9	2.3
Age (years)	20	23	25	31	33	38	40	53	59	72

7 There were seven by-elections between two general elections. The table below gives the percentage drop in support for the party in power, along with the inflation rate at that time. Find the correlation coefficient between these quantities.

Drop in support (%)	23	5	11	8	31	10	9
Inflation rate (%)	12	3	8	7	10	5	6

8 The following pairs of sample values of X and Y were obtained.

$(1, 1)$ $(2, 3)$ $(3, 5)$ $(4, 8)$ $(5, 9)$ $(6, 11)$ $(7, 13)$

Plot these points on a scatter diagram. Find the sample correlation coefficient (a) for all seven pairs, (b) for all the pairs except $(4, 8)$. What can be concluded?

9 The following pairs of sample values of X and Y were obtained.

$(1, -1)$ $(1, 0)$ $(1, 1)$ $(0, -1)$ $(0, 0)$ $(0, 1)$ $(-1, -1)$ $(-1, 0)$ $(-1, 1)$ $(3, 3)$

Plot these points on a scatter diagram. Find the sample correlation coefficient (a) for all ten pairs, (b) for the first nine pairs. What can be concluded?

10 Consider the pairs $(0, 0)$, $(1, 1)$, $(-1, 1)$, $(2, 4)$, $(-2, 4)$, $(3, 9)$, $(-3, 9)$. Show that every pair obeys the rule $y = x^2$. Show that the correlation coefficient between x and y is zero.

Significance of r

A non-zero sample correlation coefficient does *not* prove that the quantities are connected. It is possible that the correlation between the sample values may have come about by chance. Just as with means and proportions, we can test whether or not a sample correlation coefficient is significantly different from zero.

The null hypothesis in a test of correlation is that there is no connection between the variables. The alternative hypothesis is that there is a connection.

H_0: $\rho = 0$ H_1: $\rho \neq 0$ (two-tailed test)

For a one-tailed test, the alternative hypothesis will either be that $\rho > 0$ or that $\rho < 0$.

Suppose that we have collected a sample of pairs of values of size n, and that the sample correlation coefficient is r. Critical values of r are given in the tables on page 340. The values in the table are obtained assuming that:

- H_0 is true, i.e. $\rho = 0$
- the variables concerned are normal.

Suppose that $n = 10$, and that we are performing a one-tailed test at a significance level of 5 per cent. The corresponding critical value of r is 0.5494.

Significance for 1-tail test (2-tail in brackets)

$n =$	10% (20%)	5% (10%)	2.5% (5%)	1% (2%)	0.5% (1%)
5	0.6870	0.8054	0.8783	0.9343	0.9587
6	0.6084	0.7293	0.8114	0.8822	0.9172
7	0.5509	0.6694	0.7545	0.8329	0.8745
8	0.5067	0.6215	0.7067	0.7887	0.8343
9	0.4716	0.5822	0.6664	0.7498	0.7977
10	0.4428	0.5494	0.6319	0.7155	0.7646
11	0.4187	0.5214	0.6021	0.6951	0.7348
12	0.3981	0.4973	0.576	0.6581	0.7079
13	0.3802	0.4762	0.5529	0.6339	0.6835
14	0.3646	0.4575	0.5324	0.6120	0.6614

Hence if $r > 0.5494$ we shall reject the null hypothesis at this level of significance.

EXAMPLE 14.2

Eight pupils were asked how much television they had watched in the week leading up to an examination. The results, along with the mark in the examination, are given in the table below. Assuming that the data come from normal distributions, are they significant at 5 per cent to show that watching television decreases the mark obtained?

Hours watched	17	2	23	12	9	13	21	8
Mark	47	44	22	48	53	55	42	39

Solution

Let X and Y be the number of hours watched and the mark, respectively. The null hypothesis is that there is no connection between the two, i.e. that $\rho = 0$. The alternative hypothesis is that there is a connection, that $\rho < 0$. (A one-tailed test is appropriate here.)

From the formula or by using a calculator, find that $r = -0.474$. Look at the tables on page 340. For $n = 8$, the 5 per cent critical value of r is 0.6215. This is greater than 0.474.

At 5 per cent, we have not shown that there is a connection between the amount of television watched and the mark gained.

EXERCISE 14B

Throughout use a significance level of 5 per cent.

1 For each of the following, find the sample correlation coefficient between X and Y. Is there significant correlation between them? Use a one-tailed test.

a)

X	1	2	3	4	5	6
Y	23	31	28	85	56	77

b)

X	53	68	97	103	121	154	167
Y	67	38	48	61	53	71	81

c)

X	2.8	3.9	4.2	6.3	9.2
Y	6.4	5.3	7.9	4.8	0.7

2 Ten students took an IQ test, and then a Mathematics examination. The results are given below. Find the correlation coefficient between them. Assuming that both scores have normal distributions, test whether or not there is a significant connection between the scores.

Student	A	B	C	D	E	F	G	H	I	J
IQ mark	120	106	98	106	114	117	109	121	105	112
Maths mark	83	57	79	63	77	72	55	88	49	71

3 The table below gives the level of radiation in eight districts, and rate of death from cancers, in deaths per million people per year. Do the figures provide significant evidence of a connection between these quantities?

Units of radiation		23	17	26	15	6	19	11	31
Cancer deaths per million people per year		1964	1523	2916	1943	1261	1588	1041	1062

4 A sociologist investigates the connections between crime and poverty. The table below gives the crime rates and the median income for seven towns. Do the figures show a significant connection between them?

Town	A	B	C	D	E	F	G
Crime rate	23	47	10	31	19	29	38
Median income	8300	7100	9800	7500	7800	6900	7200

5, 6, 7, 8 and **9** Look at Questions 3, 4, 5, 6 and 7 of Exercise 14A. Is there significant evidence of a connection between the quantities?

14.2 Linear regression

Suppose there is positive correlation between two variables X and Y. A scatter diagram of pairs of values will show the points lying close to a straight line, as shown in Fig. 14.4. You can draw a straight line through the points.

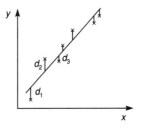

Fig. 14.4

For greater accuracy and uniformity it is preferable to calculate the equation of the line. One way is as follows.

Suppose the line is $y = ax + b$. The difference between a predicted y-value and the actual y-value is:

$$d_i = (ax_i + b) - y_i$$

These differences are shown in Fig. 14.4. We should like to make them as small as possible. There are many ways this could be done. The most mathematically convenient way is to minimise the sum of the squares of the d_i, i.e. to find the values of a and b such that:

Σd_i^2 is as small as possible

This is known as the **method of least squares**. The values of a and b are then given by:

$$a = \frac{\dfrac{1}{n}\Sigma x_i y_i - \bar{x}\,\bar{y}}{\dfrac{1}{n}\Sigma x_i^2 - \bar{x}^2}$$

$$b = \bar{y} - a\bar{x}$$

With these values of a and b, the line $y = ax + b$ is the **line of regression of y on x**. The line can be used to predict other values.

Notes

1 The value of a is related to the correlation coefficient r by

$$a = r \times \frac{S_Y}{S_X}.$$

2 The definition of b ensures that the line will go through the point $(\bar{x}, \bar{y})$, i.e. the point whose coordinates are the means of X and Y.

3 In general, the line of regression of Y on X is not the same as the line of regression of X on Y.

4 Predictions from a line of best fit are not always reliable, particularly when the values concerned are far away from the given values. The relationship between the variables might be like that shown in Fig. 14.5. The line fits the low values well, but not the high values.

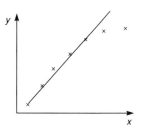

Fig. 14.5

Many scientific calculators have the facility to find the coefficients a and b automatically. Often this involves using the 'LR' mode.

In some situations the values of Y depend on the values of X. Then X is the **predictor** or **independent** variable, and Y is the **response** or **dependent** variable. Examples of such situations are:

• Suppose that we hang different weights on an elastic string. There will be a positive correlation between the weight and the stretched length of the string. The weight is the predictor variable, and the length the response variable.

• Suppose we investigate the amount of chilli pepper in the diet of a community and the incidence of stomach cancer. The amount of pepper is the predictor variable and the incidence the response variable.

Examples of cases in which we cannot label the variables as predictor and response are:

• If many pupils take examinations in both mathematics and physics, there will probably be positive correlation between the marks. The sets of marks cannot be labelled as predictor and response.

• There is likely to be correlation between frequency of visits to the doctor and age at death. Neither variable can be labelled as predictor or response.

If the variables can be labelled as predictor X and response Y, we usually find the equation of regression of the response variable on the predictor. That is, we find an equation of the form $Y = aX + b$.

EXAMPLE 14.3
The resistance R N experienced by a car at speed V m s^{-1} was measured. The results are given in the following table.

V	5	10	15	20	25
R	100	160	230	300	380

Find the line of regression of R on V. Hence predict the resistance at a speed of 30 m s^{-1}.

Solution
Here the predictor variable is V and the response variable is R. The data can be summarised as follows.

$$n = 5 \quad \Sigma V_i = 75 \quad \Sigma V_i^2 = 1375 \quad \Sigma R_i = 1170$$
$$\Sigma V_i R_i = 21\,050$$

The means of V and R are:

$$\overline{V} = \tfrac{75}{5} = 15 \quad \overline{R} = \tfrac{1170}{5} = 234$$

The formulae give the following for the constants.

$$a = \frac{\tfrac{1}{5} \times 21\,050 - 15 \times 234}{\tfrac{1}{5} \times 1375 - 15^2} = \frac{700}{50} = 14$$

$$b = 234 - 14 \times 15 = 24$$

The equation is $R = 14V + 24$.

Now put $V = 30$ into this equation.

$$R = 14 \times 30 + 24 = 444$$

The resistance at 30 m s^{-1} is predicted to be 444 N.

Note
A scatter diagram of the values and of the line is shown in Fig. 14.6. Notice how well the line fits the points.

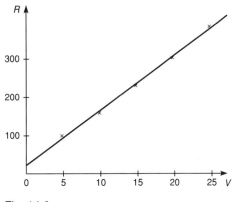

Fig. 14.6

EXERCISE 14C

1 For each of the tables below, find the equation of the line of regression of y on x.

a)

x	1	2	3	4	5	6
y	23	37	43	58	71	78

b)

x	10	20	30	40	50	60	70
y	102	91	79	71	60	49	35

c)

x	0.2	0.3	0.4	0.5	0.6	0.7
y	23	37	43	58	71	78

2 Pairs of sample values (x_i, y_i) are taken, and are summarised below. In each case find the equation of the line of regression of y on x.

a) $n = 6 \quad \Sigma x_i = 21 \quad \Sigma x_i^2 = 91 \quad \Sigma y_i = 336 \quad \Sigma y_i^2 = 21\,620 \quad \Sigma x_i y_i = 1397$

b) $n = 9 \quad \Sigma x_i = 272 \quad \Sigma x_i^2 = 9562 \quad \Sigma y_i = 632 \quad \Sigma y_i^2 = 54\,912 \quad \Sigma x_i y_i = 22\,563$

c) $n = 10 \quad \Sigma x_i = 55 \quad \Sigma x_i^2 = 385 \quad \Sigma y_i = 276 \quad \Sigma y_i^2 = 23\,674 \quad \Sigma x_i y_i = 381$

3 On successive days a patient was given a heart stimulant in increasing quantities, and her heart rate five minutes later was measured. The results are below.

Quantity of drug (mg)	0	1	2	3	4	5
Heart rate (beats/min)	48	55	62	68	75	81

Find the line of regression of h (heart rate) on q (quantity of drug). If the patient was given 6 mg, what would you expect her heart rate to be?

4 The loss of mass through evaporation of a hair shampoo is shown in the table below.

Week	1	2	3	4	5	6
Loss (grams)	1.7	2.2	2.7	3.1	3.5	3.8

Find the line of regression of L (loss) on w (week). What would you expect the loss to be after 7 weeks? Would this model be suitable for large values of w? Give reasons.

5 A disinfectant is tested on a liquid containing bacteria. After t minutes, the number of thousands, k, of bacteria remaining is given in the table below.

t	0	5	10	15	20	25
k	100	92	81	73	65	58

Find the line of regression of k on t. From your equation, when will all the bacteria be killed? Does this model still hold for large values of t?

6 The volume, V m^3, of a fixed mass of gas at constant pressure is related to its temperature, T°C by a law of the form:

$$V = a + bT$$

where a and b are constants. Experimental data are given below.

T	10	20	30	40	50	60	70
V	120	125	129	133	138	142	146

Calculate the values of a and b by linear regression.

At *absolute zero* all motion has ceased, and hence the volume of the gas will be negligible. What temperature does your model give for absolute zero?

7 The annual profit of a company, x millions of pounds, and its dividend per share, y p, are given below for eight successive years. Calculate the line of regression of y on x. If the annual profit for the next year is £37 000 000, what would you expect the dividend to be?

Year	1	2	3	4	5	6	7	8
x	29	31	21	19	33	29	17	30
y	12.3	13.1	9.7	8.3	13.4	11.8	7.8	12.8

8 An examination consists of two papers. The results for ten candidates are shown below. Find the equation of the line of regression of the Paper B mark on the Paper A mark.

An eleventh candidate scored 63 for the Paper A, but missed the second because of illness. What would you estimate for her mark in Paper B?

Paper A	87	53	59	80	70	73	66	61	52	49
Paper B	91	59	63	84	67	77	68	65	53	59

*9 Under what circumstances will regression of y on x give rise to the same line as regression of x on y?

*10 How does a scientific calculator work out the constants a and b?

Residuals

The method of least squares computes the line of best fit by minimising Σd_i^2. The terms d_i are the **residuals**.

Suppose that one of the pairs of values is inaccurate. Then it will lie well clear of the line of best fit. This point is an **outlier**. These outliers can be identified by plotting a scatter graph, and seeing which point lies away from the main trend. This is shown in Fig. 14.7. Alternatively outliers can be found by calculating the residuals and identifying any point with an exceptionally large residual.

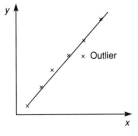

Fig. 14.7

EXAMPLE 14.4

The following table gives the length, l m, of an elastic string when different weights, w N, were suspended from it. One of the values is suspect. Calculate the line of regression of l on w. Find the residuals, and hence identify the suspect value.

w	10	20	30	40	50	60
l	15.3	8.9	12.8	16.2	19.8	23.4

Solution

Using the methods above, the line of regression is:

$$l = 0.362w + 1.74$$

For each i, calculate the difference between l_i and $0.362w_i + 1.74$. The results, given to one significant figure, are:

$$-0.06 \quad -0.07 \quad 0.2 \quad -0.009 \quad -0.03 \quad -0.04$$

Notice that the residual for the third value is considerably greater than the others.

The third value is suspect.

1 For each of the tables below, find the equation of the line of regression of *y* on *x*. In each case one value of *y* is suspect. Find the residuals, and identify the suspect value.

a)
x	10	20	30	40	50	60
y	51	63	78	87	99	110

b)
x	1	2	3	4	5	6	7
y	0.31	0.39	0.41	0.46	0.52	0.57	0.61

c)
x	100	110	120	130	140	150
y	168	141	115	91	66	48

2 The heights and weights of eight boys are given below. Find the line of regression of the weight on the height. By calculating the residuals find the boy who does not fit on the line.

Boy	A	B	C	D	E	F	G	H
Height (cm)	140	163	171	156	149	136	137	151
Weight (kg)	51	68	55	59	56	49	52	64

3 Ten companies were investigated for their percentage increase in profits over the year and the percentage increase in the dividend to shareholders. The figures are given below. Calculate the line of regression of percentage increase in dividend against percentage increase in profit. Calculate the residuals. Which company does not fit the line?

Company	A	B	C	D	E	F	G	H	I	J
Increase in profit (%)	5	3	−2	1	−8	7	12	−26	2	9
Increase in dividend (%)	6	2	0	1	−6	8	14	−23	−4	11

4 The table below gives the numbers of murder victims, classified by sex, for eight countries. Calculate the line of regression of the male rate on the female rate. Calculate the residuals, and identify any outlier.

Female rate (per 100 000)	1.42	1.38	0.95	0.61	1.02	6.23	0.80	1.25
Male rate (per 100 000)	2.40	2.13	1.58	0.70	1.72	10.2	1.48	2.15

14.3 Change of variables

Throughout this section we have been fitting straight lines to the data. However, the relationship between two variables may not always be linear. In this case a change of variables may reduce the relationship to a linear one. Below are two examples.

$y = ax^2 + b$ This is a quadratic relationship between x and y. If we let $X = x^2$, then the relationship becomes $y = aX + b$. This is a linear relationship between y and X. The techniques of this section can be used to find the constants a and b.

$y = ax^n$ This equation occurs when we know that y is proportional to a power of x, but don't know the power. Take logs of both sides.

$$\ln y = \ln ax^n = \ln a + n \ln x$$

Let $Y = \ln y$ and $X = \ln x$. The relation becomes $Y = \ln a + nX$. This is a linear relationship between Y and X. The techniques of this section can be used to find n and $\ln a$ (and hence a itself).

EXAMPLE 14.5
A model of the wind resistance acting on an aircraft is of the form

$$R = av^2 + bv$$

where R N is the force, v m s^{-1} is the speed and a and b are constants. The following table was obtained by experiment.

v	10	20	30	40	50
R	0.08	0.19	0.33	0.51	0.72

By a suitable change of variables reduce the equation to linear form. Use linear regression on the transformed variables to find a and b.

Solution
If we divide through by v, the equation becomes:

$$\frac{R}{v} = av + b$$

If we let $T = \dfrac{R}{v}$, there is now a linear relationship between T and v.

Write out an extra row for the values of T.

T	0.008	0.0095	0.0110	0.01275	0.0144

By the methods of this section find that $a = 0.000161$ and $b = 0.00631$.

The equation is $R = 0.000161v^2 + 0.00631v$.

EXAMPLE 14.6
It is thought that the population of a city has increased exponentially. Let the population x years after 1940 be y millions. If the increase is exponential the relationship between y and x is of the form $y = an^x$, where a and n are constant. A table is given below. By taking logs and changing variables reduce this relationship to a linear one. Hence find a and n.

Year after 1940	0	10	20	30	40	50
Population (millions)	4.6	5.8	7.3	9.4	12.0	15.3

Solution

Take logs of both sides.

$\ln y = \ln an^x = \ln a + x \ln n$

Let $Y = \ln y$. There is now a linear relationship between Y and x.
Write out a row for the values of Y.

Y		1.53	1.76	1.99	2.24	2.48	2.73

By the methods of this section find the line of regression of Y on x.
It is:

$Y = 0.024x + 1.52$

Hence $\ln n = 0.024$, giving $n = 1.024$. Also $\ln a = 1.52$, giving
$a = 4.6$.

The relationship is $y = 4.6 \times 1.024^x$.

EXERCISE 14E

1 In each of the following there is a relationship between X and Y of the form given. In each case
make a suitable change of variables to convert the relationship to a linear one. Calculate a line of
regression, and hence find the relationship.

a) $Y = a + \dfrac{b}{X}$

X	1	2	3	4	5	6
Y	88	47	33	26	22	19

b) $Y = a + b\sqrt{X}$

X	10	20	30	40	50	60	70
Y	0.9	2.6	3.9	5.0	5.9	6.8	7.6

c) $Y = a + bX^2$

X	-3	-2	-1	0	1	2
Y	20	12	7	5	7	12

d) $Y = ab^X$

X	0	0.1	0.2	0.3	0.4	0.5	0.6
Y	10.7	11.7	12.8	13.9	15.2	16.6	18.1

e) $Y = aX^b$

X	121	177	206	251	291	304
Y	1.42	1.52	1.56	1.62	1.67	1.68

2 The height, h cm, of a plant w weeks after germinating is thought to obey a law of the form
$h = ak^w$, where a and k are constants. The table
on the right gives values of h and w. By making
a suitable change of variables and calculating
a line of regression find the law.

w	1	2	3	4	5	6	7
h	0.41	0.57	0.78	1.07	1.46	2.01	2.76

3 A particle is placed on a slope of angle θ and
released. The distance, d m it travels from the
base of the slope is measured. The results for
different values of θ are shown on the right.

θ	5	10	15	20	25
d	0.01	0.04	0.06	0.09	0.11

It is thought that these variables are related by $d = a \sin \theta + k$, where a and k are constant. Use a change of variables and the technique of linear regression to estimate the values of a and k.

4 The pressure, $P \, \text{kg m}^{-2}$, of a fixed amount of gas at a constant temperature is related to its volume, $V \, \text{m}^3$, by a law of the form:

$$P = kV^n$$

where k and n are constant. The data on the right were found by experiment.

P	2.7	3.1	4.5	5.8	6.8	8.3
V	1.01	0.87	0.58	0.44	0.37	0.30

Make a suitable change of variables and calculate a line of regression. Hence find the law.

5 It is thought that the suicide rate, n per 100 000 per annum, is connected to the unemployment rate, u per cent, by a relationship of the form $n = au^b$, where a and b are constants. The table below gives data from ten years. Use a change of variables and the technique of regression to estimate a and b.

n	7.7	8.4	9.3	10.1	11.0	12.3	12.8	12.6	9.8	9.9
u	5	7	10	15	17	21	22	20	16	18

6 A sociologist investigates the connection between educational levels and crime rate. The table on the right gives the figures for ten towns: x per cent is the proportion of people leaving school with five GCSEs or more, and y is the number of crimes reported per 1000 of population. Two models are suggested: $y = ax^b$ and $y = cx + d$, where a, b, c and d are all constants. Find these constants, and by consideration of the relevant correlation coefficients state which is the better model.

x	43	28	61	33	50	39	25	30	45	52
y	38	69	12	55	9	28	61	52	14	11

LONGER EXERCISE

Finding ρ

In the first section of this chapter we found the correlation coefficient for sample values. Here you find the correlation coefficient for the whole population of a distribution.

To find the correlation coefficient, ρ, between X and Y you need the following.

$\quad$ E(X) and Var(X) $\quad$ E(Y) and Var(Y) $\quad$ E(XY)

The formula on page 275 can then be used.

1 Two coins are spun. Let X be 1 if the first coin shows heads, and 0 otherwise. Let Y be the number of heads shown by both coins. Below are the four possible outcomes of the spinning, each with probability $\frac{1}{4}$.

TT	TH	HT	HH
$X = 0, Y = 0$	$X = 0, Y = 1$	$X = 1, Y = 1$	$X = 1, Y = 2$

Find the correlation coefficient between X and Y.

By spinning coins or by use of a random number generator, obtain some pairs of values of X and Y. Find the sample correlation coefficient for your pairs. How close is it to the population correlation coefficient?

2 Three coins are spun. Let X be 0 or 1 depending on whether the first coins is tails or heads. Let Y and Z be defined similarly for the second and third coins respectively. Let $P = X + Y$, and $Q = Y + Z$. By listing the eight possible outcomes of the spinning find the correlation coefficient between P and Q.

3 A fair die is rolled twice. Let X be the score on the first die, and Y the total score. Find the correlation coefficient between X and Y.

4 These results can also be found using the expectation algebra of Chapter 10. Check that you obtain the same results.

EXAMINATION QUESTIONS

1 A drilling machine can run at various speeds, but in general the higher the speed the sooner the drill needs to be replaced. Over several months, 15 pairs of observations relating to speed, s revolutions per minute, and life of drill, h hours, are collected.

For convenience the data are coded so that $x = s - 20$ and $y = h - 100$ and the following summations obtained.

$$\Sigma x = 143 \quad \Sigma y = 391 \quad \Sigma x^2 = 2413 \quad \Sigma y^2 = 22\,441 \quad \Sigma xy = 484$$

a) Find the equation of the regression line of h on s.

b) Interpret the slope of your regression line.

c) Estimate the life of a drill revolving at 30 revolutions per minute.

L 1992

2 A technician monitoring water purity believes that there is a relationship between the hardness of the water and its alkalinity. Over a period of 10 days, she recorded the data in the table.

Alkalinity (mg/l)	33.8	29.1	22.8	26.2	31.8	31.9	29.4	26.1	28.0	27.2
Hardness (mg/l)	51.0	45.0	41.3	46.0	48.0	50.0	46.3	45.0	45.3	43.0

a) Plot the data on graph paper with 'Alkalinity' on the horizontal axis. Mark the mean point.

b) Given that the product moment correlation coefficient for these data is 0.913, what conclusion is it reasonable to draw? You are expected to refer to appropriate tables to support your reply.

c) The technician decides to calculate the equation for the least squares regression line of **hardness on alkalinity**. Show that this line has gradient 0.821 and find its equation.

d) Estimate the hardness of water which has a measured alkalinity of 30 mg/l.

Explain **briefly** why the technician would need to do further statistical work to be able to predict the alkalinity of water with a measured hardness of, say, 50 mg/l. (**You are not expected to carry out the work.**)

O 1991

3 Draw a diagram showing a few non-collinear points and their regression line of y on x. Mark on your diagram the distances, the sum of whose squares is minimised by the regression line.

Five shells are fired from a gun standing on level ground. After each shell is fired, the angle of elevation of the gun is increased by 1 degree. The rth shell hits the ground at a distance of y_r km from the gun. Given that

$$\Sigma y_r = 9.6 \qquad \Sigma r y_r = 29$$

find the regression line of y on r in the form $y = \alpha + \beta r$.

A shell is fired at an elevation 2.4 degrees above the initial elevation. Estimate the distance from the gun at which this shell hits the ground.

O&C 1991

4 A straight line regression equation is fitted by the least squares method to the n points (x_r, y_r), $r = 1$, 2, ..., n. For the regression equation $Y = ax + b$, show in a sketch the distances whose sum of squares is minimised, and mark clearly which axis records the dependent variable and which axis records the independent (controlled) variable.

In a chemical reaction it is known that the amount, A grams, of a certain compound produced is a linear function of the temperature $T°C$. Eight trial runs of this reaction are performed, two at each of four different temperatures. The observed values of A are subject to error. The results are shown in the table on the right.

T	10	15	20	25
A	10	15	18	16
	12	12	16	20

Draw a scatter diagram for these data.

Calculate $\overline{A}$ and $\overline{T}$.

Obtain the equation of the regression line of A on T giving the coefficients to 2 decimal places.

Draw this line on your scatter diagram.

Use the regression equation to obtain an estimate of the mean value of A when $T = 20$, and explain why this estimate is preferable to averaging the two observed values of A when $T = 20$.

Estimate the mean increase in A for a one degree increase in temperature.

State any reservations you would have about estimating the mean value of A when $T = 0$.

L 1989

5 a) Estimate, **without under-taking any calculations**, the product moment correlation coefficient between the variables in each of the scatter diagrams on the right.

b) The following table records data for the 53 pupils at a particular school who obtained at least one grade A in GCSE in 1991. X is the number of GCSE subjects passed at grade A in 1991. Y is the number of A level subjects passed at grade A in 1993.

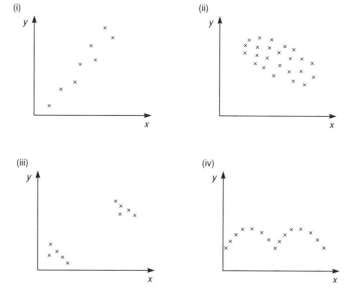

Fig. 14.8

	X					
	1	2	3	4	5	6
Y 0	8	4	7	6	7	4
1	1	2	2	0	2	2
2	0	0	3	4	1	0

(i) Calculate the product moment correlation coefficient between X and Y and comment on its value.

(ii) There are 9 pupils whose X score is 1. Calculate the mean value of Y for these 9 pupils.

Similarly calculate the mean value of Y for the pupils whose X score is each of 2, 3, 4, 5 and 6.

Comment on the use of the product moment correlation coefficient as a measure of the relationship between X and Y.

A 1994

Summary and key points

14.1 The correlation coefficient between two variables is a measure of how closely they are connected.

The sample correlation coefficient may not be the same as the population correlation coefficient. If both variables are normal, and the population correlation coefficient is zero, then critical values of the sample correlation coefficient are given in tables.

14.2 The equation of linear regression of Y on x is $Y = ax + b$, where a and b are found to minimise $\Sigma d_i^2 = \Sigma((ax_i + b) - y_i)^2$.

The values of d_i are the residuals. If a pair of values lies away from the main trend, then its residual will be large.

14.3 Sometimes a non-linear equation can be reduced to linear form by a change of variables. It is often useful to take logarithms.

Non-parametric methods

In previous chapters, when we were testing data we assumed that they came from a particular distribution. In particular, we often assumed that the data came from a normal population.

If this assumption cannot be made, then our testing methods have to be adjusted. A test which makes no assumption about the underlying distribution is a **non-parametric** or **distribution-free** test.

15.1 The sign test

A group of ten runners regularly run a certain distance. After a week's special training they run the distance again, with the results (in minutes) as below. How should we test whether their times have improved?

        12.32   13.18   12.80   13.74   25.14
        12.01   13.27   11.95   12.91   12.74

In Chapter 1 we pointed out that these sort of data are better summarised by the median than by the mean, as they are liable to be distorted by large values. Certainly we would not be justified in modelling the times by a normal distribution. The mean of these data, 14.006 minutes, is distorted by the single large value of 25.14.

Perhaps the median time, before the special training, was 13 minutes. When analysing the data we might test whether the median is significantly less than 13 minutes. Is it significant that four times are greater than 13, and six less?

In general, suppose we have n numerical data coming from an unknown distribution. Without knowledge of the population distribution, any results from a test on the **mean** of the data are unreliable. Instead we can test the **median** of the data. Under the null hypothesis that the median of the population is a particular value, m_0, we would expect half the data to be less than this value and half greater. In other words, for each data value x, we would expect that

$x - m_0$ has a positive sign with probability $\frac{1}{2}$. The test that we perform is the **sign test**. The number of values with a positive sign will have a $B(n, \frac{1}{2})$ distribution, and we test whether the number is significantly different from $\frac{1}{2}n$.

EXAMPLE 15.1

The median score for a test is 50. Ten pupils were selected at random from a school and given the test. Their results are below. Is this significant at 5 per cent to show that the median for the school is different from 50?

$$46 \quad 46 \quad 56 \quad 51 \quad 43 \quad 29 \quad 39 \quad 45 \quad 40 \quad 38$$

Solution

Let m be the median for the school. The null hypothesis is that the median is 50, and the alternative hypothesis that it is not 50.

$$H_0: m = 50 \quad H_1: m \neq 50$$

Under H_0, the number X of values greater than the median has a $B(10, \frac{1}{2})$ distribution. Here only two scores are greater than 50.

$$P(X \leq 2) = (^{10}C_2 + {}^{10}C_1 + 1)(\tfrac{1}{2})^{10} = 0.0547$$

This is greater than 0.025, the relevant probability for a two-tailed test at 5 per cent significance. The results are not significant.

We have not shown that the median differs from 50.

Comparison

The sign test can also be used on paired data. Suppose the data consists of paired values from two groups, A and B. If the two groups are equal, then there is a probability of $\frac{1}{2}$ that the A value is greater than the B value. A sign test can be performed on the differences. As above, this test will make no assumption about the population distribution of A and B.

EXAMPLE 15.2

The manufacturer of a new personal computer, the Mango, claims that it is faster than the equivalent market leader, the Pomegranate. The computers are given eight standard tasks, and the times in seconds are as below. Perform a sign test to see whether there is evidence, significant at 5 per cent, to show that the Mango is faster than the Pomegranate.

	A	B	C	D	E	F	G	H
Mango time	1.5	2.7	10.1	2.7	5.7	3.0	0.8	3.9
Pomegranate time	1.6	2.5	12.4	2.8	5.8	3.3	1.1	4.1

Solution

The null hypothesis is that the machines have the same time. The alternative hypothesis is that the Mango is faster. A one-tailed test is appropriate.

The differences are positive or negative as shown below.

A	B	C	D	E	F	G	H
+	−	+	+	+	+	+	+

Let X be the number of positive differences. Under the null hypothesis, X is just as likely to be positive as negative. This implies that $X \sim B(8, \frac{1}{2})$. The Mango was faster than the Pomegranate at seven out of eight tasks, i.e. the difference was positive on seven out of eight occasions.

$$P(X \geq 7) = 8 \times (\tfrac{1}{2})^8 + (\tfrac{1}{2})^8 = 0.035$$

This is less than 5 per cent. The alternative hypothesis is accepted.

At 5 per cent significance, we have shown that the Mango is faster than the Pomegranate.

EXERCISE 15A

1   A firm claims that the median salary of its employees is £18 000. The salaries of nine employees are listed below. Apply a sign test at a 5 per cent significance level to see whether the firm's claim is justified.

   £16 400   £14 250   £28 700   £15 200   £13 600   £9750   £11 570   £17 500   £16 250

2   The managers of a privatised bus service claim that, on 50 per cent of occasions, a passenger will have to wait no more than five minutes at a bus stop. A sceptical passenger measures the lengths of times he has to wait on eight occasions. The results, in minutes, are listed below. Apply a sign test to the claim, using a 5 per cent level of significance.

   6   7   4   12   1   27   8   9

3   A car dealer claims to sell more than 30 cars on half of the days when its business is open. Over 14 days, it sold more than 30 cars on two occasions. Apply a sign test to the claim, using a 5 per cent level of significance.

4   It is claimed that the median age at first marriage among men of a certain social group is 23. Among 20 first marriages picked at random, the age of the groom was less than 23 in three of them. Apply a sign test to the claim, using a 1 per cent level of significance.

5   A random sample of 20 companies was taken from the financial page of a paper. After a week, it was found that the share price had risen for 16 of them, and fallen for four of them. Apply a sign test to see whether this is significant at 5 per cent to show that the stock market as a whole has risen.

6 An insurance company expects that each of its sales representatives, in half the working weeks of the year, will sell more than 20 policies per week. The sales of a representative are examined for 20 weeks, and a sign test is used to decide whether his performance is substandard. If the test is at 5 per cent significance, how many weeks in which his sales were under 20 will be needed to classify his performance as substandard?

7 A battery company would like to claim that half its batteries last more than ten hours. Samples of 30 batteries from the day's batch are tested, and a sign test at 5 per cent significance is used to decide whether the batch is substandard. What number of batteries lasting under ten hours will cause the batch to be classified as substandard?

8 The annual incomes, adjusted for inflation, over two years, of ten self-employed decorators are shown below. Use a sign test at 5 per cent significance to decide whether there has been a change.

	Incomes (£1000s)									
First year	12.1	18.2	20.7	10.5	15.3	18.2	15.9	18.2	11.4	16.0
Second year	12.5	19.7	28.1	9.3	16.2	19.7	21.5	25.0	13.1	18.2

9 Nine people who normally eat cooked breakfast are persuaded to try muesli instead. After a fortnight, their weights before and after the change are compared. Use a sign test at 5 per cent significance to determine whether there has been any weight loss.

	Weights (kg)								
Before	70.2	65.3	85.9	53.2	66.3	70.0	53.8	59.2	69.0
After	69.1	66.9	84.9	53.0	65.5	70.1	53.7	58.6	68.7

10 To decide whether the stock market has risen over the period of a week, a random sample of 30 companies is taken, and a sign test applied to their share values at the beginning and the end of the week. If the test is at 1 per cent significance, how many of the share values of these sample companies would have to rise for us to conclude that the stock market as a whole has risen?

15.2 Wilcoxon signed rank test

Consider again the data consisting of the times taken to run a race.

12.32 13.18 12.80 13.74 25.14
12.01 13.27 11.95 12.91 12.74

If we use a sign test to see whether the median is 13, then we do not take into account the sizes of the values. We might want to allow for the fact that 25.14 is considerably further from the median than 13.27, for example. We can do this by ranking the differences from 13, and giving more importance to high ranks than to low.

Differences	−0.68	0.18	−0.20	0.74	12.14	−0.99	0.27	−1.05	−0.09	−0.26
Rank	6	2	3	7	10	8	5	9	1	4

The sum of the ranks of the positive differences is 24. The sum of the ranks of the negative differences is 31. Are these significantly different?

In general, a sign test takes no account of how different the values are from the median. A test which does take account of this is the **Wilcoxon signed rank** test.

Suppose we are testing whether the median of data is m_0. For each value x, find the absolute value of its difference from m_0, i.e. find $|x - m_0|$. Rank these absolute differences in order.

If some values are equal, i.e. we have **tied** ranks, then allot to each the average of the ranks they would occupy if they were slightly different. Suppose we have three values at equal 5(5=). If they were slightly different they would occupy ranks 5, 6 and 7. Hence give each the rank $\frac{1}{3}(5 + 6 + 7)$, i.e. 6.

Some of the values are less than the median, some are greater. Find the sum of the ranks for those values which are less than the median. Similarly find the sum of the ranks for those which are greater. The test statistic, T, is the smaller of these sums.

A small value of T may be significant to discredit the null hypothesis that the median is m_0. A table showing the cut-off points for T is on page 341. Its use will be shown in the following Example.

EXAMPLE 15.3
Consider again the data from Example 15.1, shown below. Use a Wilcoxon signed rank test to see whether there is evidence at 5 per cent to show that the median is not 50.

    46 46 56 51 43 29 39 45 40 38

Solution
The differences from 50, along with the ranks of their absolute values, are as follows.

Differences	4	4	−6	−1	7	21	11	5	10	12
Ranks	2=	2=	5	1	6	10	8	4	7	9

The third and fourth differences are negative, the rest positive. The sum of ranks of the negative differences is 6. The sum of ranks for the positive differences is 49. (The two ranks of 2= are allotted $2\frac{1}{2}$ each.) The smaller of the sums is 6, hence $T = 6$.

From the table, when $n = 10$, the critical value for a 5 per cent two-tailed test is 8. Our value is less than this.

for 1-tail test (2-tail in brackets)

$n =$	5% (10%)	2.5% (5%)	1% (2%)	0.5% (1%)
8	6	4	2	–
9	9	6	3	1
10	11	8	5	3
11	14	11	7	5
12	18	14	10	7

Hence at a 5 per cent significance level we reject the null hypothesis.

At a 5 per cent significance level, we conclude that the median is not 50.

Note

Examples 15.1 and 15.3 tested the same data, and the null hypothesis was rejected in 15.3 though retained in 15.1. This shows that the Wilcoxon signed rank test is more powerful than the simple sign test. This is to be expected, as it makes use of more information.

Wilcoxon paired sample signed rank test

The Wilcoxon signed rank test can also be used to test differences between two paired samples. The procedure is to find the differences between the sample values, and test whether or not the median of these differences is zero. The procedure parallels that for the sign test, except that it takes into consideration how much greater one value is than another. The procedure will be shown in the following egg sample example.

EXAMPLE 15.4

A poultry farmer wishes to test the effect of a food additive on her hens. She selected ten hens at random, and weighed their eggs before and after the food additive was given. The results, in grams, are below. Apply a Wilcoxon paired sample signed rank test to determine, at 5 per cent significance, whether the additive has increased the size of the eggs.

Before	40.3	38.7	39.4	42.1	43.7	49.8	45.0	35.7	48.2	44.1
After	41.3	40.2	41.2	42.0	44.0	49.6	44.5	36.9	50.3	46.2

Solution

The null hypothesis is that the mean mass of eggs has not changed. The alternative hypothesis is that it has increased. Write out a new row for the change in mass, and the ranks of their absolute values.

Differences	+1.0	+1.5	+1.8	−0.1	+0.3	−0.2	−0.5	+1.2	+2.1	+2.1
Rank	5	7	8	1	3	2	4	6	9=	9=

The three negative values are ranked 1, 2 and 4. The sum of these is
7. The critical value for a one-tailed test at 5 per cent is 11.

**The results are significant at 5 per cent to show that the mass has
increased.**

EXERCISE 15B

1 The data below gives the times, in minutes, that a sample of ten workers at a factory take to get to
work. Apply a signed rank test at 5 per cent significance to see whether the median time for the
whole factory is 40 minutes.

> 48   37   50   68   25   52   46   69   59   70

2 A motorcycle courier service claims that it will deliver 50 per cent of packages within 30 minutes.
The times, in minutes, for eight parcels are below. Use a signed rank test at 5 per cent significance to
see whether the claim is valid.

> 37   22   17   39   29   44   49   53

3 The median mass of a certain species of beetle is 1.5 grams. After a cold spell, a scientist thought
that their masses might have decreased. Ten were captured and weighed, with results in grams as
given below. Apply a signed rank test at 5 per cent significance to see whether the scientist was
correct.

> 1.46   1.39   1.52   1.43   1.40   1.53   1.55   1.24   1.39   1.42

4 A manufacturer of climbing ropes claims that half its ropes have a breaking strength of over 320 kg.
The breaking strengths of a sample of eight were found and are listed below. Use a signed rank test
to see whether the breaking strength is less than claimed.

> 251   305   329   316   302   321   317   327

5 A small film studio makes ten films, with profits, in £1000s, as listed below. Losses are given as negative profits. Use a signed rank test to check the assertion of the studio that half of its films make a
profit and half a loss.

> −50   −10   1000   −54   −32   20   −13   −17   −23   −5

6 Nine authors check the numbers of borrow-
ings, in 1000s, of their books from public
libraries, for this year and last year. Their
results are listed on the right. Use a paired
sample signed rank test at 5 per cent significance to see whether there has been a change.

Last year	14	28	86	7	23	12	49	31	62
This year	17	31	61	29	25	8	52	38	71

7 Eight athletes each threw a javelin twice. The results, in metres, are listed on the right. Use a paired sample signed rank test at 5 per cent significance to see whether there had been a change between the first and second throw.

First throw	23	29	17	26	32	30	32	24
Second throw	25	15	21	29	31	36	33	27

8 Two off-licences are compared by checking the prices of eight branded bottles of wine in each. The results are listed below. Use a paired sample signed rank test to see whether the difference in the prices is significant at 5 per cent.

Off-licence A	2.80	1.90	4.25	3.50	6.45	3.75	4.30	2.55
Off-licence B	2.99	1.89	4.10	3.19	6.25	3.80	3.99	2.39

15.3 Rank correlation

The correlation coefficient, r, was defined in Section 14.2. Its distribution depended on the variables X and Y being normal. If this is not the case then the significance levels of r may be wrong. If we don't know anything about the distributions of X and Y, then we need a way of measuring their correlation which does not depend on their distributions. This can be done by giving ranks to the values of X and Y, and seeing whether there is significant correlation between the ranks instead of between the values.

The correlation coefficient between the two rankings is **Spearman's rank correlation coefficient**.

Suppose that there are n pairs of values of X and Y. Let d represent the difference between the rankings. If the ranks are different, the rank correlation coefficient is given by

$$r_s = 1 - \frac{6\Sigma d^2}{n(n^2 - 1)}$$

This formula is easier to evaluate than the one for the correlation coefficient. If there are tied ranks, say two values at 5=, then allot them both a rank of $5\frac{1}{2}$. The formula above is still used, though it may be slightly inaccurate.

Critical values of Spearman's coefficient are given in the table on page 341. They are used in the same way as those for the correlation coefficient.

EXAMPLE 15.5
Ten people entered a running race and a rifle shooting contest. The results are listed below. Find the ranks of both scores, and calculate Spearman's rank correlation coefficient. Is there evidence, significant at 5 per cent, to show that there is a connection between the sports?

Person	A	B	C	D	E	F	G	H	I	J
Run time	306	241	213	278	291	287	230	206	225	254
Rifle score	0	320	410	55	0	60	160	240	0	110

Solution

The null hypothesis is that there is no connection. The alternative hypothesis is that there is. The rifle scores are unlikely to be normally distributed. In particular, three people scored 0, evidently missing the target altogether. A rank test is appropriate here.

The quickest time was 206. This has rank 1. Rank the rest of the times similarly. Rank the rifle scores. Notice that there are three people equal at the bottom. They occupy places 8, 9 and 10, so they are alloted ranks of 9. The rank table is given below.

Person	A	B	C	D	E	F	G	H	I	J
Run rank	10	5	2	7	9	8	4	1	3	6
Rifle rank	9	2	1	7	9	6	4	3	9	5

The differences between the rankings are 1, 3, 1, 0, 0, 2, 0, 2, 6, 1. These are the values of d. Apply the formula for the rank correlation coefficient.

$$r_s = 1 - \frac{6(1 + 9 + 1 + 0 + 0 + 4 + 0 + 4 + 36 + 1)}{10 \times (10^2 - 1)} = 0.66$$

The Spearman coefficient is 0.66.

The null hypothesis is that there is no connection between the rankings. The alternative hypothesis is that there is a connection. The critical value for a two-tailed test at 5 per cent is given as 0.6485.

Significance for 1-tail test (2-tail in brackets)

$n =$	10% (20%)	5% (10%)	2.5% (5%)	1% (2%)	0.5% (1%)
5	0.7	0.9	0.9	1	1
6	0.6571	0.7714	0.8286	0.9429	0.9429
7	0.5714	0.6786	0.7857	0.8571	0.8929
8	0.5476	0.6429	0.7381	0.8095	0.8571
9	0.4833	0.6000	0.6833	0.7667	0.8167
10	0.4424	0.5636	0.6485	0.7333	0.7818
11	0.4182	0.5273	0.6091	0.7000	0.7545
12	0.3986	0.5035	0.5874	0.6713	0.7273
13	0.3791	0.4780	0.5604	0.6484	0.6978
14	0.3670	0.4593	0.5385	0.6220	0.6747

This is less than the value we have found. The null hypothesis is rejected.

At 5 per cent significance, we have shown that there is a connection between the run times and the rifle scores.

EXERCISE 15C

1 For each of the tables from Question 1 of Exercise 14A, find the rankings of X and Y, and hence find the Spearman rank correlation coefficient.

2 A competition requires the entrants to rank eight properties of a car in order of decreasing importance. The organisers decide that the ranking should be as follows.

A: safety	B: reliability	C: price	D: retention of value
E: ease of handling	F: acceleration	G: maximum speed	H: looks

Two entrants give the following rankings. For each of them find the Spearman correlation coefficient with the organisers' ranking, and hence decide which entry will be considered better.

　　　CBDEAFGH　　　CDEBAGFH

3 The table on the right lists the years of service and the salaries of eight employees of a company. Find the Spearman correlation coefficient between these quantities, and test at 5 per cent significance whether there is a connection between them.

Years of service	1	4	24	5	10	2	1	9
Salary (£1000s)	12	16	14	26	48	11	15	28

4 A wine drinker was asked to taste ten bottles of wine and rank them in order of quality. The ranks, along with the prices of the bottles, are listed below. Find the Spearman's rank correlation coefficient between the quantities, and test whether they are significant at 1 per cent to show that more expensive wines are of higher quality.

Bottle	A	B	C	D	E	F	G	H	I	J
Quality	1	6	3	4	9	10	2	5	8	7
Price (£)	7.50	4.99	9.50	6.00	2.99	3.50	8.40	5.00	3.80	3.20

5 A school wishes to establish whether there is a connection between academic and sporting achievement. Eight pupils are selected and ranked. The results are on the right. What conclusions can you draw about the connection?

Pupil	A	B	C	D	E	F	G	H
Academic rank	2	3	8	5	6	1	4	7
Sporting rank	1	8	4	6	7	2	5	3

6 An examining board suspects that a marker is grading GCSE projects at random. The marker is given ten projects to rank in order, and this is compared with the board's ranking. The results are on the right. What conclusions can be drawn?

Project	A	B	C	D	E	F	G	H	I	J
Board rank	6	5	1	3	2	10	9	8	4	7
Marker's rank	6	1	2	10	9	5	8	7	3	4

7 Sketch a scatter graph of pairs of values of X and Y for which $r_s = 1$ but $r < 1$.

8 Take five pairs of positive values of X and Y for which $Y = X^2$. Show that the correlation coefficient for your values is less than 1, but that the Spearman's coefficient is equal to 1.

LONGER EXERCISE

Significance of Spearman's coefficient

For small values of n you can find or verify the critical values of Spearman's coefficient.

1 Three cards are labelled 1, 2 and 3. They are shuffled and dealt out. For each possible deal find the Spearman coefficient, r_s, between their order and 1, 2, 3. Hence find the probability distribution of r_s. Verify that $E(r_s) = 0$. Is there a critical value of r_s at 5 per cent?

2 Repeat Question 1 with four cards. (There are 24 possible orders of four numbers, so it would be a good idea to divide the labour.) What is the 5 per cent critical value?

3 With five cards, there are 120 possible orders. For a small number of these orders, r_s is at least 0.9. Find these orders. Find the 5 per cent critical value of r_s.

4 Find the 1 per cent critical value of r_s for $n = 6$.

EXAMINATION QUESTIONS

1 In order to compare the effectiveness of two mail delivery services, A and B, two samples of 12 identical deliveries were arranged. The number of hours taken for each delivery was recorded, with the following results, to the nearest $\frac{1}{2}$ hour.

Delivery	1	2	3	4	5	6	7	8	9	10	11	12
Service A	26.0	21.0	35.0	24.5	26.0	31.0	28.5	18.5	25.0	27.5	15.5	29.5
Service B	26.5	20.0	27.0	27.0	24.5	34.0	33.5	20.5	28.5	32.0	19.5	37.0

(i) It is required to test, at the 5% significance level, whether the data indicate that, on average, service A takes a shorter time for its deliveries than service B.

    a) Without assuming that the data are samples taken from normal distributions, perform a suitable test, clearly stating your hypotheses.

    b) Assuming the data are samples taken from normal distributions, perform a more suitable test.

(ii) Service A claims that its average delivery time is 24 hours. Use a non-parametric test, at the 10% significance level, to test this claim against the alternative hypothesis that the average delivery time exceeds 24 hours.

C 1994

2. A new individual programme for learning keyboard skills has been devised and it is required to compare it with the one in current use. A test is carried out by selecting 9 sets of identical twins at random. One of the twins is randomly allocated to the current programme (A) and the other is given the new one (B). At the end of each programme a common examination is given, with the results as on the right.

Twin pair	1	2	3	4	5	6	7	8	9
A score	32	43	64	30	31	59	70	50	47
B score	30	57	60	42	47	58	75	63	58

(i) Explain why a non-parametric test may be more appropriate than a parametric test for testing for a difference between the two programmes.

(ii) Perform two different non-parametric tests, at the 10% significance level, to test for a difference in average scores resulting from the two programmes. State the average (mean, median or mode) that is used in the hypotheses.

(iii) Stating any necessary assumptions, perform a parametric test of the hypothesis that the new programme results in a higher mean score than the current one. Use a $2\frac{1}{2}\%$ significance level.

C 1994

3 To test the belief that milder winters are followed by warmer summers, meteorological records are obtained for a random sample of 10 years. For each year the mean temperatures are found for January and July. The data, in degrees Celsius, are given below.

Jan.	8.3	7.1	9.0	1.8	3.5	4.7	5.8	6.0	2.7	2.1
July	16.2	13.1	16.7	11.2	14.9	15.1	17.7	17.3	12.3	13.4

(i) Rank the data and calculate Spearman's rank correlation coefficient.

(ii) Test, at the 2.5% level of significance, the belief that milder winters are followed by warmer summers. State clearly the null and alternative hypotheses under test.

(iii) Would it be more appropriate, less appropriate or equally appropriate to use the product moment correlation coefficient to analyse these data? Briefly explain why.

MEI 1992

4 A fertilizer additive is claimed to enhance the growth of marrows. To test the claim statistically, a random sample of 10 marrows is treated with varying levels of additive. The amounts of additive and the eventual weights of the marrows are given in the table.

Amount of additive (ounces)	8.2	3.5	8.8	1.6	1.9	9.9	5.8	5.5	4.4	3.9
Weight of marrow (pounds)	6.6	7.2	8.4	4.7	7.4	8.7	7.5	7.3	5.9	

(i) Rank the data and calculate Spearman's coefficient of rank correlation.

(ii) State appropriate null and alternative hypotheses for the test. Justify the alternative hypothesis you have given.

(iii) Carry out the test using a 5% level of significance. State clearly the conclusion reached.

(iv) Suppose it is discovered that the figures for the amounts of additive shown in the table were weights in grammes rather than ounces. State, with reasons, whether this does or does not invalidate your answer.

MEI 1993

5 In a national survey into whether low death rates are associated with greater prosperity, a random sample of 14 areas was taken. The areas, arranged in order of their prosperity, are shown in the table below along with their death rates. (The death rates are on a scale for which the 100 is the national average.)

	most prosperous												least prosperous
Area	A	B	C	D	E	F	G	H	I	J	K	L	M	N
Death rate	66	76	84	83	102	78	100	110	105	112	122	131	165	138

(i) Calculate an appropriate correlation coefficient and use it to test, at the 5% level of significance, whether or not there is such an association. State your hypotheses and your conclusion carefully.

(ii) A newspaper carried this story under the headline "Poverty causes increased deaths". Explain carefully whether or not the data justify this headline.

(iii) The data include no information on the age distribution in the different areas. Explain why such additional information would be relevant.

MEI 1995

Summary and key points

15.1 Suppose data comes from a population whose distribution is unknown. A sign test on the median is done by seeing whether a significant number of the data are less than the median.

Pairs of data can be tested by applying a sign test to their differences.

15.2 To apply a Wilcoxon signed rank test, rank the differences of the data from the median. Find the sum of the positive differences and the sum of the negative differences. Use tables to test whether the smaller of these sums is significantly small.

Pairs of data can be tested by applying a signed rank test to their differences.

15.3 Spearman's coefficient of rank correlation is found by giving ranks to the variables and finding the correlation coefficient between the ranks. This coefficient is independent of the distributions of the original variables. Critical values of the coefficient are given in tables.

Practical investigations II

The suggestions for practical investigations in this second set involve more theoretical work. In particular, they involve the testing of the significance of the results you find. The first three investigations ask you to revisit tasks in the first set of practical investigations, and to see how significant your results were.

Buffon's needle

This investigation asked you to throw a needle onto a floor, and to find the probability that it crosses a crack between floorboards. Your experimental probability will not be exactly the same as the theoretical probability. How different is it? Is the difference significant at 5 per cent?

Poisson distributions

Is a Poisson distribution a good model for the number of goals scored in a football match? Having obtained the data, you can use the χ^2 distribution to see whether it is a good fit.

Share values

When investigating share values, you may have asked whether there was any connection between the yield of a share at the beginning of a year and the amount by which its value had risen or fallen at the end of the year. Obtain a correlation coefficient between these figures. Is it significantly different from zero?

Random numbers

How truly random are the numbers provided by the random number generator of your calculator? If they are, the digits should come up with equal frequency. Perform a χ^2 test to see whether this is the case.

In the companion volume on Pure Mathematics, on page 507 there is a computer investigation into formulae which generate pseudo random numbers. Test whether these formulae do give digits which are random.

Astrology

Astrology is the study of the relationship between one's personal fortune and the positions of the stars and planets at one's moment of birth. Interest in astrology is widespread. The star sign columns in newspapers are very popular, and some people rely on astrology for major decisions in life.

Astrology does not claim to be able to predict with certainty. It does not claim, for example, that you are certain to be gloomy if you were born under Saturn, merely more likely to be so. The claims of astrology should be tested, not by investigating a physical cause, but by statistical analysis of the success rate of its predictions.

There are several ways the claims could be tested. You will need to find one or more people who believe that they have astrological ability. You could ask them to predict the star signs of several people. You could provide them with several life-histories and several birth dates, and ask them to match them together. In all cases you will be able to test whether the results are significantly different from those obtainable by chance.

A lot has been written on the statistical testing of astrology. The books by Michel Gauquelin, a French psychologist, are particularly recommended.

Used cars

Several questions in this book have involved exponential growth and decay. For example, the price of cars was assumed to decline exponentially. Is this true? You can obtain the prices of second-hand cars from many magazines. What formula gives the best relationship between price and age? What other factors are there?

Competitions

Many magazine competitions ask you to rank the desirable qualities of some product. Is there a best order, or is it decided arbitrarily by the competition judges? Find one of these competitions, and ask several people to do the ranking. How closely do their orders agree with each other? Are they significantly close?

Computer investigations II

In this second set of computer investigations there is theoretical as well as computer work. There are two investigations to verify statistical results, and two simulations of real life situations. All these investigations are based on a spreadsheet.

Central limit theorem

This very handy theorem tells us that the distribution of a sample mean becomes approximately normal as the sample size increases. Without this theorem, the study of Statistics would be much messier. The full proof involves advanced mathematics, so instead you can verify it using a computer.

We shall take samples of size 20 from a uniform distribution between 0 and 1. This is already provided for us by the random number function. Enter @RAND in A1, and copy across to T1. In V1 enter the sample mean, 1/20*@SUM(A1..T1). Copy A1 to V1 down for 100 rows. The V column will now contain 100 sample means.

Find the mean and variance of these 100 sample means. This can be done automatically. Are they close to the mean and variance of the corresponding normal distribution?

Sort the data into a frequency table. Your spreadsheet may have a facility to do this automatically. How close is the frequency table to that of the corresponding normal distribution? You can compare by:

a) drawing a bar-chart of the frequencies (this can be done automatically)
b) using a χ^2 goodness of fit test.

Confidence intervals

A 95 per cent confidence interval for a parameter will contain the parameter with probability 0.95. If we are trying to find a proportion π, then we take a sample of size n and find the sample proportion p. The confidence interval is then:

$$p - 1.96 \sqrt{\frac{p(1-p)}{n}} < \pi < p + 1.96 \sqrt{\frac{p(1-p)}{n}}$$

You can use a spreadsheet to investigate confidence intervals. Suppose for simplicity the (true) proportion is $\frac{1}{2}$. In A1 enter the formula @IF(@RAND<.5,1,0). This will contain 1 with probability $\frac{1}{2}$. Copy across to T1. This is our random sample of size 20. Enter the sample proportion in V1, as 1/20*(@SUM(A1..T1).

In V1 we have the sample proportion p. The left and right limits of the confidence interval can be entered in X1 and Y1, as:

$$+V1-1.96*@SQRT(V1*(1-V1)/20) \text{ and } +V1+1.96*@SQRT(V1*(1-V1)/20)$$

Does $\frac{1}{2}$ lie between X1 and Y1, i.e. does the confidence interval contain the true proportion $\frac{1}{2}$? Copy the rows A1 to Y1 down for 100 rows. In how many rows does the confidence interval contain $\frac{1}{2}$? Is it about 95?

The simulation can be varied by changing the true proportion. Does the confidence interval still contain the true proportion with probability 0.95?

Two fingered Morra

This is a simple game whose analysis provides a surprising result. Two players, A and B, simultaneously raise either 1 or 2 fingers. The pay-off is as follows.

- If both raise one finger, A pays B £1.
- If both raise two fingers, A pays B £3.
- If they raise different numbers of fingers, B pays A £2.

The game seems fair. Try playing it a few times. Who does better, A or B? Should each player aim to have equal probability of one or two fingers, or is there an advantage in having different probabilities? Might it be better to raise one finger more frequently than two?

Say that A and B play with strategies to raise one finger with probabilities p and q respectively. Set up a spreadsheet to simulate 1000 playings of the game as follows.

Put labels in row 1. In A1 and B1 enter 'A's prob.' and 'B's prob.' respectively. In D1 and E1 enter 'A's number' and 'B's number' respectively. Temporarily enter 0.5 in both A2 and B2.

A will raise one finger with probability p. So in D2 enter the formula:

$$@IF(@RAND<A\$2,1,2)$$

This will return 1 if a random number is less than p, and 2 otherwise. Hence the probability that 1 is returned is p. The \$ sign is there because you will be copying the formula down a column. Enter a similar formula in E2.

The sum of A's and B's numbers is 2, 3 or 4, and A will then win $-£1$, £2 or $-£3$ respectively. A function which returns -1, 2 and -3 at values 2, 3 and 4 respectively is

$$-4x^2 + 23x - 31 \text{ (check it!)}.$$

So in G1 enter 'A wins', and in G2 enter:

$$-4*(D2+E2)^{\wedge}2+23*(D2+E2)-31$$

Now copy rows D2 – G2 down for 1000 rows. This will provide 1000 plays of the game.

How much has A won? In A4 enter 'A's gain', and in A5 enter the formula:

$$@SUM(G2..G1001)$$

This gives A's total gain or loss. Now you are ready to investigate the game.

1 Change the values in A2 and B2, i.e. change the probabilities p and q. In particular, what happens if p has a fixed value and q varies, or vice versa?
2 There is a value of p such that, *whatever* the value of q, A will always stand to gain a certain amount. What is this value of p, and what is the amount?
3 Write A's expected gain as a function of p and q. Can you use the function to find the value of p mentioned in 2 above?

Blood bank

A blood bank keeps a stock of blood to provide transfusions. The supply of blood is fairly regular and predictable, as most donors give blood on a regular basis. Unfortunately the demand for blood is variable and unpredictable. If there is an accident a lot of blood may be required. How large a stock should the bank keep to cover all but the very worst emergencies? In this investigation you create a simplified model for blood supply and demand.

Ignore the different blood groups. Suppose the amount contributed each week is k units. Initially let k be 2. Enter 2 in A1. Suppose the initial stock is 10 units. Enter 10 in C1.

In the first model the demand for blood has a uniform distribution, taking the values 0, 1, 2, 3, 4 with equal probability 0.2. A variable which will take these values can be obtained from a random number between 0 and 1, multiplying by 5 and taking the integer value. Hence in C2 enter the formula:

+C1+A$1−@INT(5*@RAND)

Copy this formula down the C row. This will give the stock in successive weeks. Does the stock run out, or get dangerously low?

The second model for demand is more complicated. It allows for the fact that there is no upper limit on demand. Enter 10 in D1, and in D2 enter the formula:

+D1+A$1−@INT(−2.5*@LN(@RAND))

Copy this formula down. What happens?

You can adjust the initial stocks to allow for emergencies. You can also adjust the amount donated each week. What should they be to ensure that stocks do not run out?

What frequency distribution is the second model taken from? Can you find its mean?

Consolidation section D

Chapter 13

1 A particular examination is normally taken by candidates aged 16. The national average mark for this examination is 60 per cent. A school puts in 20 of its students to take the examination a year early, with the following results. Are their results significantly lower than the national average?

$$55 \quad 62 \quad 71 \quad 50 \quad 41 \quad 51 \quad 82 \quad 33 \quad 41 \quad 57$$
$$20 \quad 49 \quad 41 \quad 55 \quad 26 \quad 41 \quad 53 \quad 62 \quad 38 \quad 50$$

2 The noon temperatures over 20 days in August at a resort were as listed below. Find a 95 per cent confidence interval for the mean temperature.

$$77 \quad 71 \quad 83 \quad 66 \quad 71 \quad 80 \quad 83 \quad 92 \quad 69 \quad 70$$
$$83 \quad 85 \quad 78 \quad 90 \quad 84 \quad 82 \quad 85 \quad 91 \quad 89 \quad 84$$

3 A psychologist is investigating the sense of direction of rats. Part of the experiment is to send them through a maze, and to see at a particular junction whether they turn left, right or go straight ahead. The results are below.

	Right	Left	Ahead
Frequency	23	31	46

Is this significant at 5 per cent to show that the rats are not equally likely to take any of the three directions?

4 A woman keeps a record of how many telephone messages she receives in one-hour periods. The results are listed below. Find the mean number of messages received per hour, and test at a 5 per cent significance level whether the data could have come from a Poisson distribution.

Number of calls	0	1	2	3	4	≥ 5
Frequency	12	24	21	15	7	4

5 The times taken by 100 people to solve a dexterity puzzle are listed below. Find the mean and standard deviation of the data. Test at a 5 per cent significance level whether a normal distribution is appropriate.

Time (seconds)	20–30	30–35	35–40	40–50	50–60
Frequency	23	17	15	25	20

6 An education authority investigates different methods dealing with vandalism in schools. The results of several cases, classified by the method and by whether or not they were judged successful, are summarised below. Is there evidence, significant at 5 per cent, that there is a difference in the efficacy of these methods?

	Counselling	Punishment	Suspension
Successful	23	18	19
Not successful	29	59	31

7 The numbers of candidates passing examinations in Arabic and Japanese, classified by sex, are given in the table below. Is this significant at 5 per cent to show a connection?

	Arabic	Japanese
Female	23	49
Male	16	19

Chapter 14

8 The table below gives the results of ten basketball matches played by a particular team. Find the correlation coefficient between the points for the team and the points against.

Points for	33	51	29	48	66	53	27	40	49	30
Points against	68	55	71	36	50	60	73	62	48	62

9 The data below summarises pairs of sample values (x_i, y_i). Find the correlation coefficient.

$$n = 10 \quad \Sigma x_i = 55 \quad \Sigma x_i^2 = 385 \quad \Sigma y_i = 596 \quad \Sigma y_i^2 = 42076 \quad \Sigma x_i y_i = 3991$$

10 In Question 8, is the correlation between the points for and the points against significant at 5 per cent?

11 Using the method of least squares, find a line of linear regression for the data in Question 8, giving the points for in terms of the points against.

12 Use the data of Question 9 to calculate the line of regression of y on x.

13 The engine capacity in cm^3 of ten cars and their fuel consumption in miles per gallon are given below. Calculate the line of regression of m.p.g. on capacity. By finding the residuals, identify any outlier.

Capacity (cm^3)	1000	1400	2100	1700	1500	1200	1100	1800	2500	3000
Economy (m.p.g.)	38	25	28	30	35	36	39	28	25	24

14 The data below are thought to follow a relationship of the form $y = ax^2 + bx$. Make a suitable change of variable to convert the relationship into a linear one, and hence estimate the constants a and b.

x	2	3	4	5	6	7	8	9	10
y	10	19	30	44	60	76	100	123	150

15 The value of a particular car is thought to decline in accordance with a law of the form $V = ka^{-t}$, where £1000V is its value when it is t years old, and a and k are constant. By a suitable change of variables convert the relationship to linear form. Use the data below to estimate k and a.

t	0	1	2	3	4	5	6	7	8
V	8	6.6	5.4	4.3	3.5	2.9	2.3	1.9	1.5

Chapter 15

16 Anne buys a new cheap calculator, and suspects that its random number generator is biased towards low numbers. Of the first 30 numbers it generates, 23 are less than 0.5. Is this significant to verify her suspicions?

17 The salaries, in £1000s, earned by each partner, for ten married couples in which both husband and wife are working, are listed below. Perform a sign test to determine whether these data are significant at 5 per cent to show that men earn more than women.

Husband	23	17	26	20	19	27	16	20	25	28
Wife	21	14	29	19	12	24	15	18	18	32

18 The median score of the members of a golf club on their course is 95. The scores of nine applicants for membership are shown below. Perform a Wilcoxon signed rank test to see whether these applicants differ from the membership in ability.

92   90   89   100   91   88   102   87   94

19 Perform a Wilcoxon signed rank test on the data of Question 17 to see whether or not men earn more than women.

20 Find Spearman's rank correlation coefficient for the data in Question 8. Is it significant at 5 per cent to show a connection?

21 A competition required the entrant to list eight properties of a computer in order of importance. The judges' order, and a particular entrant's order, are shown below. Find the Spearman coefficient between the orders. Is the entrant's order significantly connected with that of the judges?

Judges' order	B	E	H	A	D	C	F	G
Entrant's order	A	H	B	G	C	D	F	E

22 The table below gives the maximum road speed, in kilometres per hour, in various countries, and their annual road death rate per million of population. Find Spearman's rank correlation coefficient between them, and comment on its significance.

Country	A	B	C	D	E	F	G	H
Maximum speed	90	96	100	112	120	128	none	none
Death rate	4	10	12	8	20	18	25	17

MIXED QUESTIONS

1   *Thy sinnes and haires may no man equall call,*
For, as thy sinnes increase, thy haires doe fall.

John Donne

What correlation is described here? From the table below find the line of regression of haires on sinnes, and predict how many sinnes are needed for complete baldness.

Sinnes (1000s)	553	716	1003	1371	1745
Haires (1000s)	23	17	14	9	5

2 A famous example of the use of the Poisson distribution occurred in the nineteenth century, when studies were done into the number of Prussian soldiers killed by horses, over the period 1875–1894. The figures are listed below.

Deaths	0	1	2	3	4
Frequency	109	65	22	3	1

Find the mean of these figures. Is a Poisson distribution with the same mean a good fit? Is it a suspiciously good fit? Below are critical values for lower cut-off points for the χ^2 distribution for certain values of v.

v	1%	5%
1	0.002	0.004
2	0.02	0.103
3	0.115	0.352
4	0.297	0.711
5	0.554	1.145

3 A 95 per cent confidence interval for a mean was $24 < \mu < 28$. It was obtained from a sample of size 15, under the assumption that the distribution was normal with variance given by the unbiased sample variance. What is the corresponding confidence interval obtained from a t-distribution?

4 A 95 per cent confidence interval for a mean was $20.5 < \mu < 29.5$ under the assumption that the unbiased sample mean was correct, and $20 < \mu < 30$ using a t-distribution. How large was the sample?

5 Sample values of X are listed below. Without any calculation, give a reason why X is unlikely to have a normal distribution.

$$20 \quad 23 \quad 29 \quad 35 \quad 39 \quad 70 \quad 97 \quad 105 \quad 299 \quad 329 \quad 900 \quad 1126$$

In fact, it is thought that $\ln X$ is normal. Find a 95 per cent confidence interval for the mean of X under this assumption.

6 It is thought that $X = aY + b$, where Y has a rectangular distribution between 0 and 1. Values of X are listed below. Find the mean and variance of these figures, and hence estimate a and b.

$$23 \quad 17 \quad 31 \quad 20 \quad 29 \quad 24 \quad 25 \quad 22 \quad 28 \quad 32$$

7 It is thought that $X = kaᶻ$, where Z has the $N(0, 1)$ distribution. Values of X are listed below. Estimate k and a.

$$2.1 \quad 3.7 \quad 5.9 \quad 10.2 \quad 11.2 \quad 24.6 \quad 56.2 \quad 95.0 \quad 102.5$$

8 Suppose there is a linear relation between y and x, and that the values of the predictor variable, x, are exact, but that the values of the response variable, y, are subject to errors which have mean 0 and variance σ^2. Then when we find the line of regression $y = ax + b$, the variance of a is $\dfrac{\sigma^2}{nS^2}$, where n is the sample size and S^2 is the (biased) sample variance of x.

Hooke's law tells us that the extension of a spring is proportional to the weight it supports. The constant of proportionality is the *stiffness* of the spring. The data below gives the length of the spring (in cm) and the mass (in kg). The masses are exact, but the measurement of the extension is subject to error which has standard deviation 0.2 cm. Find a 95 per cent confidence interval for the stiffness of the spring.

Mass	1	2	3	4	5	6
Length	12.1	13.3	14.4	15.6	16.8	17.9

9 The blood type of 100 people from a particular ethnic minority was found. The results are below. Is this significant at 5 per cent to show that the minority is not evenly spread amongst the four types?

A	AB	B	O
22	13	12	53

How would you test whether the minority has the same range of blood groups as the population as a whole?

10 There are two athletic clubs, A and B. Three members of A and four members of B are selected at random to run a race. The sum of the orders in which the A runners finished is found. Can we conclude that club A is better than club B, at a 5 per cent significance level, if the sum of these orders is:

a) 6   **b)** 7   **c)** 8?

DISCUSSION QUESTIONS

1 Suppose we want to find the usefulness of a weighing machine. Let X kg be the mass of the objects put on the machine, and Y kg be the mass it registers. If $X = Y$ then the machine is perfect.

Let ρ be the correlation coefficient between X and Y. What if $E(X) = E(Y)$ but $\rho \neq 1$?

What if $\rho = 1$ but $E(X) \neq E(Y)$?

2 Look at the tables of critical values for the correlation coefficient and the Spearman rank correlation coefficient. What do they tell you about the power of tests using these coefficients?

3 How can you distinguish between one-tailed and two-tailed tests using the χ^2 distribution?

4 When finding a line of regression by the method of least squares, we consider the vertical distances from the points to the line. Why do we not consider the perpendicular distances?

5 Numerologists claim that a person's character and fortune can be affected by the numbers associated with his or her name. A way of testing this claim would be to give an outline of someone's character and life history, along with a true and a false name. The numerologist then has to identify the correct name.

Which would be more effective: to have one person tested by 100 numerologists, or 100 people tested by one numerologist?

LONGER EXERCISES

Comparing tests

There are often several ways to test data. In Chapter 13 we have been dealing with contingency tables, to see whether there is a connection between two qualities.

If the contingency table is 2 by 2, then the test could have been done by the method of comparing proportions, as shown in Chapter 12.

Take some 2 by 2 contingency tables, and test them by the χ^2 method and by the proportion method. What are the differences between the results? Does one method give a significant result when the other doesn't?

If your data consists of matched pairs, you could test whether they come from distributions with the same average by a t-test, a sign test or a Wilcoxon signed rank test. Does one method give a significant result when the others don't?

Wald-Wolfowitz runs test

Another non-parametric test is the *Wald-Wolfowitz runs* test. Suppose we have data, coming from two groups A and B, which can be arranged in an order. The test statistic, r, is the number of blocks, or runs, of consecutive As or consecutive Bs. (A single A or B by itself counts as a run.) For example, the value of r for the sequence below is 4.

A A B A A A A A B B B B B B B

What does this test statistic tell you about A and B? In particular, what does it mean if r is small?

Suppose the groups A and B have n and m members respectively. Then if n and m are reasonably large, the distribution of r is approximately normal, with mean and variance given by

$$E(r) = \frac{2nm}{n+m} + 1 \quad \text{Var}(r) = \frac{2nm(2nm - n - m)}{(n+m)^2(n+m-1)}$$

The data below gives the salaries of 16 women and 20 men in an organisation. If you apply the runs test to the data, what will you be testing? What results do you obtain, and how do they compare with the results from other methods of testing the data?

Women				Men				
16340	17280	12820	21430	12570	25780	32650	19560	18500
20550	16410	14990	15800	18600	15900	30110	29980	17430
32690	23780	16920	17440	47300	35980	27570	17950	37120
23230	14550	13720	20630	34810	40990	53450	17830	32490

Critical values for the sign test

The tables in this book provide critical values for many tests. There isn't any table of critical values for the sign test, as it involves the comparatively simple distribution $B(n, \frac{1}{2})$. Prepare a table for the sign test, similar to those provided for the Spearman coefficient or for the Wilcoxon test. Take values of n from 8 to 12, and significance levels of 5 per cent and 1 per cent.

EXAMINATION QUESTIONS

1 A solicitor estimates how long each job will take and charges clients on the basis of these estimates. In practice a job may take more time or less time than estimated, but then there is neither an additional charge nor a refund.

A regular client complains that jobs rarely take as long as estimated so that he is being overcharged. The solicitor decides to investigate the client's claim. She consults the records on a random sample of recent jobs and determines for each the number of hours by which the estimated time exceeded the actual time taken. The figures obtained are these.

$$6.25, \quad -2.00, \quad -1.50, \quad 2.75, \quad 3.50, \quad 2.50$$

(i) Write down the null and alternative hypotheses for an appropriate significance test. Define any symbols you use, and explain why the alternative hypothesis takes the form it does.

(ii) Carry out the hypothesis test, using a five per cent significance level. State any assumption(s) required for the test to be valid.

(iii) What objection(s) might the client reasonably make regarding the solicitor's investigation?

MEI 1995

2 Two personal computers are being compared in respect of their performances in running typical jobs. Eight typical jobs selected at random are run on each computer. The table shows the values of a composite unit of performance for each job on each computer.

Job	Computer A	Computer B
1	214	203
2	198	202
3	222	216
4	206	218
5	194	185
6	236	224
7	219	213
8	210	212

It is desired to examine whether the mean performance for typical jobs is the same for each computer.

(i) State formally the null and alternative hypotheses that are being tested.
(ii) State an appropriate assumption concerning underlying normality.
(iii) Carry out the test, using a one per cent level of significance.
(iv) Provide a symmetric two-sided 95 per cent confidence interval for the difference between the mean performance times.

MEI 1995

3 An electrical component is specified by the manufacturers as having a mean lifetime of at least 1000 hours. The manufacturers regularly find the mean lifetimes for batches of five components to guard against components falling below specification. In performing hypothesis tests they rely on past records which show that lifetimes are Normally distributed with a standard deviation of 37 hours.

(i) Write down the null and alternative hypotheses under test.
(ii) Explain why no formal hypothesis test would be required for a batch with a mean lifetime of 1010 hours.
(iii) Carry out an appropriate hypothesis test at the five per cent significance level for a batch of five components with a mean lifetime of 973 hours.
(iv) After a change in the manufacturing process, the standard deviation may no longer be taken as 37 hours. The next five components to be tested have lifetimes, in hours, as follows.
   941   1002   969   988   930
Carry out an appropriate hypothesis test, at the five per cent level of significance, for these data, using the hypotheses defined in part (i). Present your conclusions carefully.

MEI 1994

4 A machine produces insulators whose lengths are normally distributed. A random sample of nine insulators yielded the following lengths in centimetres.

   5.58   6.23   5.32   6.33   5.82   6.21   6.90   5.41   5.21

The null hypothesis that the mean length of insulators produced by the machine is 6.50 cm is to be tested, using the data in this sample, against the alternative hypothesis that the mean is not 6.50 cm. Carry out this test using a two per cent significance level.

A further random sample of six insulators yielded the following lengths in centimetres.

   7.85   7.20   7.91   6.48   5.34   7.08

By combining the two samples determine if there is evidence at the five per cent significance level that the mean length is not 6.50 cm.

Stating any necessary assumptions, find a 95 per cent confidence interval for the mean length of the insulators.

Give a reason why it might not be valid to combine the two samples.

C 1994

5 A student of Statistics was heard to say that a rank correlation coefficient gives an approximation to the linear (product moment) coefficient. Sketch a scatter diagram to illustrate a situation where this statement is incorrect.

It is suspected that students who finish mathematics examinations early tend to achieve better results than those who do not. The following data show the times taken and scores of a sample of 12 randomly selected students who sat a mathematics examination.

Time in minutes (t)	25	28	32	35	40	44	47	49	52	55	59	60
Score (s)	81	59	88	79	95	86	38	44	54	48	68	73

$[\Sigma t = 526, \Sigma t^2 = 24\,614, \Sigma s = 813, \Sigma s^2 = 59\,001, \Sigma st = 34\,624]$

(i) Calculate, for the sample, the variances of s and t. Calculate also $\Sigma(s - \bar{s})(t - \bar{t})$ and hence or otherwise calculate the linear (product moment) correlation coefficient.
(ii) Calculate Spearman's rank correlation coefficient for the sample.

Hence test, at the five per cent significance level, the hypothesis that students who finish early tend to do better than those who finish later.

C 1994

6 A group of students studying A-level Statistics was set a paper, to be attempted under examination conditions, containing four questions requiring the use of the χ^2 distribution. The following table shows the type of question and the number of students who obtained good (14 or more out of 20) and bad (fewer than 14 out of 20) marks.

	Type of question			
	Contingency table	Binomial fit	Normal fit	Poisson fit
Good mark	25	12	12	11
Bad mark	4	11	3	12

a) Test at the five per cent significance level whether the mark obtained (by the students who attempted the question) is associated with the type of question.

b) Under some circumstances it is necessary to combine classes in order to carry out a test. If it had been necessary to combine the binomial fit question with another question, which question would you have combined it with and why?

c) Given that a total of 30 students sat the paper, test, at the five per cent significance level, whether the number of students attempting a particular question is associated with the type of question.

d) Compare the difficulty and popularity of the different types of question in the light of your answers to a) and c).

A 1990

7 During an investigation into visits to a health centre, interest is focused on the social class of those attending the surgery.

The table on the right shows the number of patients attending the surgery together with the population of the whole area covered by the health centre, each categorised by social class.

Social class	I	II	III	IV	V
Patients	28	63	188	173	48
Population	200	500	1600	1200	500

Use a χ^2-test, at the five per cent level of significance, to decide whether or not these results indicate that those attending the surgery are a representative sample of the whole area with respect to social class.

As part of the same investigation, the table on the right was constructed showing the reason for the patients' visits to the surgery, again categorised by social class.

	Social class				
Reason	I	II	III	IV	V
Minor physical	10	21	98	91	27
Major physical	7	17	49	40	15
Mental & other	11	25	41	42	6

Is there significant evidence to conclude that the reason for the patients' visits to the surgery is independent of their social class? Use a five per cent level of significance.

Give an interpretation of your results.

A 1991

8 In a European country registration for military service is compulsory for all eighteen year old males. All males must report to a barracks where, after an inspection some people, including all those less than 1.6 m tall, are excused service. The heights of a sample of 125 eighteen year olds measured at the barracks were as follows.

Height (m)	1.2–	1.4–	1.6–	1.8–	2.0–2.2
Frequency	6	34	31	42	12

a) Use a χ^2-test and a five per cent significance level to confirm that the normal distribution is not an adequate model for this data.

b) Show that, if the second and third classes (1.4– and 1.6–) are combined, the normal distribution does appear to fit the data. Comment on this apparent contradiction in the light of the information at the beginning of the question.

A 1992

9 An instrument panel is being designed to control a complex industrial process. It will be necessary to use both hands independently to operate the panel. To help with the design it was decided to time a number of operators, each carrying out the same task, once with the left hand and once with the right.

The times, in seconds, were as follows.

Operator	A	B	C	D	E	F	G	H	I	J	K
Left hand, x	49	58	63	42	27	55	39	33	72	66	50
Right hand, y	34	37	49	27	49	40	66	21	64	42	37

You may assume that

$\Sigma x = 554$ $\Sigma x^2 = 29\,902$ $\Sigma y = 466$ $\Sigma y^2 = 21\,682$ $\Sigma xy = 24\,053$

a) Plot a scatter diagram of the data.

b) Calculate the product moment correlation coefficient between the two variables and comment on this value.

c) Further investigation revealed that two of the operators were left-handed. State, giving a reason, which you think these were. Omitting their two results, calculate Spearman's rank correlation coefficient and comment on this value.

d) What can you say about the relationship between the times to carry out the task with left and right hands?

A 1992

10 In 1988 the Republican candidate for the Presidency of the USA was duly elected President with 54 per cent of the popular vote. The percentage of votes cast in favour of the Republican candidate at each of the elections from 1960 is given in the table.

Year	1960	1964	1968	1972	1976	1980	1984	1988
Percentage voting Republican	50.3	38.9	57.3	62.5	49.9	50.7	58.8	54.0

a) Locate and write down the median percentage vote.

b) An opposition politician, a Democrat, put forward the suggestion that the average American voter was as much a Democrat as a Republican. Suggest suitable null and alternative hypotheses (concerning the median percentage vote) to test this claim.

c) Identify all the occasions where the actual percentage is greater or less than your hypothesised median and assign a + or − appropriately. Use a binomial sign test to test the Democrat's claim explaining carefully the steps you take and making your conclusions clear.

O 1990

11 The data below shows the height above sea level, x metres, and the temperature, $y°C$, at 7.00 a.m. on the same day in summer at nine places in Europe.

Height (x)	1400	400	280	790	390	590	540	1250	680
Frequency (y)	6	15	18	10	16	14	13	7	13

a) Plot these data on a scatter diagram.

b) Calculate the product moment correlation coefficient between x and y.
(Use $\Sigma x^2 = 5\,639\,200$; $\Sigma y^2 = 1524$; $\Sigma xy = 66\,450$)

c) Give an interpretation of your coefficient.

On the same day the number of hours of sunshine was recorded and Spearman's rank correlation between hours of sunshine and temperature, based on $\Sigma d^2 = 28$ was 0.767.

d) Stating clearly your hypotheses and using a five per cent two-tailed test, interpret this rank correlation coefficient.

L 1993

Mock examinations

1 A student was asked to find the correlation coefficient of data summarised by the following.

$$n = 10 \quad \Sigma x = 55 \quad \Sigma x^2 = 385 \quad \Sigma y = 2139 \quad \Sigma y^2 = 470\,041 \quad \Sigma xy = 21\,775$$

Show that these values cannot be correct.

In fact, the last figure was written down incorrectly, and should have been 12775. Find the correlation coefficient with this amended value.

2 A factory has three machines, A, B and C, for producing steel washers. They account for 50 per cent, 30 per cent and 20 per cent of the factory's output respectively. The proportion of defective items from machines A and B is 0.01, but machine C is older and the corresponding proportion is 0.04.

A washer is picked at random from the day's production.

a) What is the probability that it is from machine C and defective?

b) What is the probability that it is defective?

c) What is the probability that it is from machine C, given that it is defective?

3 The weight in grams, of Sussex gold apples is normally distributed with mean 100 and variance 300.

a) Find the probability that a randomly selected Sussex gold apple weighs more than 110 grams.

The weight in grams of Kent russet apples is normally distributed with mean 110 and variance 400.

b) If one apple of each sort is selected, find the probability that the Kent russet apple weighs more than the Sussex gold apple.

Cartons sold in supermarkets contain two of each sort of apple. The weight of the packaging is negligible.

c) Find the probability that a carton weighs more than 400 grams.

d) Find the probability that the mean weight of 100 cartons is more than 424 grams.

4 The frequency table on the right gives details of the time, in minutes, taken by 100 members of an athletics club to run a race.

Time	10–11	11–12	12–13	13–14	14–15
Frequency	19	23	31	17	10

Construct a cumulative frequency graph, and from it estimate the median and the quartiles. Describe the skewness of the distribution.

Members of another athletics club ran the same distance, and their results are shown in the box and whisker plot in Fig. M1. Make a copy of the diagram, and on it draw a box and whisker plot for the results of the first club. Comment on the differences.

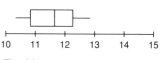

Fig. M1

5   When a markswoman fires at a target, the probability that she will hit the bull's-eye is 0.1. Assuming that each shot is independent, show that the probability that in ten shots she will get more than four bull's-eyes is 0.0016, correct to two significant figures.

By using a suitable approximation, find the probability that in 500 groups of ten shots she will score more than four bull's-eyes on fewer than two occasions.

6   A man has been told to lose weight. Over a long period when his weight remained steady at 11 stone 10 lb, he found that the standard deviation of the amount indicated by his bathroom scales was 1.6 lb.

After going on a diet, his average weight over seven days is 11 stone 8 lb. Is this significant at 5 per cent to show that his weight has declined? State any assumption made about a distribution.

Find a 95 per cent confidence interval for his weight after going on the diet.

7   The traditional treatment for a certain medical condition ensures recovery in 55 per cent of cases. A new treatment is developed, and it is to be tested on a random sample of 100 patients with the condition. A health authority will adopt the new treatment if the results are significant at 5 per cent to show that the new treatment gives a better recovery rate than the old. Calculate the minimum proportion of patients from the sample who recover under the new treatment for it to be adopted by the health authority.

What would be a Type II error in this situation? If in fact the new treatment gives a 70 per cent recovery rate, find the probability of a Type II error.

8   A survey of 200 people is carried out to investigate whether men or women are more likely to complain about poor service in restaurants. The table on the right gives the results.

	Frequently complain	Occasionally complain	Never complain
Men	12	68	30
Women	10	62	18

Using a 5 per cent level of significance, perform a χ^2 test to see whether there is a connection between sex and readiness to complain.

There were complaints that the researcher was too aggressive in the survey, and a second survey was carried out. In this second survey, the expected frequency of women who never complained fell below 5. How would you adjust the table to account for this?

After the adjustment, the value of the χ^2 statistic for the second survey was 4.34. Is this significant at 5 per cent to show that there is a connection?

PAPER 2

1 Yukiko and Mercedes are playing tennis in a tournament. The probability that Mercedes will win a given point is 0.55. Assume that the points are independent of each other. When the score is 15 all, a player will win the game if she wins three successive points.

a) Find the probability that Mercedes will win three successive points.

b) If the game was finished after three successive points, find the probability that it was won by Yukiko.

c) If they play 100 points, estimate the probability that Mercedes will win more than 60 of them.

2 A music company publishes compact discs under 378 titles. An investigation is to be carried out to see whether the company is paying the correct royalties to the performers. The following methods are suggested for choosing a sample of the discs.

  I Pick all the discs by three particular artists.

  II Pick, at random, ten discs from each of the categories Pop, Classical, Jazz.

  III Pick every tenth disc in the company's list.

Classify each of these methods of sampling. Write *brief* notes on the advantages and disadvantages of each.

The investigating authority decides instead to pick a purely random sample of 30 discs. Describe how this could be done using a table of random numbers.

3 The continuous random variable X has probability density function $f(x)$ given by:

$$f(x) = k(x^2 + 3) \quad \text{for } -2 \le x \le 2$$
$$= 0 \quad \text{otherwise}$$

a) Find k, and sketch the graph of $f(x)$.

b) From your graph, write down $E(X)$. Find the variance of X.

c) Find the probability that X is more than 1.2 standard deviations away from the mean.

4 The number of call-outs received per day by a washing-machine engineer has a Poisson distribution. The probability that he will not be called out is 0.1. Find the mean number of call-outs he receives in a day.

a) Find the probability that he will receive fewer than three call-outs in one day.

b) Find the probability that he will receive five call-outs in two days.

c) Use a suitable approximation to find the probability that in 80 days he will receive fewer than 180 call-outs.

5 The marks in an examination obtained by a group of 40 pupils are listed below. Construct a stem and leaf diagram to illustrate the data.

    60 54 58 66 71 78 51 44 40 69 60 82 75 70 80 44 60 62 54 55

    50 49 67 64 77 81 85 55 58 60 53 49 71 66 60 61 56 46 48 50

The passmark for this examination is 60, and all candidates who obtained between 55 and 59 inclusive had their papers re-marked. Discuss the shape of the diagram in the light of this information.

6 Explain the circumstances under which it is appropriate to perform a significance test on the product moment correlation coefficient.

The table below gives the ages of nine publishing houses along with the numbers of titles they have in print. Without any calculation, give a reason why it may not be appropriate to use the product moment correlation coefficient on these data. Instead calculate the Spearman rank correlation coefficient, and test at 5 per cent significance whether there is an association.

Age (years)	520	230	27	21	15	10	8	5	3
Number of titles	10 283	907	138	219	78	43	61	201	68

7 A company produces sacks of coal which are advertised as containing a minimum of 20 kg. The standard deviation of the contents of the sacks is 2 kg. Assuming that the weight is normally distributed, and that the mean weight of the sacks is 23.3 kg, show that fewer than about one in twenty will contain less than 20 kg.

Every day the company finds the average weight of a random sample of five sacks, and investigates all the day's production if this average is less than 21.5 kg. What is the significance level corresponding to this control procedure?

In fact, the mean weight of the sacks has fallen to 19.5 kg. What is the probability that this will not be recognised by the procedure above?

8 a) It is claimed that opposition to fox-hunting is greater among younger people than older. Random samples of 100 people under 30 and 200 people over 30 were found. The proportions opposing fox-hunting in the two groups were 0.44 and 0.39 respectively. Test the claim at a 5 per cent level of significance.

b) A 95 per cent confidence interval for the support for a political party is given as (48 ± 3) per cent. How large was the sample from which the interval was found?

PAPER 3

1 Describe two situations in which it is necessary to use sampling.

Explain what is meant by (a) a sample frame (b) a cluster sample, (c) a random sample. Give one advantage and one disadvantage of using a cluster sample rather than a random sample.

2 Two events A and B are such that $P(A) = 0.6$ and $P(B) = 0.7$. Explain why A and B cannot be exclusive.

Find the least and the greatest possible values of $P(A \& B)$.

If $P(A \& B) = 0.4$, find $P(A|A \text{ or } B)$.

3 a) The following table gives the frequencies of the times taken to answer the telephone by the reception of a college. Estimate the mean time and the median time. Construct a histogram to illustrate the data. What can you say about the skewness of the distribution?

Time (seconds)	0–2	2–4	4–6	6–10	10–20	20–40
Frequency	13	17	14	19	11	8

b) The data below give the noon temperature at a resort at certain dates in the summer. Construct a scatter diagram for the data.

Days after 23 June	10	15	20	25	30	35	40	45	50
Temperature (°F)	73	77	82	86	72	88	92	92	95

Identify the point which is an outlier. With this point removed, find the equation of the line of regression of temperature on date. Explain why the equation cannot be used to predict the temperature for later dates.

4 A roulette wheel has holes numbered 1 to 36. Assuming that the wheel is fair:

a) find the probability that, in five spins, two will give a number between 1 and 12 inclusive,

b) use a suitable distributional approximation to find the probability that in 90 spins, exactly four will give the number 7,

c) use a suitable distributional approximation to find the probability that in 180 spins, more than 70 will give a number between 1 and 12 inclusive.

The manager suspects the croupier of biasing the result of the spin towards low numbers, i.e. those from 1 to 12 inclusive. He monitors the results for 300 spins, and finds that these low numbers came up 115 times. Are his suspicions justified? Use a 5 per cent significance level.

5 The distance from its source that a radio station can be heard is X miles, where X is a continuous random variable with p.d.f. $f(x)$ given by:

$$f(x) = k \qquad 100 \leq x \leq 110$$
$$= 0 \qquad \text{elsewhere}$$

Find k. Write down the mean μ and median m of X.

Let Y square miles be the area of the region within which the radio station can be heard, i.e. let $Y = \pi X^2$.

For $100 \leq x \leq 110$, find $P(X < x)$, and hence find $P(Y < y)$, for $\pi 100^2 \leq y \leq \pi 110^2$. Hence find the p.d.f. of Y.

Find the mean and median of Y. Are these equal to $\pi\mu^2$ and πm^2 respectively? Comment.

6 The random variable, X, has unknown mean μ and known variance 14. A random sample of size 30 is taken from the probability distribution of X. Making use of a particular theorem, whose name should be given, estimate the probability that the sample mean $\overline{X}$ is greater than $\mu + 1$.

Another random sample is taken from the distribution, this time of size 20 and with sample mean $\overline{Y}$. Show that the following are both unbiased estimators of μ.

$$T = \tfrac{1}{2}(\overline{X} + \overline{Y}) \qquad R = 0.6\overline{X} + 0.4\overline{Y}.$$

Find the variances of T and R. Which estimator is preferable?

7 At the office of a minicab firm, the number of calls per hour for a cab has a Poisson distribution with mean 6.

   a) Find the probability that there will be no calls in 15 minutes.

   b) Find the probability that there will be at least one call within x minutes.

   Let X minutes be the waiting time until the next call. Show that the c.d.f. of X is given by:

   $$F(x) = 1 - e^{-0.1x} \qquad 0 \le x$$

   c) Find the p.d.f. of X, and sketch its graph.

   d) Find the mean and median of the waiting time. Comment on the difference.

8 A passengers' group monitors the frequency with which the buses of a coach company arrive late. The results gathered over a year are below.

Months	Jan–Mar	Apr–Jun	Jul–Sep	Oct–Dec
Frequency	53	7	38	46

   Show that these results are significant at 5 per cent to show that lateness is associated with time of year.

   It is then pointed out that there was a drivers' strike during the April to June period. Explain how this could invalidate your results. Omit the figure for this period, and test again for an association.

Mathematical appendix

Chapter 1

Two forms of variance

$$\Sigma \frac{(x_i - \overline{x})^2}{n} = \frac{\Sigma x_i^2}{n} - \overline{x}^2$$

Proof

$$\Sigma \frac{(x_i - \overline{x})^2}{n} = \Sigma \frac{x_i^2 - 2x_i\overline{x} + \overline{x}^2}{n} = \Sigma \frac{x_i^2}{n} - 2\overline{x}\Sigma\frac{x_i}{n} + \frac{n\overline{x}^2}{n} = \Sigma\frac{x_i^2}{n} - 2\overline{x}\,\overline{x} + \overline{x}^2 = \Sigma\frac{x_i^2}{n} - \overline{x}^2$$

Chapter 5

Two forms of variance

$$E((X - \overline{X})^2) = E(X^2) - \overline{X}^2$$

Proof

$$E((X - \overline{X})^2) = \Sigma(x_i - \overline{X})^2 p_i = \Sigma(x_i^2 - 2x_i\overline{X} + \overline{X}^2)p_i = \Sigma x_i^2 p_i - 2\overline{X}\Sigma x_i p_i + \overline{X}^2\Sigma p_i$$

$$= E(X^2) - 2\overline{X}\,\overline{X} + \overline{X}^2$$

(Using $\Sigma x_i p_i = E(X)$ and $\Sigma p_i = 1$. Also $\Sigma x_i^2 p_i = E(X^2)$)

$$= E(X^2) - \overline{X}^2$$

Mean and variance of uniform distribution

If X takes the values 1, 2, 3, ..., n, the mean and variance of X are given by:

$$E(X) = \tfrac{1}{2}(n + 1) \qquad \text{Var}(X) = \tfrac{1}{12}(n^2 - 1)$$

Proof

For these we shall need the following identities.

$$\sum_{i=1}^{n} i = \tfrac{1}{2}n(n + 1) \qquad \sum_{i=1}^{n} i^2 = \tfrac{1}{6}n(n + 1)(2n + 1)$$

First the mean.

$$E(X) = \sum_{i=1}^{n} i \times \frac{1}{n} = \frac{1}{n}\sum_{i=1}^{n} i = \frac{1}{n} \times \tfrac{1}{2}n(n + 1) = \tfrac{1}{2}(n + 1)$$

To find the variance, we first evaluate $E(X^2)$.

$$E(X^2) = \sum_{i=1}^{n} i^2 \times \frac{1}{n} = \frac{1}{n}\sum_{i=1}^{n} i^2 = \frac{1}{n} \times \tfrac{1}{6}n(n + 1)(2n + 1) = \tfrac{1}{6}(n + 1)(2n + 1)$$

Now use the formula $\text{Var}(X) = E(X^2) - \mu^2$.

$$\text{Var}(X) = \tfrac{1}{6}(n + 1)(2n + 1) - (\tfrac{1}{2}(n + 1))^2 = \tfrac{1}{12}(n + 1)(4n + 2 - 3(n + 1))$$
$$= \tfrac{1}{12}(n + 1)(n - 1) = \tfrac{1}{12}(n^2 - 1)$$

Chapter 6

Two forms of variance

$$E((X - \overline{X})^2) = E(X^2) - \overline{X}^2$$

Proof

$$E((X - \overline{X})^2) = \int(x - \overline{X})^2 f(x)\,dx = \int(x^2 - 2x\overline{X} + \overline{X}^2)f(x)\,dx$$
$$= \int x^2 f(x)\,dx - 2\overline{X}\int xf(x)\,dx + \overline{X}^2\int f(x)\,dx = E(X^2) - 2\overline{X}\,\overline{X} + \overline{X}^2$$

(Using $\int xf(x)\,dx = E(X)$ and $\int f(x)\,dx = 1$. Also $\int x^2 f(x)\,dx = E(X^2)$)

$$= E(X^2) - \overline{X}^2$$

Expectation and variance of the exponential distribution

Let X have the p.d.f. $f(x) = \lambda e^{-\lambda x}$, for $x \geq 0$. Then $E(X) = \dfrac{1}{\lambda}$ and $\text{Var}(X) = \dfrac{1}{\lambda^2}$.

Proof

Expectation $E(X) = \displaystyle\int_0^\infty x\lambda e^{-\lambda x}\,dx = \left[- xe^{-\lambda x} \right]_0^\infty + \int_0^\infty e^{-\lambda x}\,dx = \left[- xe^{-\lambda x} + \frac{1}{\lambda}e^{-\lambda x} \right]_0^\infty$

As x tends to ∞, $xe^{-\lambda x}$ and $e^{-\lambda x}$ tend to 0. The integral is $\dfrac{1}{\lambda}$.

Variance $E(X^2) = \displaystyle\int_0^\infty x^2\lambda e^{-\lambda x}\,dx = \left[- x^2 e^{-\lambda x} \right]_0^\infty + \int_0^\infty 2xe^{-\lambda x}\,dx$

$$= \left[- x^2 e^{-\lambda x} - \frac{2}{\lambda}\left(- xe^{-\lambda x} - \frac{1}{\lambda}e^{-\lambda x} \right) \right]_0^\infty \quad \text{(From the result above.)}$$

$$= \frac{2}{\lambda^2} \quad (-x^2 e^{-\lambda x} \text{ also tends to 0 as } x \text{ tends to } \infty.)$$

$$\text{Hence } \text{Var}(X) = E(X^2) - (E(X))^2 = \frac{2}{\lambda^2} - \frac{1}{\lambda^2} = \frac{1}{\lambda^2}.$$

Chapter 7

Expectation and variance of the binomial distribution

If $X \sim B(n, p)$, then $E(X) = np$ and $\text{Var}(X) = npq$.

Proof

We use $P(X = i) = {}^nC_i p^i q^{n-i}$, where $q = 1 - p$.

Expectation $E(X) = \sum_{i=0}^{n} i\,P(X=i)$

$$= 0 \times q^n + 1 \times npq^{n-1} + 2 \times \frac{n(n-1)}{2!} p^2 q^{n-2} + 3 \times \frac{n(n-1)(n-2)}{3!} p^3 q^{n-3} + \ldots + n \times p^n$$

$$= np\left(q^{n-1} + \frac{n-1}{1!} pq^{n-2} + \frac{(n-1)(n-2)}{2!} p^2 q^{n-3} + \ldots + p^{n-1}\right)$$

$$= np\left((q+p)^{n-1}\right) = np$$

Variance $E(X(X-1)) = \sum_{i=0}^{n} i(i-1)\,P(X=i)$

$$= 0 \times q^n + 0 \times npq^{n-1} + 2 \times 1 \times \frac{n(n-1)}{2!} p^2 q^{n-2} + 3 \times 2 \times \frac{n(n-1)(n-2)}{3!} p^3 q^{n-3}$$
$$+ \ldots + n(n-1) \times p^n$$

$$= n(n-1)p^2\left(q^{n-2} + \frac{n-2}{1!} pq^{n-3} + \frac{(n-2)(n-3)}{2!} p^2 q^{n-4} + \ldots + p^{n-2}\right)$$

$$= n(n-1)p^2\left((q+p)^{n-2}\right) = n(n-1)p^2$$

Hence $E(X^2) = E(X(X-1)) + E(X) = n(n-1)p^2 + np$

$Var(X) = n(n-1)p^2 + np - (np)^2 = np(np - p + 1 - np) = np(1-p) = npq$

Mean and variance of the geometric distribution

$$E(X) = \frac{1}{p} \quad Var(X) = \frac{q}{p^2}$$

Proof

As $|q| < 1$, the following are true

$$\sum_{i=0}^{\infty} q^i = \frac{1}{1-q}$$

Hence $\dfrac{d}{dq} \sum_{i=0}^{\infty} q^i = \sum_{i=0}^{\infty} i q^{i-1} = \dfrac{1}{(1-q)^2}$ and $\dfrac{d^2}{dq^2} \sum_{i=0}^{\infty} q^i = \sum_{i=1}^{\infty} i(i-1) q^{i-2} = \dfrac{2}{(1-q)^3}$

We use $P(X=i) = pq^{i-1}$.

Expectation

$$E(X) = \sum_{i=1}^{\infty} ipq^{i-1} = p\frac{d}{dq} \sum_{i=0}^{\infty} q^i = p\frac{1}{(1-q)^2} = p\frac{1}{p^2} = \frac{1}{p}$$

Variance

$$E(X(X-1)) = \sum_{i=1}^{\infty} i(i-1)pq^{i-1} = pq\sum_{i=1}^{\infty} i(i-1)q^{i-2} = pq\frac{d^2}{dq^2} \sum_{i=1}^{\infty} q^i$$

$$= pq\frac{2}{(1-q)^3} = pq\frac{2}{p^3} = \frac{2q}{p^2}$$

Hence $E(X^2) = \dfrac{2q}{p^2} + \dfrac{1}{p}$.

$$Var(X) = \frac{2q}{p^2} + \frac{1}{p} - \frac{1}{p^2} = \frac{2q + p - 1}{p^2}$$

$$= \frac{2 - 2p + p - 1}{p^2} = \frac{1 - p}{p^2} = \frac{q}{p^2}$$

Chapter 8

Poisson distribution

If $X \sim P(\lambda)$, then the sum of all the probabilities is 1.

Proof

We use $P(X = i) = \dfrac{\lambda^i}{i!} e^{-\lambda}$.

The expansion of e^λ is $1 + \lambda + \dfrac{\lambda^2}{2!} + \dfrac{\lambda^3}{3!} + \ldots$

The sum of all the probabilities is

$$\sum_{i=0}^{\infty} \left(\frac{\lambda^i}{i!} e^{-\lambda} \right) = e^{-\lambda} \sum_{i=0}^{\infty} \frac{\lambda^i}{i!} = e^{-\lambda} e^{\lambda} = 1$$

Expectation and variance

If $X \sim P(\lambda)$, then $E(X) = Var(X) = \lambda$.

Proof

Expectation $E(X) = \displaystyle\sum_{i=0}^{\infty} i \, P(X = i)$

$$= 0 \times \frac{\lambda^0}{0!} e^{-\lambda} + 1 \times \frac{\lambda^1}{1!} e^{-\lambda} + 2 \times \frac{\lambda^2}{2!} e^{-\lambda} + 3 \times \frac{\lambda^3}{3!} e^{-\lambda} + \ldots$$

$$= \lambda e^{-\lambda} \left(1 + \frac{\lambda^1}{1!} + \frac{\lambda^2}{2!} + \frac{\lambda^3}{3!} + \ldots \right) = \lambda e^{-\lambda}(e^{\lambda}) = \lambda$$

Variance $E(X(X - 1)) = \displaystyle\sum_{i=0}^{\infty} i(i - 1) \, P(X = i)$

$$= 0 \times \frac{\lambda^0}{0!} e^{-\lambda} + 0 \times \frac{\lambda^1}{1!} e^{-\lambda} + 2 \times 1 \times \frac{\lambda^2}{2!} e^{-\lambda} + 3 \times 2 \times \frac{\lambda^3}{3!} e^{-\lambda} + \ldots$$

$$= \lambda^2 e^{-\lambda} \left(1 + \frac{\lambda^1}{1!} + \frac{\lambda^2}{2!} + \frac{\lambda^3}{3!} + \ldots \right) = \lambda^2 e^{-\lambda}(e^{\lambda}) = \lambda^2$$

Hence $E(X^2) = E(X(X - 1)) + E(X) = \lambda^2 = \lambda$

$Var(X) = \lambda^2 + \lambda - \lambda^2 = \lambda$.

Sum of independent Poisson variables

If X and Y are independent variables with $X \sim P(\lambda)$ and $Y \sim P(\mu)$, then $X + Y \sim P(\lambda + \mu)$

Proof

$$P(X + Y = r) = \sum_{i=0}^{r} P(X + i \, \& \, Y = r - i) = \sum_{i=0}^{r} P(X = i)P(Y = r - i)$$

(Because X and Y are independent.)

$$= \sum_{i=0}^{r} \frac{\lambda^i}{i!} e^{-\lambda} \frac{\mu^{r-i}}{(r - i!)} e^{-\mu}$$

$$= \frac{e^{-(\lambda + \mu)}}{r!} \sum_{i=0}^{r} \frac{r!}{i! \, (r - i)!} \lambda^i \mu^{r-i}$$

$$= \frac{e^{-(\lambda + \mu)}}{r!} (\lambda + \mu)^r$$

This gives the probability for a $Po(\mu + \lambda)$ distribution.

Chapter 10

If X and Y are independent, then $Var(X + Y) = Var(X) + Var(Y)$

Proof

Use the formula for variance. Let $E(X) = \mu$ and $E(Y) = \lambda$.

$$\begin{aligned}
Var(X + Y) &= E((X + Y)^2) - (E(X + Y))^2 \\
&= E(X^2 + 2XY + Y^2) - (E(X) + E(Y))^2 \\
&= E(X^2) + 2E(XY) + E(Y^2) - (\mu + \lambda)^2 \\
&= E(X^2) + 2E(X)E(Y) + E(Y^2) - (\mu + \lambda)^2 \\
&= E(X^2) + 2\mu\lambda + E(Y^2) - \mu^2 - 2\mu\lambda - \lambda^2 \\
&= E(X^2) - \mu^2 + E(Y^2) - \lambda^2 \\
&= Var(X) + Var(Y)
\end{aligned}$$

Biased and unbiased sample variance

If $S^2 = \dfrac{\Sigma x_i^2}{n} - \bar{x}^2$ then $E(s^2) = \dfrac{n - 1}{n} \sigma^2$, where σ^2 is the variance of the population from which the sample comes.

Proof

The x_i are independent and identically distributed.

$$E(x_i) = \mu \text{ and } Var(x_i) = \sigma^2$$

We know that $E(\bar{x}) = \mu$ and $Var(\bar{x}) = \dfrac{\sigma^2}{n}$.

$$E(S^2) = \frac{1}{n} E(\Sigma x_i^2) - E(\bar{x}^2) = \frac{1}{n} \Sigma E(x_i^2) - (Var(\bar{x}) - \mu^2)$$

$$= \frac{1}{n}(nE(x_i^2)) - \left(\frac{\sigma^2}{n} + \mu^2\right) = (Var(x_i) + \mu^2) - \left(\frac{\sigma^2}{n} + \mu^2\right)$$

$$= \sigma^2 - \frac{\sigma^2}{n} = \sigma^2\left(1 - \frac{1}{n}\right) = \frac{n-1}{n}\sigma^2$$

Statistical tables

Table 1. Cumulative probabilities for the binomial distribution

These tables give $P(X \leq i)$, where $X \sim B(n, p)$

$n = 10$

$p =$ 0.05	0.1	0.15	1/6	0.2	0.25	0.3	1/3	0.35	0.4	0.45	0.5
$i =$											
0 0.5987	0.3487	0.1969	0.1615	0.1074	0.0563	0.0282	0.0173	0.0135	0.0060	0.0025	0.0010
1 0.9139	0.7361	0.5443	0.4845	0.3758	0.2440	0.1493	0.1040	0.0860	0.0464	0.0233	0.0107
2 0.9885	0.9298	0.8202	0.7752	0.6778	0.5256	0.3828	0.2991	0.2616	0.1673	0.0996	0.0547
3 0.9990	0.9872	0.9500	0.9303	0.8791	0.7759	0.6496	0.5593	0.5138	0.3823	0.2660	0.1719
4 0.9999	0.9984	0.9901	0.9845	0.9672	0.9219	0.8497	0.7869	0.7515	0.6331	0.5044	0.3770
5 1.0000	0.9999	0.9986	0.9976	0.9936	0.9803	0.9527	0.9234	0.9051	0.8338	0.7384	0.6230
6 1.0000	1.0000	0.9999	0.9997	0.9991	0.9965	0.9894	0.9803	0.9740	0.9452	0.8980	0.8281
7 1.0000	1.0000	1.0000	1.0000	0.9999	0.9996	0.9984	0.9966	0.9952	0.9877	0.9726	0.9453
8 1.0000	1.0000	1.0000	1.0000	1.0000	1.0000	0.9999	0.9996	0.9995	0.9983	0.9955	0.9893
9 1.0000	1.0000	1.0000	1.0000	1.0000	1.0000	1.0000	1.0000	1.0000	0.9999	0.9997	0.9990
10 1.0000	1.0000	1.0000	1.0000	1.0000	1.0000	1.0000	1.0000	1.0000	1.0000	1.0000	1.0000

$n = 20$

$p =$ 0.05	0.1	0.15	1/6	0.2	0.25	0.3	1/3	0.35	0.4	0.45	0.5
$i =$											
0 0.3585	0.1216	0.0388	0.0261	0.0115	0.0032	0.0008	0.0003	0.0002	0.0000	0.0000	0.0000
1 0.7358	0.3917	0.1756	0.1304	0.0692	0.0243	0.0076	0.0033	0.0021	0.0005	0.0001	0.0000
2 0.9245	0.6769	0.4049	0.3287	0.2061	0.0913	0.0355	0.0176	0.0121	0.0036	0.0009	0.0002
3 0.9841	0.8670	0.6477	0.5665	0.4114	0.2252	0.1071	0.0604	0.0444	0.0160	0.0049	0.0013
4 0.9974	0.9568	0.8298	0.7687	0.6296	0.4148	0.2375	0.1515	0.1182	0.0510	0.0189	0.0059
5 0.9997	0.9887	0.9327	0.8982	0.8042	0.6172	0.4164	0.2972	0.2454	0.1256	0.0553	0.0207
6 1.0000	0.9976	0.9781	0.9629	0.9133	0.7858	0.6080	0.4793	0.4166	0.2500	0.1299	0.0577
7 1.0000	0.9996	0.9941	0.9887	0.9679	0.8982	0.7723	0.6615	0.6010	0.4159	0.2520	0.1316
8 1.0000	0.9999	0.9987	0.9972	0.9900	0.9591	0.8867	0.8095	0.7624	0.5956	0.4143	0.2517
9 1.0000	1.0000	0.9998	0.9994	0.9974	0.9861	0.9520	0.9081	0.8782	0.7553	0.5914	0.4119
10 1.0000	1.0000	1.0000	0.9999	0.9994	0.9961	0.9829	0.9624	0.9468	0.8725	0.7507	0.5881
11 1.0000	1.0000	1.0000	1.0000	0.9999	0.9991	0.9949	0.9870	0.9804	0.9435	0.8692	0.7483
12 1.0000	1.0000	1.0000	1.0000	1.0000	0.9998	0.9987	0.9963	0.9940	0.9790	0.9420	0.8684
13 1.0000	1.0000	1.0000	1.0000	1.0000	1.0000	0.9997	0.9991	0.9985	0.9935	0.9786	0.9423
14 1.0000	1.0000	1.0000	1.0000	1.0000	1.0000	1.0000	0.9998	0.9997	0.9984	0.9936	0.9793
15 1.0000	1.0000	1.0000	1.0000	1.0000	1.0000	1.0000	1.0000	1.0000	0.9997	0.9985	0.9941
16 1.0000	1.0000	1.0000	1.0000	1.0000	1.0000	1.0000	1.0000	1.0000	1.0000	0.9997	0.9987
17 1.0000	1.0000	1.0000	1.0000	1.0000	1.0000	1.0000	1.0000	1.0000	1.0000	1.0000	0.9998
18 1.0000	1.0000	1.0000	1.0000	1.0000	1.0000	1.0000	1.0000	1.0000	1.0000	1.0000	1.0000
19 1.0000	1.0000	1.0000	1.0000	1.0000	1.0000	1.0000	1.0000	1.0000	1.0000	1.0000	1.0000
20 1.0000	1.0000	1.0000	1.0000	1.0000	1.0000	1.0000	1.0000	1.0000	1.0000	1.0000	1.0000

$n = 30$

$p =$	0.05	0.1	0.15	1/6	0.2	0.25	0.3	1/3	0.35	0.4	0.45	0.5
$i =$												
0	0.2146	0.0424	0.0076	0.0042	0.0012	0.0002	0.0000	0.0000	0.0000	0.0000	0.0000	0.0000
1	0.5535	0.1837	0.0480	0.0295	0.0105	0.0020	0.0003	0.0001	0.0000	0.0000	0.0000	0.0000
2	0.8122	0.4114	0.1514	0.1028	0.0442	0.0106	0.0021	0.0007	0.0003	0.0000	0.0000	0.0000
3	0.9392	0.6474	0.3217	0.2396	0.1227	0.0374	0.0093	0.0033	0.0019	0.0003	0.0000	0.0000
4	0.9844	0.8245	0.5245	0.4243	0.2552	0.0979	0.0302	0.0122	0.0075	0.0015	0.0002	0.0000
5	0.9967	0.9268	0.7106	0.6164	0.4275	0.2026	0.0766	0.0355	0.0233	0.0057	0.0011	0.0002
6	0.9994	0.9742	0.8474	0.7765	0.6070	0.3481	0.1595	0.0838	0.0586	0.0172	0.0040	0.0007
7	0.9999	0.9922	0.9302	0.8863	0.7608	0.5143	0.2814	0.1668	0.1238	0.0435	0.0121	0.0026
8	1.0000	0.9980	0.9722	0.9494	0.8713	0.6736	0.4315	0.2860	0.2247	0.0940	0.0312	0.0081
9	1.0000	0.9995	0.9903	0.9803	0.9389	0.8034	0.5888	0.4317	0.3575	0.1763	0.0694	0.0214
10	1.0000	0.9999	0.9971	0.9933	0.9744	0.8943	0.7304	0.5848	0.5078	0.2915	0.1350	0.0494
11	1.0000	1.0000	0.9992	0.9980	0.9905	0.9493	0.8407	0.7239	0.6548	0.4311	0.2327	0.1002
12	1.0000	1.0000	0.9998	0.9995	0.9969	0.9784	0.9155	0.8340	0.7802	0.5785	0.3592	0.1808
13	1.0000	1.0000	1.0000	0.9999	0.9991	0.9918	0.9599	0.9102	0.8737	0.7145	0.5025	0.2923
14	1.0000	1.0000	1.0000	1.0000	0.9998	0.9973	0.9831	0.9565	0.9348	0.8246	0.6448	0.4278
15	1.0000	1.0000	1.0000	1.0000	0.9999	0.9992	0.9936	0.9812	0.9699	0.9029	0.7691	0.5722
16	1.0000	1.0000	1.0000	1.0000	1.0000	0.9998	0.9979	0.9928	0.9876	0.9519	0.8644	0.7077
17	1.0000	1.0000	1.0000	1.0000	1.0000	0.9999	0.9994	0.9975	0.9955	0.9788	0.9286	0.8192
18	1.0000	1.0000	1.0000	1.0000	1.0000	1.0000	0.9998	0.9993	0.9986	0.9917	0.9666	0.8998
19	1.0000	1.0000	1.0000	1.0000	1.0000	1.0000	1.0000	0.9998	0.9996	0.9971	0.9862	0.9506
20	1.0000	1.0000	1.0000	1.0000	1.0000	1.0000	1.0000	1.0000	0.9999	0.9991	0.9950	0.9786
21	1.0000	1.0000	1.0000	1.0000	1.0000	1.0000	1.0000	1.0000	1.0000	0.9998	0.9984	0.9919
22	1.0000	1.0000	1.0000	1.0000	1.0000	1.0000	1.0000	1.0000	1.0000	1.0000	0.9996	0.9974
23	1.0000	1.0000	1.0000	1.0000	1.0000	1.0000	1.0000	1.0000	1.0000	1.0000	0.9999	0.9993
24	1.0000	1.0000	1.0000	1.0000	1.0000	1.0000	1.0000	1.0000	1.0000	1.0000	1.0000	0.9998
25	1.0000	1.0000	1.0000	1.0000	1.0000	1.0000	1.0000	1.0000	1.0000	1.0000	1.0000	1.0000

	$n = 40$											
$p =$	0.05	0.1	0.15	1/6	0.2	0.25	0.3	1/3	0.35	0.4	0.45	0.5
$i =$												
0	0.1285	0.0148	0.0015	0.0007	0.0001	0.0000	0.0000	0.0000	0.0000	0.0000	0.0000	0.0000
1	0.3991	0.0805	0.0121	0.0061	0.0015	0.0001	0.0000	0.0000	0.0000	0.0000	0.0000	0.0000
2	0.6767	0.2228	0.0486	0.0274	0.0079	0.0010	0.0001	0.0000	0.0000	0.0000	0.0000	0.0000
3	0.8619	0.4231	0.1302	0.0811	0.0285	0.0047	0.0006	0.0001	0.0001	0.0000	0.0000	0.0000
4	0.9520	0.6290	0.2633	0.1806	0.0759	0.0160	0.0026	0.0006	0.0003	0.0000	0.0000	0.0000
5	0.9861	0.7937	0.4325	0.3239	0.1613	0.0433	0.0086	0.0025	0.0013	0.0001	0.0000	0.0000
6	0.9966	0.9005	0.6067	0.4910	0.2859	0.0962	0.0238	0.0079	0.0044	0.0006	0.0001	0.0000
7	0.9993	0.9581	0.7559	0.6534	0.4371	0.1820	0.0553	0.0211	0.0124	0.0021	0.0002	0.0000
8	0.9999	0.9845	0.8646	0.7873	0.5931	0.2998	0.1110	0.0483	0.0303	0.0061	0.0009	0.0001
9	1.0000	0.9949	0.9328	0.8826	0.7318	0.4395	0.1959	0.0966	0.0644	0.0156	0.0027	0.0003
10	1.0000	0.9985	0.9701	0.9416	0.8392	0.5839	0.3087	0.1714	0.1215	0.0352	0.0074	0.0011
11	1.0000	0.9996	0.9880	0.9739	0.9125	0.7151	0.4406	0.2735	0.2053	0.0709	0.0179	0.0032
12	1.0000	0.9999	0.9957	0.9894	0.9568	0.8209	0.5772	0.3969	0.3143	0.1285	0.0386	0.0083
13	1.0000	1.0000	0.9986	0.9961	0.9806	0.8968	0.7032	0.5297	0.4408	0.2112	0.0751	0.0192
14	1.0000	1.0000	0.9996	0.9987	0.9921	0.9456	0.8074	0.6578	0.5721	0.3174	0.1326	0.0403
15	1.0000	1.0000	0.9999	0.9996	0.9971	0.9738	0.8849	0.7688	0.6946	0.4402	0.2142	0.0769
16	1.0000	1.0000	1.0000	0.9999	0.9990	0.9884	0.9367	0.8556	0.7978	0.5681	0.3185	0.1341
17	1.0000	1.0000	1.0000	1.0000	0.9997	0.9953	0.9680	0.9168	0.8761	0.6885	0.4391	0.2148
18	1.0000	1.0000	1.0000	1.0000	0.9999	0.9983	0.9852	0.9559	0.9301	0.7911	0.5651	0.3179
19	1.0000	1.0000	1.0000	1.0000	1.0000	0.9994	0.9937	0.9786	0.9637	0.8702	0.6844	0.4373
20	1.0000	1.0000	1.0000	1.0000	1.0000	0.9998	0.9976	0.9904	0.9827	0.9256	0.7870	0.5627
21	1.0000	1.0000	1.0000	1.0000	1.0000	1.0000	0.9991	0.9961	0.9925	0.9608	0.8669	0.6821
22	1.0000	1.0000	1.0000	1.0000	1.0000	1.0000	0.9997	0.9986	0.9970	0.9811	0.9233	0.7852
23	1.0000	1.0000	1.0000	1.0000	1.0000	1.0000	0.9999	0.9995	0.9989	0.9917	0.9595	0.8659
24	1.0000	1.0000	1.0000	1.0000	1.0000	1.0000	1.0000	0.9998	0.9996	0.9966	0.9804	0.9231
25	1.0000	1.0000	1.0000	1.0000	1.0000	1.0000	1.0000	1.0000	0.9999	0.9988	0.9914	0.9597
26	1.0000	1.0000	1.0000	1.0000	1.0000	1.0000	1.0000	1.0000	1.0000	0.9996	0.9966	0.9808
27	1.0000	1.0000	1.0000	1.0000	1.0000	1.0000	1.0000	1.0000	1.0000	0.9999	0.9988	0.9917
28	1.0000	1.0000	1.0000	1.0000	1.0000	1.0000	1.0000	1.0000	1.0000	1.0000	0.9996	0.9968
29	1.0000	1.0000	1.0000	1.0000	1.0000	1.0000	1.0000	1.0000	1.0000	1.0000	0.9999	0.9989
30	1.0000	1.0000	1.0000	1.0000	1.0000	1.0000	1.0000	1.0000	1.0000	1.0000	1.0000	0.9997
31	1.0000	1.0000	1.0000	1.0000	1.0000	1.0000	1.0000	1.0000	1.0000	1.0000	1.0000	0.9999
32	1.0000	1.0000	1.0000	1.0000	1.0000	1.0000	1.0000	1.0000	1.0000	1.0000	1.0000	1.0000

Table 2. Cumulative probabilities for the standard normal distribution

This table gives $\Phi(z)$, i.e. $P(Z < z)$, where $Z \sim N(0,1)$

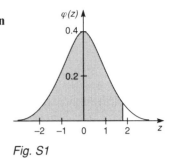

Fig. S1

z	0.00	0.01	0.02	0.03	0.04	0.05	0.06	0.07	0.08	0.09	1	2	3	4	5	6	7	8	9
0.0	0.5000	0.5040	0.5080	0.5120	0.5160	0.5199	0.5239	0.5279	0.5319	0.5359	4	8	12	16	20	24	28	32	36
0.1	0.5398	0.5438	0.5478	0.5517	0.5557	0.5596	0.5636	0.5675	0.5714	0.5753	4	8	12	16	20	24	28	32	35
0.2	0.5793	0.5832	0.5871	0.5910	0.5948	0.5987	0.6026	0.6064	0.6103	0.6141	4	8	12	15	19	23	27	31	35
0.3	0.6179	0.6217	0.6255	0.6293	0.6331	0.6368	0.6406	0.6443	0.6480	0.6517	4	8	11	15	19	23	26	30	34
0.4	0.6554	0.6591	0.6628	0.6664	0.6700	0.6736	0.6772	0.6808	0.6844	0.6879	4	7	11	14	18	22	25	29	32
0.5	0.6915	0.6950	0.6985	0.7019	0.7054	0.7088	0.7123	0.7157	0.7190	0.7224	3	7	10	14	17	21	24	27	31
0.6	0.7257	0.7291	0.7324	0.7357	0.7389	0.7422	0.7454	0.7486	0.7517	0.7549	3	6	10	13	16	19	23	26	29
0.7	0.7580	0.7611	0.7642	0.7673	0.7704	0.7734	0.7764	0.7794	0.7823	0.7852	3	6	9	12	15	18	21	24	27
0.8	0.7881	0.7910	0.7939	0.7967	0.7995	0.8023	0.8051	0.8078	0.8106	0.8133	3	6	8	11	14	17	19	22	25
0.9	0.8159	0.8186	0.8212	0.8238	0.8264	0.8289	0.8315	0.8340	0.8365	0.8389	3	5	8	10	13	15	18	20	23
1.0	0.8413	0.8438	0.8461	0.8485	0.8508	0.8531	0.8554	0.8577	0.8599	0.8621	2	5	7	9	11	14	16	18	21
1.1	0.8643	0.8665	0.8686	0.8708	0.8729	0.8749	0.8770	0.8790	0.8810	0.8830	2	4	6	8	10	12	14	16	19
1.2	0.8849	0.8869	0.8888	0.8907	0.8925	0.8944	0.8962	0.8980	0.8997	0.9015	2	4	5	7	9	11	13	15	16
1.3	0.9032	0.9049	0.9066	0.9082	0.9099	0.9115	0.9131	0.9147	0.9162	0.9177	2	3	5	6	8	10	11	13	14
1.4	0.9192	0.9207	0.9222	0.9236	0.9251	0.9265	0.9279	0.9292	0.9306	0.9319	1	3	4	6	7	8	10	11	13
1.5	0.9332	0.9345	0.9357	0.9370	0.9382	0.9394	0.9406	0.9418	0.9429	0.9441	1	2	4	5	6	7	8	10	11
1.6	0.9452	0.9463	0.9474	0.9484	0.9495	0.9505	0.9515	0.9525	0.9535	0.9545	1	2	3	4	5	6	7	8	9
1.7	0.9554	0.9564	0.9573	0.9582	0.9591	0.9599	0.9608	0.9616	0.9625	0.9633	1	2	3	3	4	5	6	7	8
1.8	0.9641	0.9649	0.9656	0.9664	0.9671	0.9678	0.9686	0.9693	0.9699	0.9706	1	1	2	3	4	4	5	6	6
1.9	0.9713	0.9719	0.9726	0.9732	0.9738	0.9744	0.9750	0.9756	0.9761	0.9767	1	1	2	2	3	4	4	5	5
2.0	0.9772	0.9778	0.9783	0.9788	0.9793	0.9798	0.9803	0.9808	0.9812	0.9817	0	1	1	2	2	3	3	4	4
2.1	0.9821	0.9826	0.9830	0.9834	0.9838	0.9842	0.9846	0.9850	0.9854	0.9857	0	1	1	2	2	2	3	3	4
2.2	0.9861	0.9864	0.9868	0.9871	0.9875	0.9878	0.9881	0.9884	0.9887	0.9890	0	1	1	1	2	2	2	3	3
2.3	0.9893	0.9896	0.9898	0.9901	0.9904	0.9906	0.9909	0.9911	0.9913	0.9916	0	1	1	1	1	2	2	2	2
2.4	0.9918	0.9920	0.9922	0.9925	0.9927	0.9929	0.9931	0.9932	0.9934	0.9936	0	0	1	1	1	1	1	2	2
2.5	0.9938	0.9940	0.9941	0.9943	0.9945	0.9946	0.9948	0.9949	0.9951	0.9952	0	0	0	1	1	1	1	1	1
2.6	0.9953	0.9955	0.9956	0.9957	0.9959	0.9960	0.9961	0.9962	0.9963	0.9964	0	0	0	0	1	1	1	1	1
2.7	0.9965	0.9966	0.9967	0.9968	0.9969	0.9970	0.9971	0.9972	0.9973	0.9974	0	0	0	0	0	1	1	1	1
2.8	0.9974	0.9975	0.9976	0.9977	0.9977	0.9978	0.9979	0.9979	0.9980	0.9981	0	0	0	0	0	0	0	1	1
2.9	0.9981	0.9982	0.9982	0.9983	0.9984	0.9984	0.9985	0.9985	0.9986	0.9986	0	0	0	0	0	0	0	0	0
3	0.9987	0.9987	0.9987	0.9988	0.9988	0.9989	0.9989	0.9989	0.9990	0.9990	0	0	0	0	0	0	0	0	0
3.1	0.9990	0.9991	0.9991	0.9991	0.9992	0.9992	0.9992	0.9992	0.9993	0.9993	0	0	0	0	0	0	0	0	0
3.2	0.9993	0.9993	0.9994	0.9994	0.9994	0.9994	0.9994	0.9995	0.9995	0.9995	0	0	0	0	0	0	0	0	0
3.3	0.9995	0.9995	0.9995	0.9996	0.9996	0.9996	0.9996	0.9996	0.9996	0.9997	0	0	0	0	0	0	0	0	0
3.4	0.9997	0.9997	0.9997	0.9997	0.9997	0.9997	0.9997	0.9997	0.9997	0.9998	0	0	0	0	0	0	0	0	0
3.5	0.9998	0.9998	0.9998	0.9998	0.9998	0.9998	0.9998	0.9998	0.9998	0.9998	0	0	0	0	0	0	0	0	0

Table 3. Critical values for the standard normal distribution

This table gives the critical values of z.

Significance for 1-tail test (2-tail in brackets)

	10% (20%)	5% (10%)	2.5% (5%)	2% (4%)	1% (2%)	0.5% (1%)
z	1.282	1.645	1.960	2.054	2.326	2.576

Table 4. Critical values for the t-distribution

This table gives the critical values of t_ν.

Significance for 1-tail test (2-tail in brackets)

$\nu =$	10% (20%)	5% (10%)	2.5% (5%)	1% (2%)	0.5% (1%)
1	3.078	6.314	12.706	31.821	63.657
2	1.886	2.920	4.303	6.965	9.925
3	1.638	2.353	3.182	4.541	5.841
4	1.533	2.132	2.776	3.747	4.604
5	1.476	2.015	2.571	3.365	4.032
6	1.440	1.943	2.447	3.143	3.707
7	1.415	1.895	2.365	2.998	3.499
8	1.397	1.860	2.306	2.896	3.355
9	1.383	1.833	2.262	2.821	3.250
10	1.372	1.812	2.228	2.764	3.169
11	1.363	1.796	2.201	2.718	3.106
12	1.356	1.782	2.179	2.681	3.055
13	1.350	1.771	2.160	2.650	3.012
14	1.345	1.761	2.145	2.624	2.977
15	1.341	1.753	2.131	2.602	2.947
16	1.337	1.746	2.120	2.583	2.921
17	1.333	1.740	2.110	2.567	2.898
18	1.330	1.734	2.101	2.552	2.878
19	1.328	1.729	2.093	2.539	2.861
20	1.325	1.725	2.086	2.528	2.845

Table 5. Critical values for the χ^2 distribution

This table gives the critical values of $\chi^2(\nu)$.

	significance level	
$\nu =$	5%	1%
1	3.84	6.64
2	5.99	9.21
3	7.82	11.34
4	9.49	13.28
5	11.07	15.09
6	12.59	16.81
7	14.07	18.48
8	15.51	20.09
9	16.92	21.67
10	18.31	23.21
11	19.68	24.73
12	21.03	26.22
13	22.36	27.69
14	23.68	29.14
15	25	30.58

Table 6. Critical values for the correlation coefficient

This table gives the critical values of r for a sample of size n.

	Significance for 1-tail test (2-tail in brackets)				
	10% (20%)	5% (10%)	2.5% (5%)	1% (2%)	0.5% (1%)
$n =$					
5	0.6870	0.8054	0.8783	0.9343	0.9587
6	0.6084	0.7293	0.8114	0.8822	0.9172
7	0.5509	0.6694	0.7545	0.8329	0.8745
8	0.5067	0.6215	0.7067	0.7887	0.8343
9	0.4716	0.5822	0.6664	0.7498	0.7977
10	0.4428	0.5494	0.6319	0.7155	0.7646
11	0.4187	0.5214	0.6021	0.6951	0.7348
12	0.3981	0.4973	0.576	0.6581	0.7079
13	0.3802	0.4762	0.5529	0.6339	0.6835
14	0.3646	0.4575	0.5324	0.6120	0.6614

Table 7. Critical values for Spearman's rank correlation coefficient

This table gives the critical values of r_s for a sample of size n.

	Significance for 1-tail test (2-tail in brackets)			
	10% (20%)	5% (10%)	2.5% (5%)	1% (2%)	0.5% (1%)
$n =$					
5	0.7	0.9	0.9	1	1
6	0.6571	0.7714	0.8286	0.9429	0.9429
7	0.5714	0.6786	0.7857	0.8571	0.8929
8	0.5476	0.6429	0.7381	0.8095	0.8571
9	0.4833	0.6000	0.6833	0.7667	0.8167
10	0.4424	0.5636	0.6485	0.7333	0.7818
11	0.4182	0.5273	0.6091	0.7000	0.7545
12	0.3986	0.5035	0.5874	0.6713	0.7273
13	0.3791	0.4780	0.5604	0.6484	0.6978
14	0.3670	0.4593	0.5385	0.6220	0.6747

Table 8. Critical values for the Wilcoxon signed rank test

This table gives the critical values of T for a sample of size n.

	for 1-tail test (2-tail in brackets)			
	5% (10%)	2.5% (5%)	1% (2%)	0.5% (1%)
$n =$				
8	6	4	2	–
9	9	6	3	1
10	11	8	5	3
11	14	11	7	5
12	18	14	10	7

Solutions

1 Analysing data

Exercise 1A Page 3

2 9.5–19.5 **3** 1.095–1.195 **4** 1–729 (ignoring leap years)

5 75.50–75.51

Exercise 1B Page 5

1 a) 26.7, 28 **b)** 156, 161.5 **c)** 0.08, 0.085 **d)** 3.82, 10

2 999 g, 1000 g **3** 0.833, 0 **4** 1.4, 1 **5** 11.2, 9, median

6 £20 600, £17 500, median **7** 4 **8** 12.41 years

10 a) 25 **b)** 154.5 **c)** 0.08 **d)** -3

Exercise 1C Page 9

1 2.12, 2, 1 **2** 1.48, 1, 1 **3** 2.24, 2, 1

4 a) 30–40, 38.9, 38.5 **b)** 30–39, 28.5, 30 **c)** 0.3–0.4, 0.319, 0.312

d) 120–124, 117.4, 119

5 32.8 min, 33.4 min **6** 59.5, 62.1 **7** 75–79. 79.7 lb, 78.4 lb

8 85–89. 81.3°, 82.3° **9** 10.0, 14.9, 14.6 cm, 14.3 cm **10** 72.0, 70.8

Exercise 1D Page 15

1 a) 9, 31.7 **b)** 16, 422 **c)** 0.25, 0.134

2 a) none **b)** 131 **c)** 2.7 **3** 5°, 50° **4** 53.4 s, 15.3 s

5 Maths: 65.7 and 7.80, French: 63.4 and 20.1

6 Bus: 46.7 min, 11.6 min, Train: 44.7 min, 2.44 min

7 A: 61.2 g, 1.83 g; B: 58.7 g, 6.29 g

8 135 1² **9** 10.2 min **10** 0.72 years **11** $\frac{1}{2}(n + 1), \frac{1}{12}(n^2 - 1)$

12 a) 4.75 **b)** 13.6 **c)** 0.228 **13 a)** 18 **b)** 79 **c)** 1.5

Longer exercise Page 16

1 27.75, 26.90, 26.04

Examination questions Page 17

1 1.29 m   2 **a)** 46.7, 12.4

3 35 y 1 m, 11 y 3 m   **a)** 33 y 10 m, 17 y 11 m   **b)** 65.0%

4 2.3, 1.41   5 54.1 m   **a)** 60 648 m^2 **b)** 55.0 m   **c)** 109.3 m^2

6 (i) -4.3, 14.0   (ii) 99.957 m, 0.14 m   (iv) -2.05, 10.2

2 Presenting data

Exercise 2A Page 23

3 positive   4 negative   5 positive   6 positive

Exercise 2B Page 26

10 38.5   11 A: 21.5, 10.5, B: 19, 11.5   12 A: 10, 10, B: 19.5, 17

Exercise 2C Page 29

1 114, 9   2 26 minutes, 21 minutes   3 53, over 77

4 £18 900, £20 400   5 9.4 mins, 15.2 mins   6 7.6%, 4.5% and 12%

7 30, 5   8 99 g, 108.5 g   9 13.3 minutes

Exercise 2D Page 32

1 12, 16 outliers, positive   2 23 outlier, negative   3 no outliers, negative

4 12 outlier, positive

Examination questions Page 33

2 **b)** 66, 52, 78   3 (i) 13.4, 11.2, 15.0   (ii) 13.2, 1.65

4 (ii) $\frac{1}{4}$ (iii) 160.6 cm

3 Probability

Exercise 3A Page 37

1 **c)** $\frac{1}{2}$ **d)** $\frac{1}{13}$ 2 **a)** $\frac{5}{36}$ **b)** $\frac{3}{8}$ **c)** $\frac{1}{6}$ **d)** $\frac{1}{6}$ 3 $\frac{1}{9}$

4 $\frac{1}{16}$ 5 $\frac{1}{6}$ 6 $\frac{1}{6}$ 7 $\frac{2}{9}$

Exercise 3B Page 40

1 A, B   2 A, B   3 **a)** $\frac{11}{12}$ **b)** $\frac{19}{24}$ 4 0.6   5 0.4

6 0.9   7 80%, 20%   8 $\frac{31}{60}$ 9 **a)** 20%   **b)** 65%

10 $P(A) + P(B) + P(C) - P(A \cap B) - P(B \cap C) - P(C \cap A) + P(A \cap B \cap C)$

Exercise 3C Page 42

1 $P(A) = \frac{1}{2}$, $P(B) = \frac{2}{5}$, $P(C) = \frac{3}{5}$, A, C independent   **2** A and C, B and C

3 0.24, 0.76   **5** $\frac{1}{2}$ **8** 80   **9** 0.1   **10 a)** 0   **b)** 0.2

11 $\frac{1}{3}$, $\frac{8}{15}$ **12** 0.8

13 a) pq **b)** $p + q - pq$ **c)** $1 - p$ **d)** $p(1 - q)$

Exercise 3D Page 45

1 a) $\frac{1}{25}$ **b)** $\frac{16}{25}$ **c)** $\frac{8}{25}$ **2** $\frac{4}{9}$ **3** $\frac{1}{3}$ **4** 0.4998

5 a) $\frac{3}{8}$ **b)** $\frac{13}{16}$ **6** 0.213   **7** 0.64   **8** $\frac{26}{59}$ **9** 0.123

10 $\frac{38}{87}$ **11** $\frac{1}{16}$ **12** 0.227   **13** 0.243   **14** $\frac{1}{3}$

15 a) $\frac{4}{27}$ **b)** $\frac{1}{3}$ **16 a)** $\frac{1}{6}$ **b)** $\frac{5}{36}$ **c)** $\frac{1}{2}$ **d)** $\frac{6}{11}$

Exercise 3E Page 49

1 a) 120   **b)** 720   **c)** 20   **d)** 720   **e)** 220   **f)** 286

2 a) $(n + 1)!$ **b)** $(n - 1)!$ **c)** n **d)** 1   **e)** ^nP_r **f)** $^nP_{n-r}$

4 3 628 800, $\frac{1}{3\,628\,800}$ **5** 1320   **6** 495   **7** 6.35×10^{11}

8 0.392   **9** 0.322   **10** 2 204 475   **11** 26 860 680

12 a) 120   **b)** 100   **13** 0.00264   **14** 350

15 a) 66   **b)** 220   **16** 0.819   **17** 10   **18** 3375

19 0.00240   **20** 0.569   **21** 0.1   **22** 0.278   **23** $\frac{1}{15}$

Exercise 3F Page 52

1 $\frac{1}{2}$, $\frac{2}{3}$ **2** $\frac{1}{6}$, $\frac{1}{2}$ **3** $\frac{1}{24}$, $\frac{13}{24}$ **4 a)** 0.703   **b)** 0.995

5 0.368   **6** 0.462   **7** $\frac{3}{8}$ **8** 0.857   **9** $\frac{1}{3}$

10 0.511   **11** 0.8   **12 a)** $\frac{3}{4}$ **b)** $\frac{2}{3}$ **13** 0.74

14 0.6   **15** 0.636

Examination questions Page 54

1 (i) $\frac{1}{4}$ **(ii)** $\frac{81}{256}$ **(iii)** $\frac{81}{1024}$ **(iv)** $\frac{1}{16}$ **(v)** $\frac{3}{4}$ **(vi)** $\frac{3}{32}$

2 (ii) $\frac{5}{8}$ **(iii)** $\frac{3}{5}$ **(v)** 0.65   **3 (i)** 0.7, 0.6   **(iii)** frequencies 12, 18, 28, 42

4 (i) $\frac{1}{4}$ **(ii)** $\frac{5}{24}$ **(iii)** $\frac{5}{8}$ **(iv)** $\frac{1}{9}$, no   **5 (i)** 0.017   **(ii)** 0.258

6 (i) 0.12   **(ii)** 0.28   **(iii)** 0.7

7 (i) 0.000 877   **(ii)** 0.421   **(iii)** 0.65   **(iv)** 0.642

4 Sampling

Exercise 4B Page 61

4 **a)** 24 Nov, 10 Jun, 16 Feb   **b)** 25 Nov, 3 Mar, 18 Jun

Exercise 4C Page 64

1 systematic   **2** quota   **3** cluster   **4** systematic

5 **a)** random   **b)** cluster   **c)** stratified

Longer exercise Page 67

$\frac{2}{3} - \frac{1}{3}p, \frac{2}{3}, \frac{1}{3}, p \approx 0.65$

Consolidation section A

Extra questions Page 69

1 **a)** 58, 56, 56   **b)** 10.25, 10.25, none   **2** 25–30. 26.8, 27.1

3 **a)** 35.8, 11   **b)** 0.0825, 0.6   **4** 7.06, 10.5   **5** 1.256, 0.000 28

6 median   **10** £33.2, £31.7, £34.3   **12** 0.1   **13** $\frac{19}{34}$

14 0.34   **15** 175 560   **16** 19 600   **17** 0.407   **18** $\frac{1}{2}, \frac{6}{7}$

19 $\frac{1}{4}$

Mixed questions Page 71

2 $\frac{r}{n}$, 50   **3** 0.1   **4** $\frac{5}{12}$ **5** 240

Examination questions Page 73

1 **a)** 29   **b)** (i) 8.54   (ii) 11.4   **3** **a)** 2   **b)** 3.5, 2, 5   **c)** 3.98

4 **a)** (i) 0.15   (ii) 0.7   (iii) 0.55   **b)** 0.3375   **5** (i) $\frac{1}{15}$ (ii) $\frac{11}{15}$ (iii) $\frac{1}{5}$

6 (i) $\frac{1}{14}$ (ii) $\frac{3}{7}$ **7** (i) 13.8   (ii) 13.7, 1.38   (iii) 14.1, 1.69   (iv) 14.1

8 (i) 6, 5   (iv) 5.5, 5   (v) lower both   (vi) positive

9 (i) 10 000   (ii) 5040   (iii) 24   (iv) $\frac{1}{24}$ (v) $\frac{1}{24}$ (vi) $\frac{7}{8}$

5 Discrete random variables

Exercise 5A Page 80

1

i	0	1	2
$P(X = i)$	$\frac{1}{4}$	$\frac{1}{2}$	$\frac{1}{4}$

2

i	0	1	2
$P(X = i)$	0.36	0.48	0.16

3

i	1	2	3
$P(X=i)$	$\frac{1}{2}$	$\frac{3}{10}$	$\frac{1}{5}$

4

i	2	3	4
$P(X=i)$	0.2	0.5	0.3

5

i	0	1	2
$P(X=i)$	$\frac{25}{36}$	$\frac{5}{18}$	$\frac{1}{36}$

6

i	0	1	2
$P(X=i)$	$\frac{1}{9}$	$\frac{4}{9}$	$\frac{4}{9}$

7

i	1	4	9	16	25	36
$P(X=i)$	$\frac{1}{6}$	$\frac{1}{6}$	$\frac{1}{6}$	$\frac{1}{6}$	$\frac{1}{6}$	$\frac{1}{6}$

8

i	0	1	2
$P(X=i)$	$\frac{1}{4}$	$\frac{1}{2}$	$\frac{1}{4}$

9

i	1	2	3	4	5	6	8	10	12
$P(X=i)$	$\frac{1}{12}$	$\frac{1}{6}$	$\frac{1}{12}$	$\frac{1}{6}$	$\frac{1}{12}$	$\frac{1}{6}$	$\frac{1}{12}$	$\frac{1}{12}$	$\frac{1}{12}$

10 $\frac{1}{30}$ **11** $\frac{1}{28}$ **12** $\dfrac{6}{\pi^2}$

Exercise 5B Page 83

1 a) 1.5, 1.45 **b)** 2.6, 1.24 **c)** 1.575, 0.382 **2** $\frac{1}{15}, \frac{11}{3}, 1\frac{5}{9}$

3 $\frac{1}{10}, 1, 1$ **4** $\frac{2}{3}, \frac{5}{9}$

5

i	0	1	3
$P(X=i)$	$\frac{4}{9}$	$\frac{4}{9}$	$\frac{1}{9}$

$£\frac{7}{9}, \frac{68}{81}$

6 2, 1

7

i	-1	1	2	3
$P(X=i)$	$\frac{125}{126}$	$\frac{75}{216}$	$\frac{15}{216}$	$\frac{1}{216}$

$(-£0.079), 1.24$

8 $£1\frac{2}{3}$ **9** $£\frac{5}{9}$ **10** $£\frac{23}{24}$ **11** £1.23 **12** $x=8$

13 $x=7$ **14** $x=0.05, y=0.45$ **15** $x=11, y=15$

16 $x=\frac{5}{28}, y=\frac{2}{21}$ **17** $k=\frac{1}{14}, \frac{8}{7}, \frac{55}{49}$ **18** $\frac{1}{84}, 3, 3$ **19** $\frac{1}{196}, \frac{29}{7}, 1.84$

20 a) 4 **b)** 11.1 **c)** 2.2 **21 a)** $\frac{41}{3}$ **b)** -4 **c)** 16

Exercise 5C Page 87

2 $5, 6\frac{2}{3}$ **3** 18, 114 **4** 4, 4 **5** 2.5, 1.25 **6** $30\frac{1}{2}, 299.9$

7 a) 8 **b)** 7

8

i	2	3	4	5	6	7	8
$P(X=i)$	$\frac{1}{16}$	$\frac{1}{8}$	$\frac{3}{16}$	$\frac{1}{4}$	$\frac{3}{16}$	$\frac{1}{8}$	$\frac{1}{16}$

5, 2.5

9

i	-5	-4	-3	-2	-1	0	1	2	3	4	5
$P(X=i)$	$\frac{1}{36}$	$\frac{1}{18}$	$\frac{1}{12}$	$\frac{1}{9}$	$\frac{5}{36}$	$\frac{1}{6}$	$\frac{5}{36}$	$\frac{1}{9}$	$\frac{1}{12}$	$\frac{1}{18}$	$\frac{1}{36}$

$0, 5\frac{5}{6}$

10

i	0	1	2	3	4	5
$P(X=i)$	$\frac{1}{6}$	$\frac{5}{18}$	$\frac{2}{9}$	$\frac{1}{6}$	$\frac{1}{9}$	$\frac{1}{18}$

1.94, 2.05

11

i	1	2	3	4	5	6
$P(X=i)$	$\frac{1}{36}$	$\frac{1}{12}$	$\frac{5}{36}$	$\frac{7}{36}$	$\frac{1}{4}$	$\frac{11}{36}$

4.47, 1.97

Exercise 5D Page 89

1

i	1	2	3
$P(X=i)$	$\frac{2}{3}$	$\frac{11}{36}$	$\frac{1}{36}$

1.36

2

i	3	4	5	6	7	8	9	10	11
$P(X=i)$	$\frac{1}{15}$	$\frac{1}{15}$	$\frac{2}{15}$	$\frac{2}{15}$	$\frac{1}{5}$	$\frac{2}{15}$	$\frac{2}{15}$	$\frac{1}{15}$	$\frac{1}{15}$

$7, 4\frac{2}{3}$

3

i	0	1	2
$P(X=i)$	$\frac{19}{34}$	$\frac{13}{34}$	$\frac{1}{17}$

4

i	0	1	2	3
$P(X=i)$	$\frac{1}{8}$	$\frac{3}{8}$	$\frac{3}{8}$	$\frac{1}{8}$

5 a)

i	0	1	2
$P(X=i)$	$\frac{49}{225}$	$\frac{112}{225}$	$\frac{64}{225}$

b)

i	0	1	2
$P(X=i)$	$\frac{1}{5}$	$\frac{8}{15}$	$\frac{4}{15}$

6 $4\frac{1}{2}$ days

7

i	2	3	4	5
$P(X=i)$	0.1	0.2	0.3	0.4

4

8

i	2	3	4	5	6	7	8
$P(X=i)$	0.25	0.3	0.19	0.16	0.07	0.02	0.01

9

i	0	1	2	3
$P(X=i)$	0.7	0.06	0.12	0.12

2.2, 0.3, 0.66

10

i	$\frac{1}{2}$	1	2
$P(X=i)$	$\frac{1}{4}$	$\frac{1}{2}$	$\frac{1}{4}$

$1\frac{1}{2}, 1\frac{1}{2}, 1\frac{1}{8}$

11 a)

i	2	3
$P(X=i)$	$\frac{2}{5}$	$\frac{3}{5}$

2.6

b)

i	2	3	4
$P(X=i)$	$\frac{3}{10}$	$\frac{2}{5}$	$\frac{3}{10}$

3

12

i	0	1	2	3
$P(X=i)$	$\frac{7}{24}$	$\frac{21}{40}$	$\frac{7}{40}$	$\frac{1}{120}$

13

i	0	1	2
$P(X=i)$	$\frac{10}{21}$	$\frac{10}{21}$	$\frac{1}{21}$

$\frac{4}{7}, 0.340$

14

i	0	1	2	3
$P(X = i)$	$\frac{1}{3}$	$\frac{1}{2}$	0	$\frac{1}{6}$

Examination questions Page 91

1 $\frac{120}{49}$, 2.57

2 (i) 0, 0.5   (ii) $-2, -1, 0, 1, 2; \frac{3}{8}$

(iii)

i	-2	-1	0	1	2
$P(X + Y = i)$	$\frac{1}{16}$	$\frac{1}{4}$	$\frac{3}{8}$	$\frac{1}{4}$	$\frac{1}{16}$

3 a)

i	0	1	2
$P(X = i)$	$(1-p)^2$	$2p(1-p)$	p^2

b) (i) yes, $p = \frac{1}{2}$ (ii) no   (iii) no   (iv) yes, $p = 1$

4 a) correct   **b)** incorrect (negative probabilities)

5 (i) **a)** $\frac{28}{45}$ **b)** $\frac{16}{45}$ **c)** $\frac{1}{45}$ (ii) **a)** $\frac{16}{25}$ **b)** $\frac{8}{25}$ **c)** $\frac{1}{25}$ **6 a)** 0.8   **b)** 4.2

6   Continuous random variables

Exercise 6A Page 97

1 a) 2   **b)** $1 - \dfrac{1}{\sqrt{2}}$ **c)** $\frac{1}{4}$ **2 b)** $\frac{1}{3}\pi$ **(c)** $1 - \dfrac{1}{\sqrt{2}}$

3 a) 1   **b)** $2\frac{2}{3}$ **c)** $\frac{1}{2}$ **4 b)** $\frac{4}{27}$

5 a) $\frac{3}{4}$ **b)** 1333 litres   **c)** $\frac{11}{16}$ **6 a)** $\sqrt[3]{6}$ **b)** $\frac{11}{16}$ **7** $k = 1$

8 $k = \frac{2}{3}$ **9** $\frac{13}{256}, 3\frac{1}{3}$ oz   **10 a)** $k = \frac{4}{16\,875}$ **b)** $\frac{16}{27}$

11 a) $k = 12$ **b)** $\frac{11}{16}$ **c)** $\frac{5}{6}$ **12 b)** $\frac{175}{256}$ **c)** $\frac{337}{3375}$

Exercise 6B Page 101

1 $\frac{1}{3}, \frac{1}{18}$ **2** $1, \pi - 3$ **4** $k = \dfrac{1}{\ln 10}$, mean = 3.91, median = 3.16

5 $0.6, \frac{1}{25}$ **6** $k = 0.000\,000\,12, \mu = 60, 0.4752$ **7** $k = \dfrac{1}{\ln 2}, E(X) = \dfrac{1}{\ln 2}, 0.529$

8 $\frac{3}{4}, 0.794$ **9** $\frac{1}{3}, 0.293$ **10** $k = \frac{3}{2500}, 6$ cm   **11** 78°

12 10 minutes   **13** $k = (n-1)$, for $n > 2$, for $n > 3$

14 $E(S) = \frac{2}{3}, T = \dfrac{10}{S}, E(T) = 20$ seconds   **15** $\frac{3}{4}$ units

16 a) 145   **b)** 10.8   **c)** 17.6   **17 a)** $\frac{4}{7}$ **b)** 2   **c** 6

Exercise 6C Page 105

1 $F(x) = 0, x < 0; \frac{1}{4}x(4 - x), 0 \le x \le 2; 1, x > 2$

2 $F(x) = 0, x < 0; x^4, 0 \le x \le 1; 1, x > 1$

3 $F(x) = 0, x < 0; \frac{1}{2}(1 - \cos x), 0 \le x \le \pi; 1, x > \pi$

4 $f(x) = 1, 0 \le x \le 1; 0$ elsewhere   5 $f(x) = 2x, 0 \le x \le 1; 0$ elsewhere, $\frac{2}{3}, \sqrt{\frac{1}{2}}$

6 $f(x) = \dfrac{2}{x^3}, 1 \le x; 0$ elsewhere; $E(X) = 2$ 7 $F(x) = 0, x < 0; 2x^{1.5} - x^3 \, 0 \le x \le 1; 1, x > 1$

8 $F(x) = 0, x < 0; 2 - \dfrac{40}{x + 20}, 0 \le x \le 20; 1, x > 20; \frac{3}{7}$

9 $F(t) = 1 - \dfrac{1000}{(t + 10)^3}$, for $t \ge 0$; $f(t) = \dfrac{3000}{(t + 10)^4}$, for $t \ge 0$; 2.6 min, 5 min

10 $f(x) = \dfrac{64}{(x + 2)^5}$, for $x \ge 0$; 3784 miles, 6667 miles

Exercise 6D Page 108

1 $F(x) = 0, x < 1; x, 1 \le x \le 2; 1, x > 2$ 3 5 minutes   4 $180°, 10\,800$

5 $f(x) = \frac{1}{180}, 0 \le x \le 180; 0$ elsewhere, 10 m

6 $f(x) = \frac{1}{10}, 150 \le x \le 160; 0$ elsewhere, $f(y) = \frac{1}{20}, 170 \le x \le 190, 0$ elsewhere, 167.5 grams

7 $\frac{1}{4}\pi, 0.206$ 8 $\frac{1}{12}(b - a)^2$ 9 $f(x) = 2x, 0 \le x \le 1, 0$ elsewhere, $E(X) = \frac{2}{3}$

Exercise 6E Page 109

1 2.77, 4.39   2 $f(t) = 0.1e^{-0.1t}, 0 \le t, 0$ elsewhere, 0.135   3 0.0347

4 $f(t) = 0.05e^{-0.05t}, 0 \le t; 0$ elsewhere, 0.221; $e^{-1} = 0.368$

5 $f(t) = \frac{1}{30}e^{-\frac{t}{30}}, 0 \le t; 0$ elsewhere, 0.264; 0.264, 138 days   7 0.0357

Examination questions Page 111

1 a) 0   b) $\frac{1}{12}\pi^2$ 2 $\frac{1}{2}(b + a), \frac{1}{12}(b - a)^2, 0.931$

3 $F(x) = 0, x < 1; 5 - x - \dfrac{4}{x}, 1 \le x \le 2; 1, x > 2; t = 1\frac{1}{3}, 1.2726$

4 (i) 10 hours, $\sqrt{1\frac{1}{3}}$ hours   (ii) $\frac{1}{8}$

5 (ii) 0.9342   (iii) $F(x) = 0, x < 0; \dfrac{\sin x + x}{\pi}, 0 \le x \le \pi; 1, x > \pi; 0.553$

6 (ii) 13.86, 7.82   (iii) $13\frac{1}{3}$ minutes   (iv) $\frac{2}{3}$

7 (i) $\frac{5}{8}, 0.0594$ (ii) $\frac{5}{16}$ (iii) 0.0305   (iv) 0.725

8 (iii) 40 mins, 10.7 mins   (iv) $F(x) = 0, x < 0; x^4(5 - 4x), 0 \le x \le 1; 1, x > 1$

9 (ii) £3000   (iii) greater   (iv) £4000, £2000

7 Binomial and geometric distributions

Exercise 7A Page 116

1 $\frac{9}{64}$ **2** $\frac{3}{8}$ **3** $\frac{5}{72}$ **4** $\frac{1}{4}$ **5** 0.422   **6** 0.395

7 $\frac{3}{8}$ **8** 0.432   **9** 0.210   **10** 0.948

Exercise 7B Page 120

1 **a)** 0.215   **b)** 0.285   **c)** 0.035   **d)** 0.196   **2** 0.155   **3** 0.173

4 0.091   **5** 0.197   **6** 0.356   **7** 0.070   **8** 0.147

9 0.212   **10** 0.217   **11** 0.146   **12** 0.172   **13** 0.329

14 0.162   **15** 0.236   **18** **a)** yes   **b)** no

Exercise 7C Page 122

1 **a)** 4, 2.4   **b)** 6, 4.2   **c)** $1, 1 - \dfrac{1}{n}$ **d)** 20, 0   **2** 9.6, 1.92

3 0.3, 0.285   **4** 2, 1.8   **5** 4.5, 2.475   **6** 17.1, 7.35   **7** $\frac{1}{3}$

8 40   **9** 500   **10** 0.2 or 0.8   **11** 0.6 and 100

12 $p = 1 - \dfrac{\sigma^2}{\mu}$ and $n = \dfrac{\mu}{1 - \dfrac{\sigma^2}{\mu}}$ **13** Missing values 0.2592, 0.2304, 0.0768; 2 and 1.2

14 1.12 and 1.5056, $p = 0.224$, variance too large

Exercise 7D Page 125

1 **a)** 0.678   **b)** 0.008   **c)** 0.0005   **d)** 0.012   **e)** 0.995   **f)** 0.608

     g) 0.396   **h)** 0.715

2 0.206   **3** **a)** 0.642   **b)** 0.075   **4** 0.461   **5** 0.353

6 0.083   **7** 0.035   **8** 0.812   **9** 0.437   **10** 0.167

Exercise 7E Page 128

1 **a)** 0.967   **b)** 0.596   **c)** 0.417   **d)** 0.100   **e)** 0.979   **f)** 0.979

     g) 0.995   **h)** 0.960   **i)** 0.238   **j)** 0.967   **k)** 0.021   **l)** 0.065

2 0.989, $i = 5$ **3** 0.316, $i = 13$ **4** $i = 28$ **5** 0.638, $i = 8$

Exercise 7F Page 130

1 **a)** 0.21   **b)** 0.6   **c)** 0.004   **d)** 0.081   **2** 0.080   **3** $\frac{1}{8}$

4 0.102   **5** **b)** 0.059   **6** 0.012   **7** 0.019   **8** 0.074

9 1   **10** $\frac{6}{11}$ **11** 0.471

Exercise 7G Page 132

1 a) 2 and 2   **b)** $1\frac{1}{2}$ and $\frac{3}{4}$ **c)** 20 and 380   **2** $\frac{1}{15}$, 210   **3** 4

5 a) 0.240   **b)** 0.064   **c)** 0.613   **d)** 0.992   **e)** 0.763   **f)** 0.028

6 a) 0.162   **b)** 0.969   **7 a)** $\frac{1}{4}$ **b)** $\frac{31}{32}$ **8** 0.389   **9** $\frac{1}{8}$

10 0.282   **11** 0.311

12

i	1	2	3
$P(X = i)$	$\frac{1}{6}$	$\frac{5}{36}$	$\frac{25}{36}$

$E(X) = 2.53$, $Var(X) = 0.583$

Examination questions Page 134

1 Missing values 0.2646, 0.0756. 1.2 and 0.84   **2** (i) 0.035   (ii) 0.138. 82.7

3 a) (i) $\frac{1}{2}$ (ii) $\frac{1}{40}$ (iii) $\frac{1}{20}$ (iv) 0.45   **b)** (i) 0.590   (ii) 0.009   (iii) 0.237

4 (i) 0.396   (ii) 0.079   (iii) 0.105   **5 a)** (i) 0.103   **b)** (i) 1   (ii) 0.760

8 Poisson distribution

Exercise 8A page 140

1 a) 0.224   **b)** 0.368   **c)** 0.090   **d)** 0.156

2 a) 0.406   **b)** 0.238   **c)** 0.713   **d)** 0.030

3 a) 0.180   **b)** 0.594   **4 a)** 0.117   **b)** 0.799

5 a) 0.067   **b)** 0.751   **6 a)** 0.224   **b)** 0.577

7 a) 0.194   **b)** 0.473   **8 a)** 0.209   **b)** 0.308

9 a) 0.162   **b)** 0.893   **10 a)** 0.223   **b)** 0.191

11 a) 0.220   **b)** 0.249   **12** $\lambda = 1$

Exercise 8B page 141

1 0.288   **2** 0.916   **3** 1.90   **4** 0.198   **5** 0.761, 0.177

6 0.267   **7** 0.135   **8** 0.818

9 1.56; 209, 327, 256, 133, 52, 16, 4, 1   **10** 0.068

Exercise 8C page 143

1 0.6. 0.099

2 a) 0.335   **b)** 0.195   **c)** 0.670   **d)** 0.090   **e)** 0.463   **f)** 0.713

g) 0.896   **h)** 0.310   **3** 0.350   **4** 0.261   **5** 0.423

6 0.670   **7** 0.960   **8** 0.451   **9** 0.181. 0.018   **10** 0.908

Exercise 8D page 145

1 a) 0.271 **b)** 0.368 **2 a)** 0.427 **b)** 0.107

3 0.607 **4 a)** 0.366 **b)** 0.697 **5 a)** 0.054 **b)** 0.119 **c)** 0.005

6 a) 0.0009 **b)** 0.918 **7 a)** 0.354 **b)** 0.134

8 a) 0.670 **b)** 0.145 **9 a)** 0.020 **b)** 0.25

10 a) 0.217 **b)** 0.444 **11** 0.221

Exercise 8E page 146

1 0.175 **2** 0.161 **3** 0.900 **4** 0.330 **5** 0.128

6 0.147, 0.320 **7** 0.119, 0.021 **8** 0.105 **9 a)** 0.134 **b)** 0.082

Exercise 8F page 149

1 0.228, 0.821, 4 **2** 0.084, 6 **3** 0.191, 4 **4** 0.037, 0.23

5 1.49, 5 **6** 0.016, 0.042 **7** 0.972, 0.011 **8** 0.996, 0.364

9 0.017, 0.85 **10** 0.0078, 0.007

Examination questions Page 150

1 a) 0.271 **b)** 5.3 **2 a)** 0.908 **b)** 9

3 0.016, 0.908, 0.004, 0.0003

4 a) (i) 0.67032 **(ii)** 0.06155 **(iii)** 0.14813 **b)** $e^{-0.4n}$, 5 **c) (i)** 1.5 **d)** 0.594

5 600 m. Po(2.5). 0.082, 0.109. 0.779. 0.207

6 (i) B(40 000, 0.000 005) **(ii) (A)** 0.819 **(B)** 0.164 **(C)** 0.018

(iii) 250 000 **(iv) (A)** 0.235 **(B)** 0.247

7 a) 0.515 **b)** 0.031 **c)** 0.454 **d)** 0.333 **e)** 0.265 **f)** 0.407

Consolidation section B

Extra questions Page 159

1 $\frac{12}{25}$

2

i	1	2	3	4	5	6	8	10	12
P($X = i$)	$\frac{5}{36}$	$\frac{1}{6}$	$\frac{5}{36}$	$\frac{1}{6}$	$\frac{5}{36}$	$\frac{1}{6}$	$\frac{1}{36}$	$\frac{1}{36}$	$\frac{1}{36}$

3 1.92, 1.114 **4** 4.08, 6.08 **5** 13p **6** 19

7

i	1	2	3	4	6	9
P($X = i$)	$\frac{1}{9}$	$\frac{2}{9}$	$\frac{2}{9}$	$\frac{1}{9}$	$\frac{2}{9}$	$\frac{1}{9}$

4, 5.78

8

i	0	1	2
P($X = i$)	$\frac{28}{153}$	$\frac{80}{153}$	$\frac{5}{17}$

1.11, 0.465

9 $\frac{3}{4}$ **10** 1.2, 0.4   **11** $F(x) = \frac{1}{16}x^3(8 - 3x), 0 \le x \le 2$

12 a) $F(x) = \frac{1}{4}x^2, f(x) = \frac{1}{2}x$ **b)** $1\frac{1}{3}, \frac{2}{9}, £5$ **13** 20.8 mins, 30 mins

14 0.258, 0.287   **15 a)** 0.201   **b)** 0.678   **16** 2.75, 2.06

17 2, 1.6   **18** 0.0752   **19 a)** 0.1024   **b)** 0.866   **20** 5, 20

21 0.150, 0.907   **22** 0.248   **23 a)** 0.607   **b)** 0.09

24 a) 0.156   **b)** 0.971   **25 a)** 0.373   **b)** 1.10, 3

Mixed questions Page 161

1 a) 0, 0   **b)** n, 0   **c)** 0, 0   **d)** 1, 0   **e)** ∞, ∞

2 a) binomial   **b)** Poisson

4 $P(X = i) = (i - 1)\frac{1}{6^2}\left(\frac{5}{6}\right)^{i-2}, i \ge 2, P(X = i) = {}^{i-1}C_{n-1}\frac{1}{6^n}\left(\frac{5}{6}\right)^{i-n}, i \ge n$

5 16.7 m, 17.3 m   **6 a)** 0.118   **b)** 0.125; £2.43   **7** 0.590. 1.22   **8** 0.308

9 50.5, 833.25   **a)** 50, 833.33   **b)** 50.5, 816.75   **c)** 50, 816.75   **d)** 50.5, 833.33

10 b) 0.074   **c)** $k = \dfrac{1}{1 - e^{-\lambda}}, 0.458$ **d)** $k = \dfrac{6}{\pi^2}, 0.936$

Examination questions Page 164

1 b) $6\frac{2}{3}$ **c)** 6.22

2 (i) 0.819   (ii) 0.407   (iii) 0.122

3 (i) $\frac{1}{13}, \frac{1}{13}$ (ii) 2.77, 0.331

    (iii) 50, 25, 15, with probabilities $\frac{1}{13}$; 0, with probability $\frac{10}{13}$; 6.92 pence   (iv) £6.15

4 (ii) 7.83

5 (i) 0.066   (iii) 0.24

6 a) $a = 3, 0.577$ **b)** (i) $\frac{30}{81}, \frac{11}{81}$ (ii) $7\frac{2}{9}, \frac{5}{3}, 3\frac{8}{9}$

7 (i) $a = 1$ (iii) 0.586   (iv) 1   (v) $\frac{1}{7}$

8 a) $E(X) = \dfrac{1}{\lambda}, F(X) = 1 - e^{-\lambda x}$ **b)** both $= (1 - e^{-\lambda t})^2$ **d)** $\dfrac{3}{2\lambda}$

9 Normal distribution

Exercise 9A Page 169

1 a) 0.977   **b)** 0.957   **c)** 0.949   **d)** 0.936   **e)** 0.090   **f)** 0.021

   g) 0.371   **h)** 0.150

2 a) 0.984   **b)** 0.749   **c)** 0.976   **d)** 0.069   **e)** 0.389   **f)** 0.022

   g) 0.389   **h)** 0.026   **i)** 0.015   **j)** 0.960   **k)** 0.681   **l)** 0.980

m) 0.086   **n)** 0.309   **o)** 0.083   **p)** 0.130   **q)** 0.845   **r)** 0.328

s) 0.977   **t)** 0.882   **u)** 0.901   **v)** 0.508   **w)** 0.981   **x)** 0.466

y) 0.100   **z)** 0.010   **3**   **a)** 0.893   **b)** 0.228   **c)** 0.788, 1%

Exercise 9B Page 171

1   0.674, 0.348

2   **a)** 0.842   **b)** 0.619   **c)** −1.126   **d)** −0.073   **e)** 0.303   **f)** −0.659

   g) −1.426   **h)** 1.96   **i)** 2.576   **3**   over 1.282

Exercise 9C Page 173

1   **a)** 0.933   **b)** 0.748   **c)** 0.841   **d)** 0.718   **e)** 0.579   **f)** 0.421

2   **a)** 7.56   **b)** 12.5   **c)** 2.16   **d)** −14.0   **3**   0.132   **4**   0.043

5   0.091   **6**   0.023, 135   **7**   64%, 72   **8**   0.057

9   0.202. 991 cm^3 **10**   31%, under 107 minutes   **11**   20.003 cm and 20.017 cm

12   47%, within 0.8 m   **13**   0.288, £2 530 000   **14**   0.066, 57.7 m.p.h.

15   10.6%, 42.9 grams, greater

Exercise 9D Page 176

1   **a)** 7.9   **b)** 1.91   **c)** 7.80   **2**   **a)** 1.35   **b)** 12.6   **c)** 9.29

3   **a)** −1.65, 9.09   **b)** 15.8, 33   **c)** 4.42, 1.49   **d)** −0.92, 1.77   **e)** 6.64, 5.71

4   61 gram^2 **5**   14.8 cm   **6**   17.8 in   **7**   110, 130

8   145 min, 222 min^2 **9**   17.4 m, 4.96 m   **10**   10.04 cm, 0.022 cm, 35%

Exercise 9E Page 178

1   **a)** 0.974   **b)** 0.003   **c)** 0.179   **d)** 0.179   **2**   0.06   **3**   0.029

4   0.183   **5**   0.896   **6**   0.125   **7**   0.026   **8**   0.202, 0.06

9   0.215, 0.835   **10**   43   **11**   21   **12**   18   **13**   148

Exercise 9F Page 180

1   **a)** 0.048   **b)** 0.952   **2**   0.02   **3**   0.11   **4**   0.974

5   0.262, 229   **6**   0.89, 117   **7**   40

Examination questions Page 181

1   **a)** 0.106   **b)** 1.028 kg   **2**   **(i)** 0.45   **(ii)** 0.1   **(iii)** 0.484

3   **(i)** 0.227   **(ii)** 9.34   **4**   **a)** 0.97   **b)** 78   **c)** 10

5 a) 0.106, 42   **b)** 0.940   **c)** 0.714

6 (i) 0.887   **(ii)** 0.994; 18, N(18, 18), 0.278

7 (ii) $60 - \mu = -0.807\sigma$, $65 - \mu = 0.332\sigma$; $\mu = 63.5$, $\sigma = 4.39$

(iii) consistent   **(iv)** not consistent

10 Combinations of random variables

Exercise 10A Page 187

1 a) 7   **b)** 1   **c)** 17   **d)** 11   **e)** 2   **f)** -6 **g)** 21   **h)** 5

2 745 ml

3 a) 5   **b)** 5   **c)** 30   **d)** 35   **e)** 2   **f)** 8   **g)** 20   **h)** 27

i) 19   **j)** 51   **k)** 86   **l)** 519

4 145 grams, 50 grams^2 **5** 55 ml, 9 ml^2 **6** 89 s, 9 s^2

7 a) $a = \frac{1}{2}, b = 3$ **b)** $a = 2, b = 3$ **8** $\frac{2}{3}X + 31\frac{2}{3}$

Exercise 10B Page 190

1 $10, \frac{1}{5}, 400$ **2** $0.7 \text{ cm}^2, 84$ **3 a)** more efficient

4 a) more efficient   **5** $a = 0.6, b = 0.4$ **6 b)** more efficient

7 $a = \frac{3}{4}, b = \frac{1}{4}$ **8** $a = \frac{2}{3}, b = \frac{1}{3}$

Exercise 10C Page 192

1 a) $20\frac{2}{3}$ **b)** 0.13   **c)** 732.8   **2** 9   **3** 12.6

4 a) 550   **b)** 11 500   **c)** 0.542   **5** 49.4   **6** 5.40 g^2

7 1050 m^2 **8** 8.93

Exercise 10D Page 194

1 a) N(7, 6)   **b)** N(1, 6)   **c)** N(17, 44)   **d)** N(14, 22)

2 a) 0.910   **b)** 0.428   **c)** 0.673   **d)** 0.643   **3** 0.048

4 a) 0.079   **b)** 0.079   **c)** 0.240   **5 a)** 0.019   **b)** 0.939   **c)** 0.151

6 a) 0.589   **b)** 0.044   **7 a)** 0.76   **b)** 0.28   **8** 0.319

9 0.966   **10** 0.353, 10.2 minutes to 8   **11** 0.118. 21 minutes past 1

12 5.47 gallons

Exercise 10E Page 196

1 a) 0.943   **b)** 0.215   **c)** 0.886   **d)** 0.126

2 a) 6.04   **b)** 3.53   **c)** 1.24   **3** 0.11   **4** 0.376

5 0.023 **6** 0.99 **7** $k = 58.7$ **8** 26.5 min

9 $k = 0.0051$ **10** $m = 2.3$

Exercise 10F Page 198

1 0.626 **2** 0.421 **3** 0.013 **4** $0, \frac{1}{3}; 0.219$ **5** 0.034

6 1.5, 0.75; 0.767 **7** 18.5, 107.9; 0.132

Examination questions Page 199

1 (i) N(9.9, 0.36) (ii) A, 0.253; B, 0.033; C, 0.714

2 **a)** (i) 0.091 (ii) 22.8 min **b)** 22 min **c)** N(3, 58), 0.653 **d)** Blue Star

3 (i) 0.253 (ii) 0.058 (iii) 0.104

4 (i) 0.798 (ii) 0.323 (iii) 0.132 (iv) 0.228

5 **a)** 0.377 **b)** 0.623 **c)** 0.906 **6** $N(\mu_1 + \mu_2, \sigma_1^2 + \sigma_2^2), N(\mu_1 - \mu_2, \sigma_1^2 + \sigma_2^2)$

a) 0.0228 **b)** 0.988 **c)** 0.083 **d)** 0.209

11 Tests 1

Exercise 11A Page 206

1 $z = 2.24$, significant **2** $z = 1.41$, not significant **3** $z = 1.24$, not significant

4 $z = 1.83$, significant **5** $z = 1.36$, not significant **6** $z = 1.81$, significant

7 $z = 2.80$, significant **8** $z = 1.94$, not significant **9** $z = 2.4.$, significant

10 $z = 1.79$, not significant **11** 11.8 V, $z = 1.41$, not significant

12 1000.6 cm^3, $z = 3.49$, significant

Exercise 11B Page 210

7 $\overline{X} > 226.6$ kg, 0.363 **8** 0.253 **9** 0.293

10 Under 57.7 kg, 0.591 **11** Under 4940 N. 0.05 **12** Under 1.8 kg, 0.211

Exercise 11C Page 214

1 $\mu = 15\,000, \mu < 15\,000$ **2** $\mu = 6, \mu \neq 6$ **3** $T = 100, T < 100$

4 $\mu = 320, \mu \neq 320$ **8** $z = 1.67$, not significant **9** $z = 2.32$, significant

10 $z = 1.41$, not significant **11** $z = 2.83$, significant

12 $z = 0.75$, not significant **13** $z = 2.53$, not significant

14 £18 380, $z = 0.743$, not significant **15** 72.1, $z = 1.82$, not significant

16 4.3, 0.065, $z = 3.53$, not justified

Exercise 11D Page 218

1 **a)** $2.15 < \mu < 6.45$ **b)** $1008 < \mu < 1022$ **c)** $0.024 < \mu < 0.056$ **d)** $50.4 < \mu < 55.6$

2 **a)** $1.48 < \mu < 7.12$ **b)** $1006 < \mu < 1024$ **c)** $0.019 < \mu < 0.061$ **d)** $49.6 < \mu < 56.4$

3 $56 < \mu < 66$ **4** $29.2 < \mu < 34.8$, reject claim

5 $1.039 < \mu < 1.047$, reject claim   **6** 3.84 kg, $3.53 < \mu < 4.15$

7 $61, 52.5 < \mu < 69.5$ **8** $6.57, 4.04, 6.18 < \mu < 6.96$

9 $31.52, 12.7, 30.5 < \mu < 32.5$, accept claim

Examination questions Page 219

1 960 seconds

2 **a)** 0.034 **b)** 0.069, not significant   **3** **a)** $7.73, 37.0$ **b)** accept claim

4 **(i)** $\overline{X} > 53.5$ **(ii)** $0.28, 0.72$ **5** **a)** $z = 1.79$, significant

6 **a)** $1.43, 0.656, 0.145$ **b)** $1.15 < \mu < 1.72$, sufficient

7 **a)** $100.3 < \mu < 104.5$ **b)** reject claim   **c)** 20

12 Tests 2

Exercise 12A Page 225

1 **a)** $z = 1.71$, not significant   **b)** $z = 1.48$, not significant   **c)** $z = 2.29$, significant
   d) $z = 1.86$, not significant

2 **a)** significant   **b)** not significant   **c)** significant   **d)** significant

3 $z = 1.1$, not significant   **4** $z = 1.76$, significant

5 $z = 1.94$, significant   **6** $z = 1.24$, not significant

7 $z = 2.24$, significant   **8** $z = 1.51$, not significant, $-2.4 < \mu - \mu' < 18.4$

9 $z = 2.18$, significant $0.14 < \mu - \mu' < 2.66$

10 149.4 lb, 169.2 lb. $z = 1.77$, significant   **11** $z = 0.74$, not significant

Exercise 12B Page 228

1 not significant, significant   **2** significant   **3** at least 15 heads, not significant

4 significant   **5** not significant   **6** at least 16 over 140, significant

7 ≥ 18 right, significant   **8** significant

Exercise 12C Page 231

1 **a)** $z = 1.3$, not significant   **b)** $z = 2.02$, significant   **c)** $z = 1.92$, not significant
   d) $z = 0.56$, not significant   **2** $z = 3.18$, significant

3 $z = 2.03$, significant   **4** $z = 1.42$, not significant   **5** $z = 1.71$, significant

6 $z = 2.61$, significant   **7** $z = 1.48$, not significant

8 $z = 1.04$, not significant   **9** $z = 1.69$, not significant

10 $59, 0.38$ **11** $374. 0.06$ **12** $z = 1.82$, not significant

13 $z = 1.92$, significant   **14** $z = 1.80$, not significant

Exercise 12D Page 233

1 **a)** $z = 0.95$, not significant   **b)** $z = 2.24$, significant   **c)** $z = 1.77$, not significant

     d) $z = 2.5$, significant   **2** $z = 0.80$, not significant

3 $z = 2.28$, significant   **4** $z = 1.49$, not significant   **5** $z = 2.75$, significant

6 $z = 2.34$, significant

Exercise 12E Page 236

1 **a)** $z = 0.82$, not significant   **b)** $z = 2.67$, significant   **c)** $z = 0.44$, not significant

2 $z = 1.01$, not significant   **3** $z = 2.55$, significant

4 $z = 1.05$, not significant   **5** $z = 1.25$, not significant

6 $z = 1.32$, not significant   **7** $z = 2.64$, significant

Exercise 12F Page 238

1 **a)** $0.36 < \pi < 0.44$ **b)** $0.27 < \pi < 0.33$ **c)** $0.69 < \pi < 0.81$ **d)** $0.68 < \pi < 0.72$

2 **a)** $0.34 < \pi < 0.46$ **b)** $0.26 < \pi < 0.34$ **c)** $0.67 < \pi < 0.83$ **d)** $0.67 < \pi < 0.73$

3 $0.09 < \pi < 0.15$ **4** $0.53 < p < 0.67$ **5** $0.19 < p < 0.28$

6 $0.76 < \pi < 0.84$

7 **a)** $42\% < \pi < 48\%$ **b)** $47\% < \pi < 51\%$ **c)** $46\% < \pi < 49\%$

8 $0.26 < \pi < 0.39, 8430, 14\,600$ **9** $0.28 < p < 0.42, 35\,000$

10 $53\% < \pi < 67\%, 2300$

Examination questions Page 240

1 241 yds, 144. $239 < \mu_A < 243, z = 2.62$, significant

2 (i) 0.028 (ii) 0.131 (iii) 0.261, not significant at 5%

3 (i) 0.202 (ii) 0.041 (iv) 11 (v) 3

4 **b)** (i) £3320 $<$ difference $<$ £16 680 $\dfrac{(25\,000)^2}{n_1} + \dfrac{(20\,000)^2}{(100 - n_1)}, n_1 = 56, n_2 = 44$

5 **a)** (i) $\frac{3}{8}, 0.22 < \pi < 0.53$ **b)** (i) 20% (ii) 90

6 **a)** $p = 0.09$, significant   **b)** $z = 1.39$, not significant

7 (i) 0.0755 (ii) 0.323

8 (i) 3.24 cm, 2.71 cm² (ii) 3.05 cm, 3.01 cm² (iii) $-0.24 < \mu_1 - \mu_2 < 0.62$

(iv) not significant

Consolidation section C

Extra questions Page 244

1 0.913. 0.396 **2** 0.760. 2.860 **3** 0.103 **4** 525.6 grams

5 8.3, 19 **6** 0.208 **7** 0.227 **8 a)** 10 **b)** 31 **c)** 4

9 a) 294 **b)** 90 **c)** 94 **d)** 334 **e)** 120 **f)** 31 **g)** 185

10 $Y = 0.8X + 21$ **11 a)** $10, \frac{1}{2}$ **b)** 200 **12** 4.3, 4.23

13 a) 0.797 **b)** 0.162 **c)** 0.550 **14 a)** 0.016 **b)** 0.294

15 0.119 **16** 0.770 **17** $z = 1.5$, not significant

18 $z = 2.71$, significant **19** Over 52.2, under 47.8, 0.237

20 $30.9 < \mu < 34.3$ **21** 1638, 22 755, $1564 < \mu < 1712$, significant

22 $z = 1.04$, not significant **23** $z = 1.82$, significant

24 $z = 2.34$, significant **25** $45.5\% < \pi < 50.5\%$, not rejected

Mixed questions Page 246

2 a) 400 **b)** 690 **3** 2.5, 2.08, 98.6% **5** not significant, significant

6 not significant, significant **7** not significant **8** 6, not significant

9 21, significant **10** $315 < X < 1200$ **11** 0.674. 0.798

Examination questions Page 249

1 a) 0.251 **b)** 0.587. $P(X \geq 4) = 0.066$, not significant

2 c) 0.311 **d)** 0.149 **e)** 0.697 **3 a)** (i) 0.159 (ii) 0.562 **b)** 0.957

4 (i) 22.6% (ii) 21.1% **5 d)** 0.989

6 (i) 0.067 (ii) 0.309 (iii) 20, 125, normal (iv) 0.037 (v) 6 minutes

7 a) (i) 0.124 (ii) 0.789 **b)** (i) 126.5 g, 225 g² (ii) accept claim

8 $0.26 < \pi < 0.38$

9 (i) 0.954 (ii) 0.209, 0.975

10 (i) 0.0175 (ii) 507.3 grams (iii) 14

11 (i) 0.159 (ii) 0.885 (iii) 0.278

12 $0.102\sqrt{(p(1 - p))}, 0.1\sqrt{(p(1 - p))}$. T_2 better

13 t- and χ^2 distributions

Exercise 13A Page 257

1 $t_9 = 1.82$, not significant   **2** $t_7 = 3.31$, significant   **3** $t_8 = 2.53$, not significant

4 $t_{10} = 1.84$, not significant   **5** $t_9 = 3.43$, significant   **6** $t_9 = 1.46$, not significant

7 $t_7 = 2.24$, significant   **8** $t_5 = 1.63$, not significant

Exercise 13B Page 259

1 **a)** $102 < \mu < 112$ **b)** $3.80 < \mu < 3.85$ **c)** $0.009 < \mu < 0.012$

2 $69.8 < \mu < 80.4$ **3** $111 < \mu < 122$ **4** $52 < \mu < 71$

5 $42 < \mu < 58$ **6** $0.12 < \mu < 0.30$ **7** $0.65 < \mu < 3.85$

Exercise 13C Page 263

1 $\chi^2(5) = 7.9$, fair   **2** $\chi^2(3) = 9.4$, biased   **2** $\chi^2(2) = 28.5$, different

4 $\chi^2(2) = 5.43$, not significant   **5** 0.487, $\chi^2(2) = 3.44$, good fit

6 0.1, $\chi^2(1) = 0.275$, good fit   **7** $\lambda = 2.4$, $\chi^2(4) = 10.07$, not good fit

8 $\chi^2(1) = 0.312$, good fit

9 $\mu = 85.8$, $\hat{\sigma}^2 = 165$, frequencies $10.9, 21.64, 30.2, 23.7, 13.5$ $\chi^2(2) = 3.07$, good fit.

10 $\mu = 134.5$, $\hat{\sigma}^2 = 45.9$, $\chi^2(3) = 7.27$, good fit

Exercise 13D Page 267

1 $\chi^2(1) = 16.9$ (17.8 without Yates), significant   **2** $\chi^2(2) = 3.07$, not significant

3 $\chi^2(2) = 8.5$, significant   **4** $\chi^2(4) = 24.2$, significant

5 $\chi^2(2) = 8.7$, not significant   **6** $\chi^2(4) = 28.2$

7 $\chi^2(1) = 7.03$ (8 without Yates), significant difference   **8** $\chi^2(2) = 10.9$, significant

9 $\chi^2(2) = 8.5$, significant   **10** $\chi^2(2) = 3.5$, not significant

11 $\chi^2(4) = 24$, significant

Examination questions Page 270

1 **(i)** $\overline{X} = 9627$, $s^2 = 123\,823$ **(ii)** $t_5 = 2.6$, justified   **(iii)** $\frac{1}{64}$

2 **(ii)** $72.5, 95, 67.5, 15$ **(iii)** $\chi^2(3) = 3$, no evidence of change

3 **a)** $\chi^2(1) = 0.71$ (1.15 without Yates), independent   **b)** $\chi^2(2) = 2.41$, independent

4 **a)** frequencies: $8, 8, 4, 10, 9, 7, 5, 3, 6$ **b)** $\chi^2(3) = 23.6$, not good model

5 **a)** 23.5 **b)** $\chi^2(7) = 14.4$, theory rejected   **6** $\chi^2(1) = 3.4$, suitable model

7 $\chi^2(2) = 11.1$, significant

8 **a)** $\chi^2(4) = 7.07$, no significant difference   **b)** evidence significant

14 Correlation and regression

Exercise 14A Page 277

1 **a)** 0.881 positive   **b)** -0.983 negative   **c)** 0.546 positive

2 **a)** 0.798   **b)** -0.012 **c)** 0.120   3 0.804   4 -0.915

5 0.351   6 0.964   7 0.825   8 **a)** 0.996   **b)** 1

9 **a)** 0.574   **b)** 0

Exercise 14B Page 280

1 **a)** 0.805, yes   **b)** 0.618, no   **c)** -0.883, yes   2 0.548, no (two-tailed)

3 no   4 yes   5 yes   6 yes   7 no   8 yes

9 yes

Exercise 14C Page 283

1 **a)** $y = 11.2x + 12.5$ **b)** $y = -1.09x + 113$ **c)** $y = 112x + 1.27$

2 **a)** $y = 12.6x + 11.8$ **b)** $y = 2.58x - 7.78$ **c)** $y = -13.8x + 103.4$

3 $h = 6.6q + 48.3$, rate $= 88$ 4 $L = 0.423w + 1.35$, loss $= 4.3$ g

5 $k = -1.71t + 99.5$, 58 minutes   6 $V = 0.432T + 116$, $-270°$

7 $y = 0.361x + 1.72$, 15.1 p   8 $B = 0.917A + 9.67$

Exercise 14D Page 286

1 **a)** $y = 1.18x + 40.1$, -0.9, -0.7, 2.6, -0.2, 0.01, -0.8, 78 suspect

  b) $y = 0.0489x + 2.71$. -0.01, -0.02, -0.008, -0.007, 0.004, 0.005, -0.004, 0.39 suspect

  c) $y = -2.43x + 408$, 2.5, -0.2, -2.0, -1.7, -2.4, 3.8, 48 suspect

2 $W = 0.323H + 8.2$, boy C   3 $D = 0.942P + 0.617$. company I

4 $m = 1.64f - 0.0073$, 0.08, -0.1, 0.03, -0.3, 0.05, -0.02, 0.2, 0.1, fourth an outlier

Exercise 14E Page 288

1 **a)** $Y = 5.39 + \dfrac{82.7}{X}$ **b)** $Y = -3.15 + 1.28\sqrt{X}$ **c)** $Y = 5.27 + 1.65X^2$

  d) $Y = 10.7 \times 2.4^X$ **e)** $Y = 0.59X^{0.18}$ 2 $h = 0.3 \times 1.4^w$

3 $d = 0.3 \sin \theta - 0.01$ 4 $P = 2.7V^{-0.923}$ 5 $a = 4.53$, $b = 0.313$

6 $y = 220\,000x^{-2.46}$, $y = -1.80x + 108$, second better

Examination questions Page 290

1 **a)** $h = 217 - 3.09s$ **c)** 124 hours

2 **b)** significant at 1%   **c)** $H = 0.821A + 22.6$ **d)** 47.2 mg/l

3 $y = 1.86 + 0.02r$, 1.93 km

4 $\overline{A} = 14.875$, $\overline{T} = 17.5$, $A = 0.49T + 6.3$, $A(20) = 16.1$, 0.49

5 b) (i) 0.106   (ii) $\frac{1}{9}, \frac{1}{3}, \frac{2}{3}, \frac{4}{5}, \frac{2}{5}, \frac{1}{3}$

15 Non-parametric methods

Exercise 15A Page 296

1 $p = 0.02$, not justified   **2** $p = 0.14$, not significant   **3** $p = 0.006$, reject claim

4 $p = 0.003$, reject claim   **5** $p = 0.006$, significant   **6** 5 or fewer

7 20 or more   **8** $p = 0.02$, significant   **9** $p = 0.09$, not significant

10 22 or more

Exercise 15B Page 300

1 $T = 7$, median not 40   **2** $T = 9$, claim retained   **3** $T = 7$, mass decreased

4 $T = 10$, not significant   **5** $T = 15$, not significant   **6** $T = 14$, not significant

7 $T = 9.5$, not significant   **8** $T = 7$, not significant

Exercise 15C Page 303

1 a) 0.89   **b)** -0.99 **c)** 0.6   **2** 0.738 and 0.595, first better

3 0.53, not significant   **4** 0.89, significant

5 $r_s = 0.26$, no significant correlation   **6** $r_s = 0.079$, no significant correlation

Examination questions Page 304

1 (i) **a)** sign: $p = 0.073$, not significant, Wilcoxon: $T = 17$, significant

    b) $t_{11} = 1.59$, not significant   (ii) $T = 24.5$, not significant

2 (ii) Sign test, $p = 0.49$, not significant Wilcoxon, $T = 6$, not significant

    (iii) $t_8 = 2.76$, significant   **3** (i) 0.636   (ii) not significant correlation

4 (i) 0.61   (iii) reject H_0 (one-tailed test)

5 (i) $r_s = 0.95$, significant to show association

Consolidation section D

Extra questions Page 312

1 $t = 3.39$, significant   **2** $77 < \mu < 84$ **3** $\chi^2(2) = 8.2$, significant

4 $\lambda = 1.916$, $\chi^2(3) = 0.16$, good fit   **5** 39.15, 10.7, $\chi^2(2) = 4$, good fit

6 $\chi^2(2) = 6.68$, significant   **7** $\chi^2(1) = 1.93$ (with Yates, 1.38), not significant

8 -0.711 **9** 0.970   **10** significant   **11** $y = 89.1 - 0.795x$

12 $y = 8.64x + 12.1$ **13** $y = 43.1 - 0.00713x$, second car

14 $y = 1.23x^2 + 2.56x$ **15** $V = 8.08 \times 1.23^{-t}$ **16** significant

17 not significant **18** $T = 12$, not significant **19** $T = 14$, not significant

20 -0.772, significant **21** $r = -0.048$, not significant

22 0.80, significant at 5%

Mixed questions Page 315

1 $y = 28.8 - 0.0141x$. 2 000 000 **2** $\lambda = 0.61$. $\chi^2(1) = 0.06$, not significant

3 $23.8 < \mu < 28.2$ **4** 13 **5** $41.8 < \mu < 250$

6 25.1, 23.7, $a = 16.9$, $b = 16.7$ **7** $a = 4.11$, $k = 16.0$ **8** $1.07 < a < 1.25$

9 $\chi^2(3) = 44.2$, significant

10 a) significant **b)** not significant **c)** not significant

Examination questions Page 318

1 (ii) $t = 1.49$, not significant **2** (iii) $t = 1.09$, not significant $-10.3 < d < 3.8$

3 (iii) $z = 1.63$, not significant (iv) $t = 2.5$, significant

4 $t = 3.24$, significant, $t = 0.75$, not significant $5.824 < \mu < 6.825$

5 (i) 327, 130, -1012.5, -0.41 (ii) -0.448, not significant

6 a) $\chi^2(3) = 12$, significant **c)** $\chi^2(3) = 4.4$, not significant

7 $\chi^2(4) = 7.97$, not significant $\chi^2(8) = 18.1$, significant

8 a) $\chi^2(2) = 9.0$ **b)** $\chi^2(1) = 3.0$

9 b) 0.296, not significant **c)** E, G, 0.954, significant

10 a) 52.35 **c)** not significant **11 b)** -0.975, significant **d)** significant

Mock examinations Page 323

Paper 1

1 0.995 **2 a)** 0.008 **b)** 0.016 **c)** 0.5

3 a) 0.282 **b)** 0.647 **c)** 0.704 **d)** 0.143

4 12.3, 11.3, 13.1 **5** 0.809

6 $z = 3.31$, significant, 11 st 6.8 lb $< \mu < $ 11 st 9.2 lb **7** 64, 0.078

8 $\chi^2(2) = 1.47$, not significant, significant

Paper 2

1 a) 0.166 **b)** 0.354 **c)** 0.135 **3 a)** $k = \frac{3}{52}$ **b)** 0. 1.66 **c)** 0.322

4 2.30, **a)** 0.595   **b)** 0.173   **c)** 0.364   **6** 0.7, significant

7 2%, 0.013   **8** **a)** $z = 0.83$, not significant   **b)** 1065

Paper 3

2 $0.3, 0.6, \frac{2}{3}$ **3** **a)** 8.43 s, 5.57 s, positive   **b)** $(30, 72)$, $T = 0.517d + 70.1$

4 **a)** 0.329   **b)** 0.134   **c)** 0.048, $z = 1.78$, significant

5 $k = 0.1$, $\mu = m = 105, 0.1(x - 100), 0.1\left(\sqrt{\dfrac{y}{\pi}} - 100\right), \dfrac{0.05}{\sqrt{\pi y}}$, 34 662, 34 636, no, yes

6 $0.072, 0.292, 0.28, R$

7 **a)** 0.223   **b)** $1 - e^{-0.1x}$ **c)** $f(x) = 0.1e^{-0.1x}$ **d)** 10 minutes, 6.93 minute

8 $\chi^2(3) = 34.3$, $\chi^2(2) = 2.47$, not significant

Index

Index